A Manual of Physical Methods

in Organic Chemistry

By the Same Author

R. A. Raphael, E. C. Taylor, and Hans Wynberg, editors.
Advances in Organic Chemistry: Methods and Results.

FREDERIK SIXMA
1923–1963

Frederik Leonardus Johannes Sixma was born in Amsterdam on February 5, 1923. He studied chemistry at the University of Amsterdam from 1939–1948, receiving his Ph.D. *cum laude* for a dissertation entitled "Substitution in Aromatic Compounds; the effect of temperature and catalyst." After a short postdoctoral fellowship with J. D. Roberts he returned to the post of lecturer in organic chemistry at his alma mater.

When Wibaut, his mentor, retired in 1956, Sixma was appointed to the chair of Physical Organic Chemistry at the University of Amsterdam.

In 1960 he accepted the Research Directorship of The States Mines' Central Laboratory and became one of its Managing Directors in 1961. That same year he partially resumed his academic career by serving as extraordinary Professor at Eindhoven Technical University. His many publications covered a wide variety of topics in the field of kinetics, ozonolysis, and aromatics, and the isomerization of aliphatic halides.

A tragic traffic accident in February, 1963, ended the career of one of the Netherlands' most outstanding organic chemists. To his memory this book is dedicated.

Hans Wynberg, Groningen, Holland, July, 1964

A Manual of Physical Methods in Organic Chemistry

The Late F. L. J. Sixma

Director of Research, State Mines, Holland

Hans Wynberg

Professor of Chemistry, The University, Groningen, Holland

JOHN WILEY & SONS, INC. New York · London · Sydney

To Fritz

Preface

The purpose of this manual is threefold. It is to provide tested and detailed directions for use in a laboratory course at the undergraduate or graduate level, to serve as an introduction to a new technique for the individual researcher, and to enable any scientist to acquaint himself rapidly with a physical method in order to evaluate its usefulness in his work.

The present manual is a translation, revision, and expansion of the manual originally written for use in the Department of Organic Chemistry of the University of Amsterdam. It is natural that no attempt has been made to be as comprehensive as the many-volume *Technique of Organic Chemistry* series, or as thorough as a monograph on any single subject. The manual is intended as a well-tested introduction to the many physical methods confronting the practicing chemist. Its continuing intensive use in the laboratories in Amsterdam and Groningen has shown that the book fills a real need.

HANS WYNBERG

Groningen, Holland, 1964

Contents

A Manual of Physical Methods

in Organic Chemistry

I

Chromatography and
related techniques

I

Countercurrent distribution

1-1 Introduction

Separations based on countercurrent distribution depend on the differences in the partition coefficients of various components with respect to two liquid phases.

Although separatory funnels can be used to effect separations in this manner, the method would become cumbersome. Using the apparatus developed by Craig simplifies the technique greatly; furthermore, complete automation is possible.

The method is especially important for achieving separations under very mild conditions (of temperature and pH, for instance) and thus is ideally suited for mixtures of peptides, hormones, vitamins, antibiotics, and light-, heat-, or air-sensitive compounds. The method is frequently employed in cases where column or gas-phase chromatography or fractional distillation fails.

The method is not successful with:

(*a*) Compounds of limited solubility.
(*b*) Strongly polar compounds (e.g., salts).
(*c*) Completely non-polar compounds (saturated hydrocarbons).
(*d*) Compounds whose molecular weight is above *ca*. 6000.

1-2 Principle

The countercurrent distribution apparatus consists of a train of tubes connected in series. Each unit contains an extraction tube and a decantation tube (Fig. 1-1). Every tube contains L ml. of the lower (stationary) phase (heavier liquid) and U ml. of the upper (mobile) phase (lighter liquid).

Equilibration of the solute between the two liquid phases is achieved by tilting back and forth, rocking from position I to III and back (Fig. 1-2). In position III separation of the two phases is possible, and careful turning to position IV allows the top phase to enter the decantation tube, while the bottom phase remains behind. The top phase is transferred to the next tube in position I. The first tube (known as the 0th tube in the theoretical treatment) is filled with U ml. of the top phase and a new cycle can start.

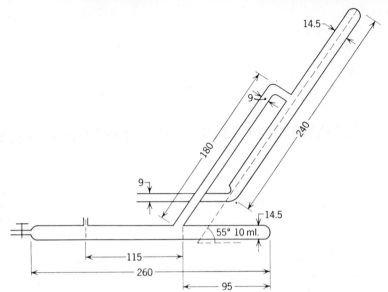

Fig. 1-1. Cell for countercurrent distribution (dimensions in millimeters).

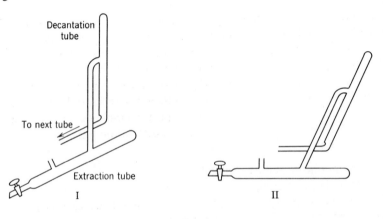

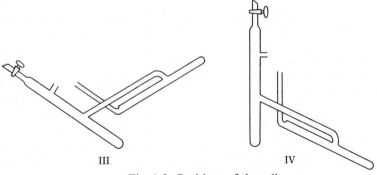

Fig. 1-2. Positions of the cell.

4

1-3 Theory

1-3a THE SIMPLE CASE

The components of the mixture move with the mobile phase with different speeds depending upon their distribution coefficients. The distribution of a substance over the various tubes can be calculated as follows.

Assume experimental conditions so that, upon equilibration, a substance is distributed equally between the top and bottom phases. After the first cycle each

Table 1-1 Fraction of Solute in Each Tube after n Cycles

Tube	0	1	2	3	4	5	6	7	8	9	10	11	
0	1												$\times 2^0$
1	1	1											$\times 2^{-1}$
2	1	2	1										$\times 2^{-2}$
3	1	3	3	1									$\times 2^{-3}$
4	1	4	6	4	1								$\times 2^{-4}$
5	1	5	10	10	5	1							$\times 2^{-5}$
6	1	6	15	20	15	6	1						$\times 2^{-6}$
7	1	7	21	35	35	21	7	1					$\times 2^{-7}$
8	1	8	28	56	70	56	28	8	1				$\times 2^{-8}$
9	1	9	36	84	126	126	84	36	9	1	1		$\times 2^{-9}$
10	1	10	45	120	210	256	210	120	45	10	1		$\times 2^{-10}$
11	1	11	55	165	330	462	462	330	165	55	11	1	$\times 2^{-11}$

of the first two tubes will contain one half of the original substance. After n cycles, the distribution among the first $(n + 1)$ tubes is given by the terms of the binomial expansion: $(\frac{1}{2} + \frac{1}{2})^n$ (see Table 1-1).

1-3b FUNDAMENTAL PROCEDURE

All fractions undergo the same number of transfers during the fundamental procedure. The number of cycles (n) is equal to the number of times that the mobile phase is transferred to the next tube. This number is equal to the number of times that fresh mobile phase is added to the 0th tube. After n cycles $(n + 1)$ tubes will have been used. Tubes are numbered starting with 0 $(0, 1, 2, \ldots, r)$.

Assuming that the partition coefficient K is constant, independent of the concentration (linear partition isotherm), then

$$K = \frac{C_{\text{mobile phase}}}{C_{\text{stationary phase}}}$$

Under these conditions the partition coefficient of a substance for a particular solvent is a characteristic physical property.

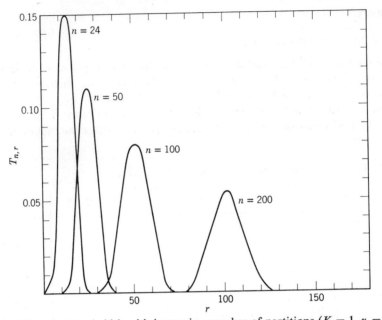

Fig. 1-3. Bandwidth with increasing number of partitions ($K = 1$, $\alpha = 1$).

When the volumes of the mobile and stationary phases are equal, then

$$p = \text{fraction of solute in mobile phase} = \frac{K}{(K + 1)}$$

$$q = \text{fraction of solute in stationary phase} = \frac{1}{(K + 1)}$$

$$p + q = 1$$

When these volumes are not equal, then

$$p = \frac{\alpha K}{(\alpha K + 1)}$$

$$q = \frac{1}{(\alpha K + 1)}$$

$$p + q = 1$$

where $\alpha = V_{\text{mobile phase}}/V_{\text{stationary phase}}$.

The fraction of solute in each tube can now be calculated (see Table 1-1). It is given by the terms of the binomial expansion $(p + q)^n = 1$. The individual terms of the expansion are equal to

$$T_{n,r} = \frac{n!}{(n - r)!r!} p^r q^{n-r} \tag{1-1}$$

When this function is plotted vs. the number of the tube (r), a theoretical distribution curve is obtained (see Fig. 1-3). The absolute bandwidth increases with an increase in n (i.e., the solute is distributed over more tubes); however, the bands become narrower relative to one another, since with an increase in n the solute is found in a smaller fraction of the total number of tubes used.

Position of the Maximum. From formula 1-1 it follows that

$$T_{n,r+1} = \frac{n-r}{r+1}\frac{p}{q} T_{n,r} \qquad (1\text{-}2)$$

The slope of the distribution curve is positive for $T_{n,r}/T_{n,r-1}$ larger than 1, and negative when this fraction is smaller than 1. At the maximum (for $n = $ odd, compare Table 1-1)

$$T_{n,r} = T_{n,r+1}$$

$$\frac{n-r_{max}}{r_{max}+1}\frac{p}{q} = 1 \rightarrow \boxed{r_{max} = p(n+1)-1} \qquad (1\text{-}3)$$

When n is odd, the maximum concentration is found in two tubes, namely in $p(n+1)$ and in $[p(n+1)-1]$. When n is large (>20), r_{max} equals pn to a good approximation.

$$(1\text{-}3a)$$

Calculation of the Partition Coefficient from the Distribution Curve. From the position of the maximum we find

$$r_{max} = \frac{\alpha K}{(\alpha K + 1)}(n+1)-1$$

$$K = \frac{r_{max}+1}{\alpha(n-r_{max})} \qquad (1\text{-}4)$$

K may be calculated from the concentration ratios of neighboring cells (formula 1-2):

$$\boxed{K = \frac{r+1}{\alpha(n-r)}\frac{T_{n,r+1}}{T_{n,r}} = \frac{r}{\alpha(n-r+1)}\frac{T_{n,r}}{T_{n,r-1}}} \qquad (1\text{-}5)$$

1-3c LARGE NUMBER OF TRANSFERS

Formula 1-1 becomes cumbersome for a large (>20) number of transfers. The following method can then be used:

$$d\ln T_{n,r} = \frac{dT_{n,r}}{T_{n,r}} = \left[\frac{(n-r)p}{rq}-1\right]dr$$

The origin of the coordinate system is taken at the maximum of the partition curve (Fig. 1-4), and the number of the tube counting from the maximum is called x. Then:

$$r = np + x$$

$$n - r = nq - x$$

$$d\ln T_{n,r} = \left[\frac{(nq-x)p}{(np+x)q}-1\right]dx = \frac{-(p+q)x}{npq+qx}dx$$

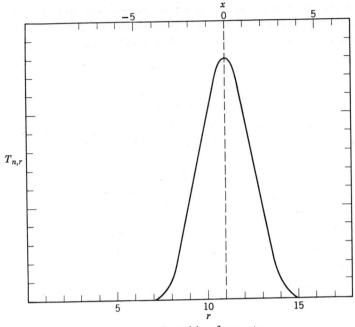

Fig. 1-4. Transition from r to x.

Near the maximum qx is small compared to npq, and we may write

$$d \ln T_{n,r} = \frac{-x}{npq}\, dx \qquad (1\text{-}6)$$

This equation is not valid further away from the maximum, but then $T_{n,r}$ becomes negligible (for $n > 20$).

Integration of formula 1-6 yields

$$T_{n,r} = C \exp\left(\frac{-x^2}{2npq}\right)$$

C is found by calculating the value of $T_{n,r}$ at the maximum with the aid of formula 1-1 and substituting:

$$\boxed{T_{n,r} = (2\pi npq)^{-\frac{1}{2}} \exp\left(\frac{-x^2}{2npq}\right)} \qquad (1\text{-}7)$$

1-3d SEPARATION [7]

The ratio of the partition coefficients (separation factor) is of importance in determining the separability of two compounds.

$$\beta \equiv \frac{K_2}{K_1} = \frac{p_2 q_2}{p_1 q_1} \quad (K_2 > K_1)$$

The maxima are found at np_1 and np_2 after n transfers. The more β differs from 1 the easier is the separation. When $\beta = 1$ a separation is clearly impossible.

In the tube containing a maximum amount of the first component we find:

$$(T_{n,r})_{max} = (2\pi n p_1 q_1)^{-1/2}$$

For those tubes in which the amount of substance equals $e^{-1} T_{max}$ the equation

$$e^{-1} = \exp\left(\frac{-x^2}{2np_1q_1}\right)$$

holds. The number of these tubes therefore equals

$$x_e = \pm(2np_1q_1)^{1/2}$$

Thus the width of the "band" between the two e^{-1} limits is

$$L_e = 2(2np_1q_1)^{1/2} = 2.82(np_1q_1)^{1/2} \tag{1-8}$$

Similarly the bandwidths between the 1% and 10% limits are

$$\left.\begin{array}{l} L_{1\%} = 6(np_1q_1)^{1/2} \\ L_{10\%} = 4.3(np_1q_1)^{1/2} \end{array}\right\} \tag{1-9}$$

When C and D are the 1% limit, Fig. 1-5 shows that

$$AE - AB = BE = BD + CE - CD$$
$$CD = BD + CE - AE + AB$$

The overlap therefore equals

$$CD = 3(np_1q_1)^{1/2} + 3(np_2q_2)^{1/2} - np_2 + np_1$$
$$= n^{1/2} \cdot 3(p_1^{1/2}q_1^{1/2} + p_2^{1/2}q_2^{1/2}) - n(p_2 - p_1)$$

The number of transfers necessary to obtain a 1% separation is given by ($CD = 0$)

$$(n_{1\%})^{1/2} = \frac{3(p_1^{1/2}q_1^{1/2} + p_2^{1/2}q_2^{1/2})}{p_2 - p_1} \tag{1-10}$$

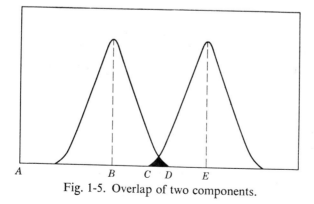

Fig. 1-5. Overlap of two components.

$L_{10\%}$ and $n_{10\%}$ can be calculated similarly:

$$L_{10\%} = \frac{4.3}{6} L_{1\%} = 0.7 L_{1\%}$$

$$(1\text{-}11)$$

$$n_{10\%} = \frac{2.15^2}{3} n_{1\%} = \tfrac{1}{2} n_{1\%}$$

These relationships are valid only when the mixture contains equal amounts of both components (see § 2-3d).

1-3e   SINGLE WITHDRAWAL METHOD

The operation can be continued upon completion of the fundamental procedure by collecting the mobile phase of the last tube in a fraction collector after every transfer (see § 3-2). This procedure is closely related to the elution method used in chromatography (see § 2-3).

When n transfers have been completed, the amount of substance *in the mobile phase* of the last tube (the one about to be eluted) is equal to

$$T_{n,r} = \frac{n!}{r!(n-r)!} \, p^r q^{n-r} p$$

$$(1\text{-}12)$$

Here n varies for every fraction separated (since it is equal to the number of transfers completed at that time), but r is a constant for every fraction and is equal to the total number (R) of tubes in the apparatus.

$$T_{nR} = \frac{n!}{R!(n-R)!} \, p^{R+1} q^{n-R}$$

T_{nR} can be plotted as a function of n. The change to a continuous function, by moving the origin to the maximum, can now be made just as in § 1-3c. When n_{max} is equal to the total number of transfers which have been carried out at the moment that the maximum is being eluted,

$$R = p n_{max}, \quad n_{max} = \frac{R}{p}$$

Then

$$T_{nR} = \left(\frac{2\pi n_{max} q}{p}\right)^{-\frac{1}{2}} \exp\left(\frac{-x^2 p}{2 n_{max} q}\right)$$

$$(1\text{-}13)$$

The bandwidth within the e^{-1} limits may be found as follows:

$$\frac{T_{nR}}{T_{max}} = e^{-1} = \exp\left(\frac{-x^2 p}{2 n_{max} q}\right)$$

$$x_e = \left(\frac{2 n_{max} q}{p}\right)^{\frac{1}{2}} = \frac{2 R q}{p}$$

$$L_e = 2.82 \left(\frac{R q}{p}\right)^{\frac{1}{2}}$$

$$(1\text{-}14)$$

In a similar manner,

$$L_{1\%} = 6\left(\frac{Rq}{p}\right)^{\frac{1}{2}}$$
$$L_{10\%} = 4.3\left(\frac{Rq}{p}\right)^{\frac{1}{2}}$$

(1-15)

The number of tubes needed to achieve a 1% separation is (compare Fig. 1-5)

$$3\frac{(Rq_1)^{\frac{1}{2}}}{p_1} + 3\frac{(Rq_2)^{\frac{1}{2}}}{p_2} - \frac{R}{p_2} + \frac{R}{p_1} = 0$$
$$R^{\frac{1}{2}} \cdot 3(p_2 q_1^{\frac{1}{2}} + p_1 q_2^{\frac{1}{2}}) = R(p_1 - p_2)$$
$$R_{1\%} = 9\left(\frac{p_2 q_1^{\frac{1}{2}} + p_1 q_2^{\frac{1}{2}}}{p_1 - p_2}\right)^2$$

(1-16)

To achieve a 10% separation the coefficient is 4.5 instead of 9. All these relationships are valid only for a mixture containing equal amounts of the two components (see also § 2-3d).

1-3f SEPARATION OF ACIDS FROM BASES

In order to separate weak acids, a solvent mixture is used consisting of a buffer solution and an organic solvent. The ionization of the acid in the aqueous phase [2] is given by

$$A\!-\!H \xrightleftharpoons{K_a} A^{\ominus} + H^{\oplus}, \qquad K_a = \frac{[H^{\oplus}][A^{\ominus}]_2}{[AH]_2}$$

Only the undissociated acid will dissolve in the organic phase [1]. So here

$$K = \frac{[AH]_1}{[AH]_2}$$

The "observed partition coefficient" is therefore

$$K' = \frac{[AH]_1}{[AH]_2 + [A^{\ominus}]_2} \quad (K' < K)$$

but

$$[A^{\ominus}]_2 = K_a \frac{[AH]_2}{[H^{\oplus}]_2}$$

Therefore

$$K' = \frac{K}{(1 + K_a/[H^{\oplus}]_2)}$$

If we use a buffer when $[H^{\oplus}] \ll K_a$, then

$$K' = \frac{K[H^{\oplus}]_2}{K_a}$$

or

$$\boxed{\log K' = \log K - pH + pK_a}$$

(1-17)

For weak bases similar expressions may be derived. For a dibasic acid

$$pK_{a1} < pH < pK_{a2}$$

should be used.

1-4 Miscellaneous Remarks

(*a*) When larger quantities have to be separated the mixture is placed in several other tubes in addition to tube 0.

(*b*) When complications due to association, dissociation, or non-linear partition isotherms arise, the literature [2] should be consulted.

(*c*) For examples and appropriate solvent pairs the reviews of Craig and Craig [2] and von Metzsch [5] are useful.

(*d*) Formula 1-1 should be used when $n < 20$, while formula 1-7 is appropriate for n and $r > 20$. The results of the analysis are plotted against the tube number (r). A smooth curve is drawn through the points, and for each component the position of the maximum is determined (not necessarily an integer). K is calculated, using formula 1-4. By means of formula 1-5 K is again calculated, using the remaining points on the graph. Taking an average value of K, a theoretical partition curve is now calculated with formula 1-1 or 1-7. All points of the theoretical partition curve are multiplied by the factor $F = T_{exp}^{max}/T_{calc}^{max}$ when the calculated maximum is equal to T_{calc}^{max} and the maximum found experimentally is T_{exp}^{max}. The results calculated in this manner are also drawn on the graph.

(*e*) The graph should further contain:

Name	Volume of mobile phase
Date	Volume of stationary phase
Mixture	Phase analyzed (n)
Solvent system used	K_{calc} for each component
Number of tubes	
Number of transfers	

1-5 Small Countercurrent Apparatus

A manually operated apparatus consisting of twelve tubes is used in the experiments described in § 1-6.

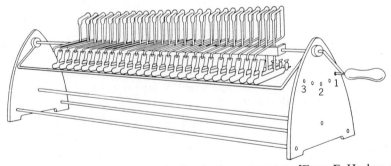

Fig. 1-6. Hand-operated countercurrent distribution apparatus. [From E. Hecker, *Chem. Ing. Tech.*, **25**, 505 (1953).]

The dimensions of the tubes (Fig. 1-1) are chosen so that the volume from the bottom of the tube to the decantation connection is 10 ml. The decantation arm of each tube is connected to the extraction part of the next tube. All twelve connected tubes are mounted in a frame which can be rotated about its longitudinal axis to allow the tubes to take up the position shown in Fig. 1-2.

The apparatus is provided with a stop to prevent rotation beyond position III during equilibration. This stop must be removed before the tubes in position III can be rotated to the decantation position IV. A second stop at the front of the apparatus is used to fix the frame in positions I, III, and IV.

Warning. Do not use silicon grease on the stopcocks of the tubes.

Cleaning the Apparatus. All cells are filled with alcohol, the stopcocks are closed, and the apparatus is tilted several times *first* between positions III and IV and then between positions I and III. All cells are emptied and the operation is repeated, using distilled water. The apparatus is emptied again and left, fixed in position I with all stopcocks open.

1-6 Examples

1-6a SEPARATION OF 2- FROM 8-METHYLQUINOLINE

Solvents. Mutual saturation is essential and is accomplished as follows. Cyclohexane (125 ml., spectrograde) and citric acid–disodiumphosphate buffer (150 ml., pH $\simeq 3.6$; cf. *Handbook of Chemistry and Physics*) are shaken together in a separatory funnel for 5 min.

Filling the Apparatus. Fix the frame in position III (see Fig. 1-2), pour 10 ml. of the buffer solution into tubes 2 through 11 *via* the stopcocks and 20 ml. into tube 1. Close the stopcocks. The excess buffer solution in tube 1 is allowed to pass through tubes 2 through 11 by *slowly* tilting the frame, starting in position IV, *via* positions III and II to position I. The excess is allowed to drain from the apparatus. In this way the bottom half of the extraction tubes will be filled.

Using a funnel with a long, thin stem (apparatus in position III), pipette 10 ml. of a solution of 2- and 8-methylquinoline in cyclohexane (obtainable from assistant) into tube 0; an additional 10 ml. of cyclohexane layer is added to this tube.

Tilting. Tilt the frame *carefully* and *slowly* 25 times between positions III and I. Fix the frame in position III to allow the phases to separate (2 min.) and then turn the frame carefully to position IV (the cyclohexane enters the decantation tube); the apparatus is kept in position IV for $\frac{1}{2}$ min. and then slowly turned to position I (the cyclohexane flows to the extraction tube). Wait another $\frac{1}{2}$ min. The apparatus is now fixed in position III again, 10 ml. of fresh cyclohexane is added to the 0 tube, and the entire cycle is repeated. When the top phase has reached extraction tube 11, and the 0 tube has been filled once again with 10 ml. of cyclohexane, the frame is tilted another 25 times and the liquid phases are allowed to separate in *position I.*

Analysis, Calculation, and Reports (see § 1-4). Empty each tube separately and determine the extinction E of the twelve cyclohexane layers at 316 nm. (1 cm. cell), using the cyclohexane saturated with buffer solution as the reference solvent. Plot E against the tube number r (0.1 unit on the E coordinate = 1 unit on the r coordinate = 2 cm.).

Calculate the partition coefficient of 2-methylquinoline, using the extinctions of the following pairs of tubes: 0–1, 1–2, and 2–3. The partition coefficient of 8-methylquinoline is calculated, using the extinctions of tubes 8–9, 9–10, and 10–11. The following formula is used:

$$K = rE_r(n - r + 1)^{-1}(E_{r-1})^{-1}$$

where K = partition coefficient;

$\quad n$ = number of transfers (11 in this case);

$\quad E_r$ = extinction of tube r.

Using the partition coefficient thus found, calculate the theoretical partition of the two isomeric methylquinolines between the cyclohexane layers.

$$E_0 = K(K + 1)^{-(n+1)}$$

$$E_r = E_{r-1}(n - r + 1)Kr^{-1}$$

The theoretical curve (adjusted to the same scale as the experimental curve) is also drawn on the graph.

Note

(*a*) Show how the formulas used above are derived.

(*b*) Put the cyclohexane left after the experiment has been completed into a labeled bottle.

1-6b   THE SEPARATION OF 3,4,5-TRIHYDROXYBENZOIC ACID AND 4-HYDROXYBENZOIC ACID [8]

Solvents. Ether/water. In a separatory funnel, 150 ml. of peroxide-free ether is shaken with 150 ml. of distilled water for 5 min.

Filling and Tilting the Apparatus. As in example 1-6a, tube 0 is filled with 10 ml. of a solution of the two benzoic acids (see assistant).

Analysis. The aqueous layers are carefully drained into Erlenmeyer flasks while the ether layers are drained into separatory funnels. The aqueous layer is titrated, using $0.01N$ NaOH, with 2–3 drops of bromothymol blue as indicator.

To each of the ether layers from tubes 0 through 8, 10.00 ml. of $0.01N$ NaOH is added from the burette, while 20.00 ml. of $0.01N$ NaOH is added to the ether from cells 9 through 11. Each separatory funnel is shaken for 3 min., the layers are allowed to separate, and the sodium hydroxide layer is drained into an Erlenmeyer. The ether layer is washed twice with distilled water, this being added to the corresponding Erlenmeyer. The excess hydroxide is titrated, using $0.01N$ HCl and 4–5 drops of bromothymol blue indicator.

Note. A solution of trihydroxybenzoic acid turns green upon shaking with excess base.

Calculations and Reports (see § 1-4). A tabulation (see Form 1-1) is made of the number of millimoles of acid (to the nearest 0.01 mmole) which are found in the top and bottom layers of every tube. The columns thus obtained are added.

A graph is drawn, showing the number of millimoles of acid in the top and bottom layer of each tube combined vs. the number of the tube (0.01 mmole = 10 mm. and 1 tube = 20 mm.).

The partition coefficients K_1 and K_2 of both acids are calculated from the tabulation by means of formula 1-5. Using these partition coefficients, the theoretical partition coefficients of these acids are calculated (taking a 1 mole basis for each of the acids). The theoretical results for the first acid are multiplied for every tube with the factor

$$F_1 = \frac{^1T^{max}_{exp}}{^1T^{max}_{theor}}$$

The analogous factor for the second acid is

$$F_2 = \frac{^2T^{max}_{exp}}{^2T^{max}_{theor}}$$

The newly obtained theoretical values for every cell are added, and the results plotted on the graph.

Form 1-1

Cell	Mmoles Acid in		K	Mmoles Acid in Ether + Water Layer	
	Ether Layer	Aqueous Layer		Exp.	Theor.
0					
1					
2					
3					
4					
5					
6					
7					
8					
9					
10					

1-6c SEPARATION OF PHTHALOYLAMINO ACIDS [9]

Solvents. Ethyl acetate/phosphate buffer solution (pH $\simeq$ 5.5; *Handbook of Chemistry and Physics*). One hundred and fifty milliliters of ethyl acetate and 150 ml. of the buffer solution are shaken for 5 min.

Filling and Tilting. Follow example 1-6a. Tube 0 is filled with 10 ml. of the solution, which contains 10 mg. of each of the two amino acids. When the transfers are complete the amino acids are brought into the upper layer. To accomplish this (after the upper phase has reached tube 11) the two phases are allowed to separate in position III (not in position I).

Add 1 ml. of 8M phosphoric acid from a graduated pipette to every tube and tilt the tubes 25 times. Allow to separate in position I.

Analysis, Calculation, and Reports. The tubes are drained separately, and the extinction at 300 nm. of the top phase is determined with an ultraviolet spectrophotometer. The reference solvent is ethyl acetate saturated with buffer solution. The directions used in example 1-6a are applicable from here on.

Notes

(*a*) Good separations may be achieved with the following acid pairs:

Phthaloylglycine–phthaloylphenylalanine.

Phthaloylglycine–phthaloyl-α-aminobutyric acid.

(*b*) Preparation of phthaloyl derivatives [10].

Dissolve 10 moles of the amino acid and 10 mmoles of sodium carbonate in 15 ml. of water. Add 10 mmoles of N-carboethoxyphthalimide. Stir the mixture until virtually all of the N-carboethoxyphthalimide is dissolved (10–15 min.). Filter the solution and acidify with 6N HCl. The precipitate formed is redissolved by carefully warming the solution, which is then allowed to cool slowly.

An alternative procedure [11] consists in taking equimolar quantities of the amino acid and phthalic acid and heating them to 180° in a heavy-wall test tube, using a Woods metal bath. Stir the mixture for 10 min.; then raise the temperature to 185° and keep there for 5 min. Cool and crystallize the product from water (1:9 by volume).

1-6d SEPARATION OF NICOTINAMIDE AND BENZAMIDE

Solvents. Shake 150 ml. of ethyl acetate with 150 ml. of water for 15 min., separate the layers, and use them as mobile and stationary phases.

Filling and Tilting the Apparatus. Follow example 1-6a. To cell 0, 150 mg. of nicotinamide and 100 mg. of benzamide dissolved in the stationary phase are added. To tube 1, 10 ml. of the mobile phase is added. During the distribution process this phase will precede all others and will be in the decantation tube of cell 11 at the end of the experiment.

Analysis by Weighing. At the end of the distribution process both layers are emptied out of each cell into numbered and tared evaporating dishes. The cells are rinsed with acetone. The contents of the decantation tube II is treated just like the other fractions. This "blank" gives an indication of the amount of stopcock grease dissolved in the mobile phase during the distribution.

The evaporating dishes are placed in a vacuum desiccator, which is evacuated at the aspirator. As soon as the ethyl acetate has evaporated the pressure will drop sharply. The dishes are placed in a drying oven at 60–70° overnight and finally for a few hours in a desiccator over calcium chloride. Determine the total amount of acid amides in each cell by weighing. Calculations and reporting are done as in example 1-6a.

1-6e   EQUIPMENT

24 Erlenmeyers (100 ml.)	2 Pipettes (10 ml.)
Separatory funnel (500 ml.)	Thin-stemmed funnel
3 Separatory funnels (50 ml.)	Beaker (800 ml.)
Graduate cylinder (10 ml.)	12 Evaporating dishes
Graduate cylinder (250 ml.)	

Fig. 1-7. Fully automatic countercurrent apparatus of F. A. von Metzsch (Glastechnische Werkstätten Hermann Kühn, Hospitalstrasse 4c, Göttingen, Germany). The apparatus contains 100 cells in two rows of 50.

1-7 Large Apparatus for Countercurrent Distribution

Many types of apparatus for countercurrent distribution are currently commercially available. An example is the one pictured in Fig. 1-7, currently in use in the author's laboratory.

1-8 References

1. H. M. Rauen and W. Stamm, *Gegenstromverteilung*, Springer Verlag, Berlin, 1953.
2. L. C. Craig and D. Craig in *Technique of Organic Chemistry*, A. Weissberger, ed., Interscience Publishers, New York, 1956, 2nd Ed., Vol. III, Part I, p. 149.
3. J. R. Weisiger in *Organic Analysis*, J. Mitchell, I. M. Kolthoff, and E. S. Proskauer, eds., Interscience Publishers, New York, 1954, Vol. II, p. 277.
4. O. Jübermann in *Methoden der organischen Chemie*, Houben-Weyl, ed., G. Thieme Verlag, Stuttgart, 1958, Band I/1, pp. 227–339.
5. F. A. v. Metzsch, *Angew. Chem.*, **65**, 586 (1953), and **68**, 323 (1956); *Chem. Ing. Tech.*, **25**, 66 (1953).
6. L. C. Craig, *J. Biol. Chem.*, **155**, 519 (1944).
7. M. Verzele, *Bull. soc. chim. Belges*, **62**, 619 (1953).
8. R. P. Linstead, J. A. Elvidge, and M. Whalley, *A Course in Modern Techniques of Organic Chemistry*, Butterworths Scientific Publications, London, 1955, Ch. 5, p. 27.
9. R. W. Cowgill and A. B. Pardee, *Experiments in Biochemical Research Techniques*, John Wiley and Sons, New York, 1957, p. 19.
10. G. H. L. Nefkens, G. I. Tesser, and R. J. F. Nivard, *Rec. trav. chim.*, **79**, 688 (1960).
11. J. H. Billman and W. F. Harting, *J. Am. Chem. Soc.*, **70**, 1473 (1948).
12. E. Hecker, *Verteilungsverfahren im Laboratorium*, Verlag Chemie, Weinheim, 1955.
13. L. Alders, *Liquid-Liquid Extraction*, Elsevier Publishing Co., Amsterdam 1959, 2nd ed.
14. B. Keil in *Laboratoriumstechnik der Organischen Chemie*, Akademie Verlag, Berlin, 1961, pp. 467–534.
15. K. B. Wiberg, *Laboratory Technique in Organic Chemistry*, McGraw-Hill Book Co., New York, 1960, pp. 179–190.
16. A. E. Werner and M. Waldichuk, "Continuous Liquid-Liquid Extractor," *Anal. Chem.*, **34**, 1674–1676 (1962).
17. Robert Ewald Treybal, *Liquid Extraction*, McGraw-Hill Book Co., New York, 1963. 2nd ed.
18. P. K. Hietala, *Acta Chem. Scand.*, **14**, 212–214 (1960)(in English).

2

Chromatography

2-1 Introduction

When components of a mixture are separated by making use of their differences in partition coefficients between two phases, the term *chromatography* is applied. A mobile phase is used to carry the mixture through a column. The presence of a second (stationary) phase influences the movement of the components to a different extent. Thus a separation is achieved.

Several systems may be distinguished; they may be based upon differences in:

(*a*) Adsorption.
(*b*) Partition between two liquid phases.
(*c*) Partition between a liquid and a gas phase.
(*d*) Ion exchange.

Depending upon the phases used, several distinct methods, each applicable to a specific area, are known (Table 2-1). Many experimental factors influence the choice of the best method. Some examples using these different techniques are listed in Table 2-2.

2-2 Different Methods of Developing a Chromatogram

In addition to a variation in the phases used a change in the method of developing the chromatogram may sometimes be useful. This is illustrated with adsorption chromatography.

(*a*) *Frontal Analysis* [9] (Fig. 2-1). At the top of the column a solution of the unknown mixture is added continuously, while the concentration of the components leaving the column is determined (as a function of the volume). Figure 2-2 shows the result of such an analysis. The component which is least strongly absorbed (A) is eluted first; the second component (B) follows, while component (C), which is absorbed the strongest, leaves last. This method is suitable for analysis only, since a real separation of the components is not achieved.

(*b*) *Displacement Analysis* [10] (Fig. 2-3). A given quantity of the mixture is added to the top of the column, and a developing liquid (desorbent, X) is used

Table 2-1

Stationary Phase	Mobile Phase	Method	Example in Chapter
Solid	Gas	Gas (adsorption) chromatography	8
Solid	Liquid	Adsorption chromatography	4
Liquid	Gas	Gas-liquid partition chromatography	7
Liquid	Liquid	Partition chromatography	3
		Paper chromatography	6

Table 2-2

Gas Adsorption Chromatography	Gas-liquid Partition Chromatography	Adsorption Chromatography	Partition Chromatography	Chromatography over Ion-exchange Resins
Gases: H_2, O_2, N_2, CO_2, etc. Hydrocarbons (up to C_4)	Volatile compounds (up to b.p. 200° with special techniques to ~300°)	Solid and liquid organic compounds, such as olefins, aromatics, carbohydrates, steroids, porphyrines, carotenoids	Solid and liquid organic compounds, such as amines, esters, fatty acids, hydrocarbons, proteins	Amino acids, peptides, nucleotides, carbohydrates

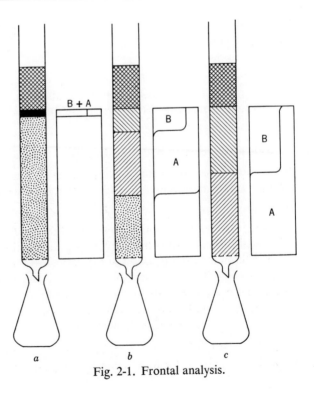

Fig. 2-1. Frontal analysis.

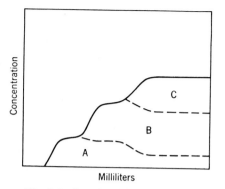

Fig. 2-2. Result of frontal analysis.

which is absorbed more strongly than the components of the mixture. Elution with a solution of a desorbent is also feasible. The mixture is displaced by the desorbent and separates in such a fashion that the component which is absorbed least strongly moves up front (Fig. 2-4).

Only a little of the unknown mixture and the solvent is used in displacement analysis. However, because of the effect of the adsorption of one component upon the adsorption of the others, this method is not uniformly successful.

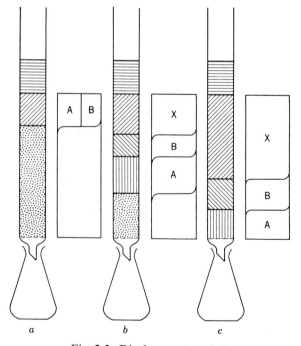

Fig. 2-3. Displacement analysis.

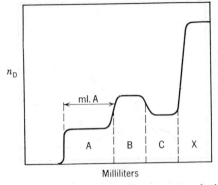

Fig. 2-4. Result of displacement analysis.

(c) *Elution Analysis* [11] (Fig. 2-5). A given amount of the mixture is added to the top of the column, and a suitable solvent is used to elute the components. The components of the mixture move through the column with varying speeds, depending upon the extent to which they are adsorbed. Thus bands are formed which leave the column one after the other (Fig. 2-6).

Distinct zones are obtained with sufficiently slow moving components. By cutting up the column and extracting these zones it is often possible to isolate the

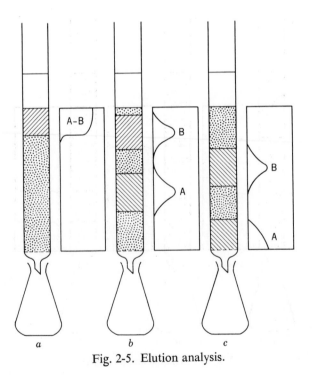

Fig. 2-5. Elution analysis.

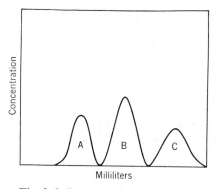

Fig. 2-6. Result of elution analysis.

components. Another method is to elute the column with solvents of increasing solvent power (roughly polarity, e.g., petroleum ether, benzene, ether, acetone, alcohol; see p. 36).

Table 2-3   Summary of Chromatographic Techniques

Stationary Phase	Solid		Liquid	
Mobile Phase	Gas	Liquid	Gas	Liquid
Frontal analysis	James and Phillips (1953) [6]	Tiselius (1940) [9]	Griffiths and Phillips (1954) [12]	Phillips *et al.* (1952) [14]
Displacement analysis	Turner (1943) [7]	Tiselius (1943) [10]		Levi (1949) [15]
Elution analysis	Cremer *et al.* (1951) [8]	Tswett (1906) [11]	James and Martin (1952) [13]	Martin and Synge (1941) [16]

2-3   Partition Chromatography (Elution Analysis I)

2-3a   PLATE THEORY [1]

Partition chromatography and countercurrent distribution are closely related. Thus a similar theoretical treatment is possible.

The chromatographic column is divided into a number of hypothetical "plates," which correspond to the tubes of the countercurrent apparatus. Assume that equilibrium conditions exist between the mobile and stationary phases with a theoretical plate and that the continuous liquid movement in the column is equal (in the limit) to the discontinuous transfer of the mobile phase. The relationships derived in Chapter 1 (§ 1-3e) can now be applied.

Let the number of theoretical plates of the column equal R; then, according to formula 1-13:

$$T_{nR} = \left(\frac{2\pi n_{max} q}{p}\right)^{-\frac{1}{2}} \exp\left(\frac{-x^2 p}{2 n_{max} q}\right)$$ (2-1)

and

$$n_{max} = \frac{R}{p}$$ (2-2)

where n_{max} = number of times the mobile phase has moved to a next plate at the moment that the maximum is being eluted;

$p = \alpha K/(\alpha K + 1)$;
$q = 1/(\alpha K + 1)$;
$\alpha = V_m/V_s$ = ratio of volumes of mobile to stationary phase in a theoretical plate;
$K = C_m/C_s$ = ratio of the concentration of the substance being chromatographed in the mobile and stationary phase;
T_{nR} = fraction of starting substance.

In order to use symbols for quantities which can be measured directly it is necessary to introduce:

V_{max} = retention volume = amount of liquid which has left the column at the instant the maximum is being eluted = $n_{max} V_m$;
V = total volume of the mobile phase present in the column = RV_m.

Formula 2-2 then becomes:

$$n_{max} = \frac{V_{max}}{V_m} = \frac{R}{p} = \frac{V}{pV_m}$$

$$\boxed{\text{Retention volume} = V_{max} = \frac{V}{p}}$$ (2-3)

V can be determined readily by chromatographing a small amount of a substance insoluble in the stationary phase $(K \gg 1)$; then

$$V_{max} = V$$

2-3b   DETERMINATION OF THE NUMBER OF THEORETICAL PLATES OF A COLUMN FROM THE HEIGHT OF THE MAXIMUM

Just before the maximum is eluted from the column, that fraction of the material put on the column, which is present in the last plate, can be calculated with formula 1-7:

$$T_{nR} = (2\pi npq)^{-\frac{1}{2}} \exp\left(\frac{-x^2}{2npq}\right)$$

For the maximum $x = 0$. If the original amount put on the column is T_0, then, at the instant described above, the last plate contains

$$T_{nR} = T_0 (2\pi n_{max} pq)^{-\frac{1}{2}}$$

pT_{nR} is present in the mobile phase (volume V_m) and is being eluted. Thus the concentration of the solution which leaves the column at the maximum is

$$C_{\max} = \frac{pT_0}{V_m}(2\pi n_{\max}pq)^{-\frac{1}{2}}$$

using 2-2

$$C_{\max} = \frac{pT_0}{V_m}(2\pi Rq)^{-\frac{1}{2}}$$

but

$$V_m = \frac{V}{R} = \frac{pV_{\max}}{R}$$

so

$$C_{\max} = T_0\frac{R}{V_{\max}}(2\pi Rq)^{-\frac{1}{2}}$$

and

$$\boxed{R = \left(\frac{C_{\max}V_{\max}}{T_0}\right)^2 2\pi q} \tag{2-4}$$

2-3c NUMBER OF THEORETICAL PLATES FROM BANDWIDTH

According to formula 1-15, the following equation pertaining to the single withdrawal of the countercurrent distribution method is valid:

$$L_{10\%} = 4.3\left(\frac{Rq}{p}\right)^{\frac{1}{2}}$$

Using transfer numbers, we switch to volumes (compare Fig. 2-7):

$$\frac{V_{10\%}}{L_{10\%}} = V_{\max}/n_{\max}$$

$$V_{10\%} = \frac{V_{\max}}{n_{\max}} 4.3\left(\frac{Rq}{p}\right)^{\frac{1}{2}}$$

Since $n_{\max} = R/p$,

$$V_{10\%} = 4.3 \cdot V_{\max} Rq$$

$$\boxed{R = 18.5 \cdot q\left(\frac{V_{\max}}{V_{10\%}}\right)^2} \tag{2-5}$$

2-3d SEPARATION

The number of theoretical plates (R) necessary to effect a specific separation can be found with the aid of formula 1-16:

$$R_{10\%} = 4.3\left(\frac{p_2q_1^{\frac{1}{2}} + p_1q_2^{\frac{1}{2}}}{p_1 - p_2}\right)^2 \tag{2-6}$$

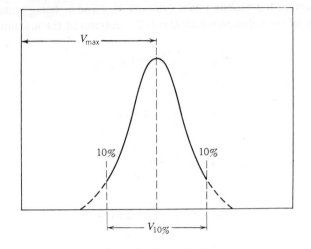

Fig. 2-7. Bandwidth.

The amount of one component which falls within the band of another component can be found in an analogous manner [4]. The result is shown in Fig. 2-8. The separation factor is β. When unequal amounts of both components are present, the impurity is

$$\eta = \frac{2m_1m_2}{m_1^2 + m_2^2}\,\eta_{1:1}$$

Example. Separation of a Mixture Containing Two Substances in a Mole Ratio of 1:1. If the separation factor $\beta = 1.2$, one component may overlap the band of the other component by 5% when $R \cong 350$. In case the mole ratio is 9:1, then

$$2m_1m_2/(m_1^2 + m_2^2) = 2 \times 0.1 \times 0.9/(0.1^2 + 0.9^2) = 0.22$$

On the η ordinate we read $0.22 \times 5 \times 10^{-22} = 1.1 \times 10^{-2}$; thus $R \cong 700$.

2-3e CONTINUOUS FLOW

A better approximation of partition chromatography takes into consideration that the mobile phase flows continuously from one plate to the next. This is a fundamental difference between countercurrent distribution and chromatography. Thus we deal with a Poisson function [2], instead of with a binominal distribution.

In the case of a large number of partition cycles (when V_{max}/V_m is large), both distribution curves can be approximated to a reasonable degree with a Gaussian curve [3]. Thus the results using the closer approximation no longer differ from those obtained with the formulas derived above.

2-3f RATE THEORY

The theory of chromatographic processes has been given a kinetic treatment also. The increase in bandwidth during the elution can be considered in terms of a diffusion process [2, 3]. This treatment leads to results similar to the ones obtained with the plate theory.

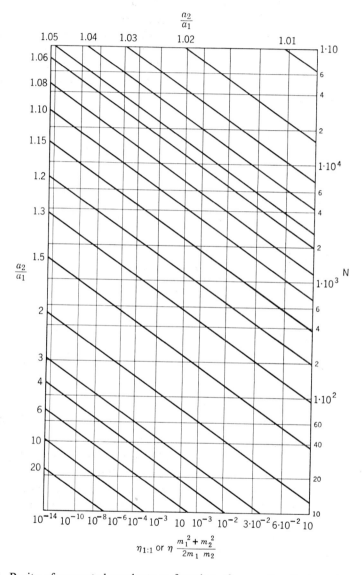

Fig. 2-8. Purity of separated products as function of separation factor a_2/a_1, number of theoretical plates N, and mass ratio m_1/m_2. Note: $a_2/a_1 = \beta$. [From E. Glueckauf. *Trans. Faraday Soc.*, **51**, 34 (1955).]

2-4   Adsorption Chromatography (Elution Analysis II)

2-4a   PLATE THEORY

Adsorption chromatography and countercurrent distribution may, in principle, be given a similar theoretical treatment even though the relationship between the two is not as close as that between partition chromatography and countercurrent distribution. The symbols p, q, and K need redefinition, however.

K expresses the ratio of the amount of substance adsorbed to its concentration in the mobile phase. When we are dealing with a linear adsorption isotherm (linear chromatography), K will be constant. Then $p = K/(K + 1)$ is equal to the fraction of the substance adsorbed, and $q = 1/(K + 1)$ is equal to the fraction which is present in the mobile phase at equilibrium.

The following formulas hold again:

$$\text{Retention volume} = V_{\max} = \frac{V}{p} \tag{2-3}$$

$$R = \left(\frac{C_{\max} - V_{\max}}{T_0}\right)^2 2\pi q \tag{2-4}$$

$$\text{Number of plates} = R = 18.5 \cdot q \left(\frac{V_{\max}}{V_{10\%}}\right)^2 \tag{2-5}$$

Number of plates needed to effect a 10% separation

$$R_{10\%} = 4.5\left(\frac{p_2 q_1^{\frac{1}{2}} + p_1 q_2^{\frac{1}{2}}}{p_1 - p_2}\right)^2 \tag{2-6}$$

2-4b   EXTRUSION TECHNIQUE

In case the components of the mixture move very slowly through the column ($K \ll 1$), the process should be interrupted before the components are eluted. The adsorbent can be pushed carefully out of the column and cut into suitable pieces. The formulas derived for the fundamental procedure of the countercurrent distribution must be applied in this case.

2-4c R_F-VALUE

The R_F-value is frequently used to indicate the speed with which a substance moves through the column. By definition it is the ratio of the displacement velocity of the substance to that of an ideal standard substance which does not dissolve in the stationary phase (or which is not adsorbed by the stationary phase).

Again the formulas applicable to the fundamental procedure are used.

For our substance:

$$r_{\max} = np$$

For the standard ($1/K = 0$, $p = 1$):

$$r'_{\max} = n$$

$$R_F = \frac{r_{\max}}{r'_{\max}} = p = \frac{\alpha K}{1 + \alpha K}$$

2-5   References

1. M. Verzele and F. Alderweireldt, *Bull. soc. chim. Belges*, **64,** 579 (1955); M. Verzele F. Alderweireldt, and M. Vandewalle, *ibid.*, **66,** 570 (1957).
2. A. J. P. Martin and R. L. M. Synge, *Biochem. J.*, **35,** 1358 (1941); J. J. van Deemter, F. J. Zuiderweg, and A. Klinkenberg, *Chem. Eng. Sci.*, **5,** 271 (1956).
3. A. Klinkenberg and F. Sjenitzer, *Chem. Eng. Sci.*, **5,** 258 (1956).
4. E. Glueckauf, *Trans. Faraday Soc.*, **51,** 34 (1955).
5. H. C. Cassidy, *Fundamentals of Chromatography*, Vol. X in *Technique of Organic Chemistry*, A. Weissberger, ed., Interscience Publishers, New York, 1957.
6. D. H. James and C. S. G. Phillips, *J. Chem. Soc.*, 1600 (1953) and 1066 (1954).
7. N. C. Turner, *Natl. Petrol. News*, **35,** R-234 (1943).
8. E. Cremer and F. Prior, *Z. Elektrochem.*, **55,** 66 (1951); E. Cremer and R. Müller, *ibid.*, **55,** 217 (1951).
9. A. Tiselius, *Arkiv Kemi, Mineral. Geol.*, **B14,** no. 22 (1940).
10. A. Tiselius, *Arkiv Kemi, Mineral. Geol.*, **A16,** no. 18 (1943).
11. M. Tswett, *Ber. deut. botan. Ges.*, **24,** 316, 384 (1906).
12. J. H. Griffiths and C. S. G. Phillips, *J. Chem. Soc.*, 3446 (1954).
13. A. T. James and A. J. P. Martin, *Biochem. J.*, **50,** 679 (1952).
14. J. H. Griffiths, D. H. James, and C. S. G. Phillips, *Analyst*, **77,** 897 (1952).
15. A. A. Levi, *Discussions Faraday Soc.*, **7,** 124 (1949).
16. A. J. P. Martin and R. L. M. Synge, *Biochem. J.*, **35,** 1358 (1941).
17. M. Lederer, ed., *Journal of Chromatography*, Elsevier Publishing Co., Amsterdam, Vol. I. 1958, and Vols. VII and VIII, 1962.

3

Partition chromatography

3-1 Introduction

Partition chromatography is a method of separation which is based upon the difference in partition coefficients of the components of a mixture when distributed between two liquid phases. The stationary phase is fixed by means of an inert solid substance, while the mobile phase flows through the column.

The solid phase (carrier) is chosen so as to minimize adsorption of the components of the mixture. Silica gel is commonly used as carrier, with water or a suitable buffer solution as the stationary phase. Elution is carried out using a liquid immiscible with water.

In some cases the choice of a lipophile liquid as stationary phase may be advantageous. This phase can be used in conjunction with rubber, glass powder, or Hyflo Super Cel (made water repellent with silicones). Elution is then carried out with an aqueous liquid (*reversed phase chromatography*).

Figure 3-1 shows a column used for partition chromatography. *No* stopcock grease should be used.

3-2 Fraction Collector (Fig. 3-2)

Depending on the desired volume of each fraction (1–20 ml.), the weight is adjusted so that the switch makes contact just before the siphon is filled.

3-3 Examples

3-3a SEPARATION OF ALIPHATIC ACIDS [3, 4]

Liquids. Chloroform: shake with water, dry (CaCl$_2$), and pass over a column of alumina (or distill).

Butanol: shake with 0.1N NaOH, dry (Na$_2$CO$_3$), distill.

Mobile phase: shake the chloroform 3 times with half its volume of water, and separate. Add the appropriate amount of butanol, followed by 15 ml. of water for every 100 ml. of liquid. Shake and separate (explain the need for all these operations).

Stationary Phase. Silica gel, prepared from water glass according to the

30

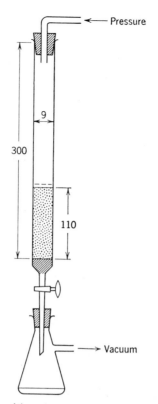

Fig. 3-1. Column for partition chromatography (dimensions in millimeters).

Fig. 3-2. Fraction collector.

directions of Gordon, Martin, and Synge [6], is used as carrier. Commercial water glass (140° Tw.—Jos. Crosfield, Ltd., Warrington) is diluted to 3 vol. with distilled water containing a little methyl orange. $10N$ HCl is added in a thin stream with vigorous stirring, addition being interrupted at intervals and stirring continued to get efficient mixing. The solution changes first slowly and then rapidly to a thick porridge, and all but the smallest lumps are broken up by stirring. When the mixture is permanently acid to thymol blue, addition of HCl is stopped and the mixture is kept 3 hr. It is filtered on a Buchner funnel and washed with distilled water (approx. 2 l./250 g. dry gel) without allowing the precipitate to crack. The gel is then suspended in $N/5$ HCl and aged 2 days at room temperature. It is again filtered and washed in the same way with distilled water (approx. 5 l./250 g. dry gel) until the washings are free from methyl orange.

The SiO_2 is dried for 1 hr. at 110° before the experiment and allowed to cool in a vacuum desiccator overnight. Finely powdered silica gel (4 g.) is mixed in a mortar with 1 ml. of bromocresol solution (50 mg. in 25 ml. of water $+$ 0.7 ml. of appr. $0.1N$ ammonia). *Carefully* add a few drops of 5% ammonia with constant stirring to the (yellow-colored) gel until the color has changed to light blue-green. Then add 2 ml. of water, followed, in small portions, by 25–30 ml. of 1% butanol-chloroform (vol./vol.) while stirring constantly.

Filling the Column. Take a column (Fig. 3-1) of 30 cm. length and 9 mm. internal diameter. Add a few milliliters of butanol-chloroform (close the stopcock) and place a cotton plug (wetted with butanol-chloroform) in the column (see Fig. 3-1) in such a manner that no airbubbles are trapped. Using a funnel, pour the green slurry into the column and remove all trapped air bubbles by rotating the column between both hands. Remove excess liquid (using pressure) until the stationary phase no longer flows upon tilting the column.

Dissolve 0.5 mmol of acetic acid, propionic acid, and butyric acid in 10 ml. of the 1% butanol-chloroform solution; add 1 ml. of this solution to the column. When this has been adsorbed, add 1 ml. of the eluent. Develop the column with 5% butanol-chloroform (vol./vol.) (using slight positive pressure) until the first of the three (yellow) zones which were formed (butyric acid) is eluted. Elution is continued, using 10% butanol-chloroform (vol./vol.) until the second band (propionic acid) is eluted. The acetic acid is eluted using 15% butanol-chloroform (vol./vol.). Collect 1-ml. fractions.

Add an equal amount of water to each fraction and titrate with $0.01N$ NaOH (indicator phenol red; microburette) until the solution turns red. Shake well (usually the solution will turn yellow again) and titrate until the solution remains red upon shaking. Now titrate 1 ml. of the original solution as well as a blank.

Calculate the number of millimoles of acid in each fraction and plot this number either against the number of milliliters of eluate or against the number of the fraction. Compare the amount of acid after and before the separation and calculate the loss (in per cent) incurred during the separation.

Report. Prepare a table containing the number of milliliters of NaOH used, the calculated number of millimoles of acid, and the number of the fraction (or milliliters of eluate).

Plot the number of milliequivalents vs. the number of milliliters of eluate (10^{-6} mole = 1 cm., 1 fraction = 1 cm.). Calculate the amount recovered and the percentage loss.

3-3b SEPARATION OF HIGHER-MOLECULAR-WEIGHT FATTY ACIDS [5] (Reversed phase partition chromatography)

Stationary Phase. Hyflo Super Cel is used as carrier. Dry the Super Cel at 110°, cool, and allow to stand for a week in a vacuum desiccator over dichloro-dimethylsilane. The Super Cel has now become water repellent and floats on water. Wash the Super Cel with methanol until free from acid (check with bromothymol blue) and shake together 8 g. of Super Cel and 8 ml. of paraffin oil (use a mechanical shaker) until the mixture is homogeneous and no lumps are present.

Mobile Phase. A 60% acetone-water (vol./vol.) mixture is shaken with paraffin oil, and the acetone-water layer is used as aqueous phase.

Filling the Column. Add the mobile phase to the stationary phase in small portions and with constant stirring, thus preventing any lumps from forming. Use a column having a diameter of 10 mm. and a length of 30 cm. A few milliliters of the mobile phase is added to the column, and a cotton plug, wetted with mobile phase, is placed at the bottom. All air bubbles are removed. The slurry is added slowly to the column, taking care, by using a tamping rod and moving the column, that no air bubbles are trapped. The excess liquid is drained from the column.

Add a solution containing lauric acid, myristic acid, palmitic acid, and stearic acid (2 mg. of each acid dissolved in 1 ml. of mobile phase) to the column. Elution is started immediately upon adsorption of the acids. Collect 5-ml. fractions and titrate, using 0.01 N NaOH against phenol red (microburette).

Report. See § 3-3a.

3-3c EQUIPMENT

Bromocresol green	Mortar and pestle
Chloroform	10 Pipettes (1 and 0.1 ml.)
Butanol	Separatory funnel (500 ml.)
Vacuum desiccator	Graduate cylinder (100 ml.)
Porcelain dish	10 Erlenmeyers (100 ml.)
Column (300 × 9 mm.)	Round-bottom flask (250 ml.)
Funnel	Fraction collector
Tamping rod	

3-4 References

1. E. Lederer and M. Lederer, *Chromatography*, Elsevier Publishing Co., Amsterdam, 1954, Division III, p. 65.
2. H. G. Cassidy, *Fundamentals of Chromatography*, Vol. X in *Technique of Organic Chemistry*, A. Weissberger, ed., Interscience Publishers, New York, 1957.
3. S. R. Elsden, *Biochem. J.*, **40**, 252 (1946).
4. M. H. Peterson and M. J. Johnson, *J. Biol. Chem.*, **174**, 775 (1948).
5. G. A. Howard and A. J. P. Martin, *Biochem. J.*, **46**, 532 (1950).
6. A. H. Gordon, A. J. P. Martin, and R. L. M. Synge, *Biochem. J.*, **37**, 79 (1943).

4

Adsorption chromatography

4-1 Introduction

Adsorption chromatography is a method of separation which is based on the difference in adsorption of the components of a mixture on a solid. This solid adsorbent (in finely divided form) is contained in a column. The solution containing the mixture is passed through this column.

4-2 Apparatus

Figure 4-1 shows a column used in adsorption chromatography. Uniform packing of the adsorbent is essential to increase regular bands. It may be achieved by adding the dry adsorbent to the column while tapping the column continuously (*dry packing*) or by making a slurry from the adsorbent and the liquid (*wet packing*). A slight variation consists of slowly adding the finely powdered solid (through a funnel) to the column containing the liquid. Dry packing frequently causes the appearance of air bubbles.

4-3 Adsorbents and Eluents

In order to effect proper separation the choice of adsorbents and eluents is important. This choice depends upon the physical as well as the chemical properties of the mixture. The following considerations should be borne in mind.

In order of decreasing activity adsorbents may be arranged approximately as shown in Table 4-1.

The activity of some of these adsorbents may be varied, depending upon initial preparation. The activity of aluminum oxide, for instance, is very sensitive to the moisture content (see § 4-7).

Solvents, arranged approximately in order of increasing polarity (ability to elute a polar substance), are as shown in Table 4-2. Mixtures of solvents are

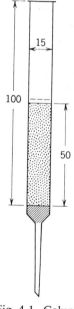

Fig. 4-1. Column for adsorption chromatography (dimensions in millimeters).

Table 4-1   Adsorbents

Activated carbon	
Iron oxide	
Magnesium silicate	
Aluminum oxide	
Silica gel	
Aluminum hydroxide	Decreasing
Calcium hydroxide	adsorbent
Calcium carbonate	power
Calcium sulfate	
Talcum powder	
Sugar	
Starch	
Powdered cellulose	↓

frequently used in order to obtain a polarity best suited to the problem. The experiment described in § 4-6 can be exceedingly useful in this connection. A rapid insight is gained into the partition coefficients and separability of the mixture.

The eluents must be of high purity and free of moisture, since water is adsorbed strongly by most adsorbents. Thus 50 mg. of water (1 drop!) is sufficient to displace 1 g. of cholesterol from alumina. This is the amount of water normally present in 6 ml. of ether! Traces of alcohol (for instance, in ethyl acetate, ether, or chloroform), peroxides (in ethers and hydrocarbons), olefins (in commercial hydrocarbons), heterocyclic compounds and phenols (in aromatic hydrocarbons), or free acids (in halogenated hydrocarbons) can all hamper proper separations.

Table 4-2   The Eluotropic Series

Petroleum ether (hexane)	
Cyclohexane	
Carbon disulfide	
Carbon tetrachloride	
Benzene	
Dichloromethane	
Chloroform	
Ether	
Tetrahydrofuran	Increasing
Ethyl acetate	polarity
Acetone	
n-Butanol	
Ethanol	
Methanol	
Phenol	
Water	
Acetic acid	
Pyridine	↓

4-4 Examples

4-4a PURIFICATION OF ANTHRACENE

A 15 mm. diameter column of appropriate length is filled (using wet packing) to a height of about 10 cm. with 25 g. of alumina (activity Brockmann II). (Use a column equipped with a stopcock. Do *not* use stopcock grease.) The column is filled half way with hexane, and a cotton plug wetted with hexane is placed in the bottom. The alumina is added through a funnel in a careful, slow stream to the column while the glass is tapped continuously.

When all the alumina has been added, the hexane is drained from the tube until its level is about 1 cm. above that of the alumina. The drained liquid is added to the column, and this process is repeated until the alumina no longer moves downward. The top of the alumina is carefully smoothed. Take care that at least 1 cm. of liquid is present at all times above the alumina. A small disk of filter paper, placed on top of the alumina, prevents disturbance of the surface.

With an addition funnel, a solution containing 50 mg. of technical grade anthracene in 50 ml. of hexane is added at a rate of 1–2 drops/sec., while the solution is drained at the bottom at a similar rate. If necessary, suction (aspirator) may be applied to the bottom of the column, but care must be taken that no evaporation of the solvent occurs.

When all the anthracene has been added, the column is developed with 30 ml. of hexane. Three bands visible in ultraviolet light can be distinguished:

(*a*) Top band, blue fluorescence: *carbazole*.
(*b*) Middle band, yellow-green fluorescence: *naphthacene*.
(*c*) Bottom band (broad) blue fluorescence: *anthracene*.

Elution is continued, using 40 ml. of a mixture of benzene and hexane (1:1, vol./vol.); receivers are changed as soon as the bottom band leaves the column. Pure anthracene is obtained by evaporating the solvent under reduced pressure. The yield (about 45 mg.) is determined, and the melting point recorded. Compare the melting point with that of the crude starting material and with that recorded in the literature.

Clean and dry the column. Put the used alumina in the appropriate container.

4-4b SEPARATION OF ANTHRACENE FROM NAPHTHALENE [4]

A column is filled to a height of 20 cm. with 50 g. of alumina (activity Brock-mann I) according to the technique described in § 4-4a. A solution containing 50 mg. of anthracene and 50 mg. of naphthalene in 100 ml. of hexane is added to the column (1–2 drops/sec.). Elute with 100 ml. of hexane. The same three bands are visible in ultraviolet light as before. The naphthalene band coincides with the anthracene band but is not fluorescent.

Using another 200 ml. of hexane, continue the procedure. Check on· the appearance of naphthalene by evaporating a drop of the eluate on a watchglass.

Change the receiver just before the appearance of the anthracene. Continue elution with about 150 ml. of benzene-hexane (1:1, vol./vol.). Evaporate all fractions under reduced pressure; determine yield and melting points of both compounds.

Compare with starting materials and literature value. Clean the column.

4-4c SEPARATION OF CAROTENOIDS AND OTHER COLORING MATTERS

One pound of grated carrots (or spinach greens) is divided among 4 Erlenmeyers; small glass splinters, 50 ml. of hexane, and 25 ml. of ethanol are added to each flask and the flasks are shaken for 1 hr. on a shaker. The pulp is squeezed well in a towel and rinsed with 150 ml. of methanol. If necessary, centrifuge the liquid (20 min. at 3000 r.p.m.). Separate layers, dry the hexane layer over Na_2SO_4, remove the solvent under reduced pressure, and keep the residue in a vacuum desiccator (in the dark).

Fill a chromatograph column (1.7 cm. diameter) as in §4-4a, using in succession 8 g. of alumina (Brockmann III), 5 g. of calcium carbonate (80–100 mesh, dried at 100° for 30 min.), and 7 g. of saccharose (80–100 mesh). Make a slurry of each of the adsorbents separately, using 15, 30, and 20 ml. of hexane, respectively. Then add these slurries to the column in the proper sequence, using tamping rod and tapping to ensure absence of air bubbles. Rinse any adsorbent from the inside of the column with hexane, before adding a new component. Place a disk of filter paper on top of the column and maintain a 2-cm. liquid layer on top of the adsorbent at all times. Apply the crude mixture of vegetable dyes to the column, using 10 ml. of hexane. The top of the column is now connected to the compressed air, and the pressure is regulated so that the liquid flows from the column at a rate of about 1 drop/sec. Two 10-ml. portions of hexane are added to the column upon adsorption of the initial crude extract.

The column is developed with hexane-benzene. (4:1, vol./vol.). A number of colored zones (depending on the starting material) become visible:

(a) A dark green band in the saccharose layer = chlorophyll-b.
(b) A second green band in the saccharose–calcium carbonate layer = chlorophyll-a.
(c) An orange band in the calcium carbonate layer = xanthophyllene.
(d) A red band in the bottom layer = carotenoids.

Interrupt the elution process when the (c) and (d) zones are well separated. Carefully extrude the adsorbent and cut out the red band. The column will crumble when it becomes too dry. Extract the carotenoids with hexane containing 0.02% methanol, remove the solvent under reduced pressure, weigh the residue, and keep it in the dark in a vacuum desiccator.

Dissolve a small amount in CS_2 and determine its absorption spectrum (Chapter 19).

4-4d SEPARATION OF CAROTENOIDS

Fill a column (length 30 cm., diameter 3 cm.), using the wet method with a 3:1 mixture of magnesium oxide and Super Cel. The mixture of carotenoids (25 mg., obtained as in § 4-4c) is dissolved in the minimum quantity of petroleum ether (or hexane) and put on the column, rinsing with three 5-ml. portions of hexane. Develop the column with hexane until the colored zones are well separated. Drain the column, extrude the adsorbent, and cut out each zone. The bands are extracted with hexane-ethanol (20:1, vol./vol.), and the absorption spectrum of each extract is determined.

The middle fraction (β-carotene) is evaporated to dryness and then taken up in the minimum amount of warm benzene, 2–3 times its volume of hot methanol is added, and the solution is allowed to stand in the refrigerator overnight. The red needles are removed by filtration, washed with a little cold methanol, and dried (in the dark) in a drying pistol at 60–80° over P_2O_5.

The melting point is determined (on a Koffler block), as well as its extinction ($E_{1\,cm.}^{1\%}$). Properties of pure β-carotene: m.p. 183°, $E_{1\,cm.}^{1\%} = 2350$ (at 465 nm. in benzene).

4-4e SEPARATION OF CHLOROFORM AND ACETONE (Frontal analysis)

Silica gel is used as adsorbent. It is powdered in a mortar and passed through a sieve. Use material between 200 and 325 mesh. Take 60 g. and dry at 110° in a drying oven to constant weight.

Note. Do not place other items in the drying oven at the same time since they may be adsorbed by the silica gel.

Fill a column (1 cm. diameter, 100 cm. length) with the dried silica gel, using the dry method. Do not use stopcock grease. With a tamping rod, place a cotton plug at the bottom of the column. The narrow bottom part of the column is placed loosely in a cork. A 1-cm. layer of silica gel is put into the column. By allowing the column to drop gently into the cork, the silica gel is divided as evenly as possible. The process is repeated until the column is filled to a height of 60 cm. A disk of filter paper is placed on top of the adsorbent.

A mixture containing 5 ml. of chloroform and 5 ml. of acetone is carefully poured into the column (stopcock open at the bottom). When this mixture has been adsorbed, the column is developed with methanol. The displacement velocity of the liquid front in the column may be adjusted with the bottom stopcock and should not be faster than 2 cm./min. Collect twenty 1-ml. fractions and determine the refractive index at 20° (n_D^{20}) of every fraction. Plot n_D^{20} against the number of the fraction and compare the results with the refractive indices of acetone, chloroform, and methanol.

At the completion of the experiment the moist adsorbent should be removed from the column and rinsed free of all solvents.

Note. A 1:1 chloroform-acetone mixture cannot be separated by fractional distillation, since a (maximum) azeotrope is formed at this composition.

4-4f SEPARATION OF BENZENE AND CYCLOHEXANE (Frontal analysis)

Prepare a silica gel column as described in § 4-4e. Add a mixture containing 5 ml. of benzene (b.p. 80.1°) and 5 ml. of cyclohexane (b.p. 81.4°). Use methanol as desorbent. Follow the directions given in § 4-4e. (Between pure benzene and pure methanol a few fractions are collected which will separate into two layers, so that no accurate n_D^{20} can be determined.)

4-4g SEPARATION OF HEPTANE AND TOLUENE

Using 5 ml. of heptane and 5 ml. of toluene and methanol as desorbent, follow the directions given in § 4-4e.

4-4h EQUIPMENT

3 Columns	(1 × 60 cm.; 1.7 × 20 cm.; 1.7 × 30 cm.)
2 Separatory funnels	(100 ml.)
3 Round-bottom flasks	(300 ml.)
2 Tamping rods	
Watchglass	
Graduate cylinder	(100 cc.)
Funnel	(6 cm.)
2 Evaporating dishes	
2 Porcelain dishes	

4-5 Determination of Activity of Alumina by Method of Brockmann [5]

4-5a INTRODUCTION

The activity of alumina depends on the moisture content. According to Brockmann, a simple classification may be made by using the following azo dyes:

(*a*) Azobenzene.
(*b*) 4-Methoxyazobenzene.
(*c*) Phenylazonaphthol-2.
(*d*) Sudan red.
(*e*) 4-Aminoazobenzene.
(*f*) 4-Hydroxyazobenzene.

The test solutions consist of two successive dyes in this series; as shown in the table at the top of p. 41. The activity of the alumina decreases from I to V.

4-5b APPARATUS

Use a column similar to the one shown in Fig. 4-1. Place a cotton plug in the bottom, add a 5-cm. layer of alumina, and cover with a disk of filter paper. Add the alumina through a funnel while constantly tapping the tube.

Activity:	I	II		III		IV		V
Mixture of dyes:	$\begin{array}{c}1\\a+b\end{array}$	$\begin{array}{c}1\\a+b\end{array}$	$\begin{array}{c}2\\b+c\end{array}$	$\begin{array}{c}2\\b+c\end{array}$	$\begin{array}{c}3\\c+d\end{array}$	$\begin{array}{c}3\\c+d\end{array}$	$\begin{array}{c}4\\d+e\end{array}$	$\begin{array}{c}5\\e+f\end{array}$
Results under standard conditions } In the column: In eluate:								

4-5c PROCEDURE

Dissolve 20 mg. of each of the two dyes in 10 ml. of benzene (thiophene-free, distilled from KOH), and add benzene to a total volume of 50 ml.

Put 10 ml. of the test solution into the column. Just before its complete adsorption add the developing solution from a separatory funnel. Use 20 ml. of a 1:4 (vol./vol.) benzene-hexane mixture. A flow of 20–30 drops/min. suffices.

After use the alumina can be recovered and saved. Start with test mixture 3 for an unknown alumina sample in order to save time.

4-5d EQUIPMENT

4 Columns (in rack)	Nickel crucible
4 Separatory funnels (100 ml.)	Iron pan
4 Erlenmeyers (100 ml.)	Crucible tongs
5 Containers with test solutions	Graduate cylinder (50 ml.)
Container with eluent	Flat board (or plate)
Container with alumina	6 Containers with dyes
Vacuum desiccator	5 Extra columns
6 Disks of filter paper	2 Porcelain dishes
Funnel	Iron ring
Bunsen burner	3 Iron dishes

4-6 Determination of Activity of Alumina by Method of Hesse [6, 7]

4-6a INTRODUCTION

A different method of determining the activity is based on the amount of a dye absorbed under standard conditions. This method is easily applicable to all types of compounds. Conversely, this method can be used to determine the eluent ability of different solvents for a specific substance when the activity of the alumina is known. The next example describes the determination of the activity of alumina using azobenzene.

4-6b SHAKE TEST

Weigh 2 g. of alumina into a 25-ml. Erlenmeyer (with rubber stopper), and add 10 ml. of a 0.1 molar solution of azobenzene in benzene-hexane (1:4 vol./vol.).

Dry the solvents thoroughly before use. Shake the mixture well for 5 min., allow the alumina to settle (centrifuge if necessary), determine the extinction of the solution, and compare with that of the test solution. The samples must be diluted properly before the extinction determination (use the benzene-hexane mixture). The percentage adsorption is determined by using the formula:

$$A = 100 - 100EV/E_0V_0$$

where V = dilution of the sample after shake test;

E = extinction of the sample after dilution;

E_0 = extinction of the test solution after dilution;

V_0 = dilution of test solution.

4-6c PROBLEM

Determine A for alumina containing, respectively, 0, 3, 6, 10, and 15% water. Determine also the Brockmann activity of these five kinds of alumina.

4-7 Preparation of Various Alumina Having Different Activities [5, 7]

Alumina I. Alumina is heated in a porcelain dish in small portions at 500° for at least 3 hr. with frequent stirring. Cool (about 1 hr.) and keep in a vacuum desiccator.

Alumina II. A 3-cm. layer of alumina is placed on the bottom of a large pan, which is heated for 4–6 hr. over a large flame. Stir frequently. Cool in a desiccator and allow to stand exposed to the air, spread out on a flat surface, for about 30 min.

Alumina II–V. Weigh off 10 g. of alumina (activity I) in a 100-ml. Erlenmeyer. Add the appropriate amount of distilled water with a pipette. Stopper tightly with a rubber stopper, heat on a steambath, and shake well until all lumps have disappeared. Allow to cool for at least 15 min.

Activity:	I	II	III	IV	V
% water:	0	3	6	10	15

Other Adsorbents. For the preparation and regeneration of other adsorbents see directions in [1] and [2], p. 220.

4-8 References

1. E. Lederer and M. Lederer, *Chromatography*, Elsevier Publishing Co., Amsterdam, 1954.
2. H. G. Cassidy, *Fundamentals of Chromatography*, Vol. X in *Technique of Organic Chemistry*, A. Weissberger, ed., Interscience Publishers, New York, 1957.
3. H. G. Cassidy, *Adsorption and Chromatography*, Vol. V in *Technique of Organic Chemistry*, Interscience Publishers, New York, 1951.
4. R. P. Linstead, J. A. Elvidge, and M. Whalley, *A Course in Modern Techniques of Organic Chemistry*, Butterworths Scientific Publications, London, 1955, p. 3.
5. H. Brockmann and H. Schodder, *Ber.*, **74B**, 73 (1941).
6. G. Hesse, I. Daniël, and G. Wohlleben, *Angew. Chem.*, **64**, 103 (1952).
7. K. J. Keuning, G. J. van Dijk, and M. J. Wiggers-de Vries, *Rec. trav. chim.*, **76**, 747 (1957).

5

Thin-layer chromatography

5-1 Introduction

Thin-layer chromatography is a special application technique of adsorption chromatography, in which thin layers (appr. 250 μ) of adsorbents such as silica and alumina are spread on a glass plate. Like paper chromatography (see Chapter 6), it is a micromethod ($<$ 1 mg. of substance). It has advantages over paper chromatography, such as

(*a*) Rapidity of equilibration and development (about 1 hr.).
(*b*) The possibility of using higher temperatures.
(*c*) Scope for application of identifying reagents.

The basic principles of thin-layer chromatography are the same as those of column-adsorption chromatography. That is why thin-layer chromatography (TLC) can rapidly give a preliminary indication of how larger quantities of material can be separated by means of column chromatography. The silica gel used in thin-layer chromatography most closely resembles the alumina of activity II (see p. 42).

The relative displacement is expressed in a similar fashion to that used for paper chromatography:

$$R_X = \frac{\text{displacement of substance}}{\text{displacement of standard}}$$

A mixture frequently employed as a standard contains 0.2% of each of the following components dissolved in benzene: DPA (N,N-dimethyl-*p*-phenylazoaniline), butter yellow(*p*-N,N-dimethylaminoazobenzene), Sudan red, and indophenol.

5-2 Choice of Eluent

The series given in § 4-3 can serve to indicate roughly the solvents of increasing polarity (ability to elute). To determine the solvent most suitable for a particular mixture the following method is used.

A small amount of the unknown mixture is placed at several different points on the layer of silica gel. The mixture is allowed to dry, and a capillary is placed in the middle of each spot. Different solvents are allowed to flow to each spot through the capillary. Small circular chromatograms are formed in this fashion, and the solvent or solvent system giving the best separation can be determined easily and rapidly.

5-3   Preparation of the Plates

The layers are applied to glass plates which should be cleaned thoroughly before their use. Several of the plates (20 × 20 cm.) are placed on a suitable holder, while another plate (20 × 5 cm.) is placed at the beginning and at the end. To prepare five plates, 15 g. of silica gel G (Merck) and 30 ml. of water are mixed well in a mortar. The silica gel G contains plaster of Paris and consequently should be applied immediately after mixing. The slurry in the mortar is poured into the applicator (Fig. 5-1); the latter is placed on the starter plate, opening down,

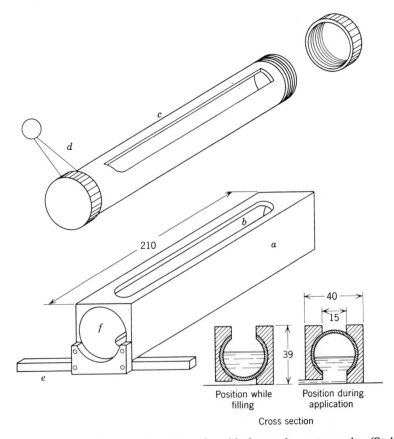

Fig. 5-1. Apparatus used to make plates for thin-layer chromatography (Stahl). *a.* Holder and cut-outs (*b*) on top and bottom. *c.* Inner cylinder (fits inside *f*). *d.* Handle to turn inner cylinder. *e.* Guide.

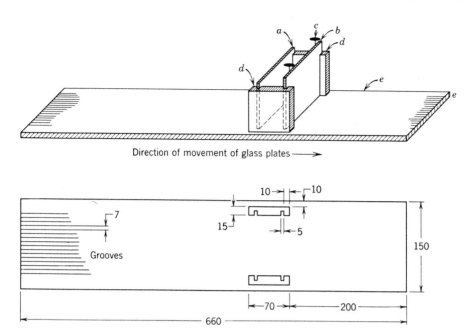

Fig. 5-2. Applicator for thin-layer chromatography (dimensions in millimeters). *a.* Slide. *b.* Adjustable slide. *c.* Set screws used to adjust thickness of layer. *d.* Slide holders. *e.* Plate, provided with grooves. These grooves in the direction indicated are 2 mm. wide, 1 mm. deep, and separated 7 mm. from one another. Apparatus of this type (Camag TLC) can be purchased from Microchemical Specialties Co., 1825 Eastshore Highway, Berkeley 10, California.

and passed over the plates with one rapid movement. *The applicator should be cleaned at once.*

After the plates have been air-dried they are placed in an oven at 105°C. for 30 min. They may be kept in a desiccator.

The apparatus shown in Fig. 5-2 may be used to prepare plates with varying layer thicknesses. It is filled between slides *a* and *b* with a silica paste, consisting of a mixture of 84 g. of silica gel G [Anasil B (Analytical Engineering Laboratories, Inc., Hamden, Conn.) may be used instead of silica gel G, Merck], 70 ml. of water, and 70 ml. of methanol. The glass plates are pushed through the apparatus, one directly following the other, in the direction $a \rightarrow b$.

5-4 General Procedure

Two centimeters from one of the sides of the glass plate a starting line is drawn. With a capillary as pipette, 0.002–0.01 cc. of the unknown, a comparison mixture, and a solution of needed reference compounds are applied to the plate, using a spacing of about 3 cm. The spots are kept as small as possible (diameter 5 mm.), if necessary by drying in a current of hot air. The amount of substance applied in this fashion varies between 1 and 500 γ.

The plate is placed vertically (starting line at the bottom) in the developer, a basin containing the eluent to a 0.5 cm. depth. The eluent rises through capillary action; thus a "rising chromatogram" is obtained. After the liquid front has risen at least 10 cm. (20–40 min.) the plate is taken out of the developer and dried. If necessary, the spots can then be made visible with a suitable reagent.

Used plates can be washed with water and then reused. Not only pure solvents but also solvent mixtures may be used as eluents. One difficulty that may be encountered, however, is an apparent increase in the R_X-value of the same substance as the distance from the edges of the plate increases; these "border effects" are probably caused by unequal evaporation of the components in the solvent mixture. Working in an atmosphere saturated with the solvent mixture used is recommended in these cases. A simple way of accomplishing this is by covering the inside of the developer basin with filter paper (Whatman 3); the solvent is soaked up and evaporates rapidly.

5-5   Examples

5-5a   AZOBENZENES

Mixture.   The mixture is composed of

1. Azobenzene.	4. Sudan red.
2. 4-Methoxyazobenzene.	5. 4-Aminoazobenzene.
3. Sudan yellow.	6. 4-Hydroxyazobenzene.

The reference solutions contain 25 mg. of substance in 10 ml. of benzene.

Test Solution.   0.5% of butter yellow, Sudan red, and indophenol in benzene.

Application.   With a capillary pipette, 0.01 ml. of the reference solution, 0.01 ml. of the unknown, and 0.002 ml. of the test mixture are applied to the plate.

Development.   Eluent: benzene. Cover the inside walls of the basin with filter paper (Whatman 3) soaked in benzene. Allow the liquid to rise to about 15 cm. (30–40 min.). Remove the plate from the developing chamber, delineate the liquid front with a pencil, and calculate the R_X-values with respect to butter yellow. Determine the R_F-value of the test mixture. Copy the chromatogram on translucent paper and color the spots accordingly.

5-5b   PHENOLS

Mixture.   The mixture is composed of

1. Pyrogallol.	5. β-Resorcylic acid.
2. Catechol.	6. Gallic acid.
3. Caffeic acid.	7. Gentisic acid.
4. Salicylic acid	

The reference solutions contain 100 mg. of substance dissolved in 10 ml. of benzene-ethanol (1:1), except the caffeic acid solution, which contains only 50 mg. of substance in 10 ml. of benzene-ethanol (1:1).

Test Solution.   As in § 5-5a.

Application. Apply 0.01 ml. of the caffeic acid solution, 0.005 ml. each of the other reference solutions, 0.005 ml. of the mixture, and 0.002 ml. of the test solution.

Eluent. Ether containing 2% glacial acetic acid.

Development. Saturate the chamber as in § 5-5a and develop for 30 min. or until the liquids have traveled 10–15 cm. Record the liquid front with a pencil while the plate is still in the chamber. Dry the plate in a current of warm air until the odor of acetic acid is no longer noticeable. Spray the plate with 1% aqueous $FeCl_3$ solution. Observe the plate also, using an ultraviolet lamp. Calculate the R_X-values with respect to DPA and the R_F-value of DPA. Copy the chromatogram on translucent paper and color the spots.

5-5c EQUIPMENT

Glass plates (20 × 20 cm.)	Capillary pipette
Glass plate (20 × 5 cm.)	Azobenzenes
Silica gel	Phenols
Applicator	Benzene

5-6 References

1. K. Randerath, *Dünnschicht Chromatographie*, Verlag Chemie, Weinheim/Bergstr., 1962.
2. E. V. Truter, *Thin Layer Chromatography*, Interscience Publishers, a division of John Wiley and Sons, New York, 1963.
3. J. G. Kirchner, *Anal. Chem.*, **23**, 420 (1951).
4. E. Stahl, *Chem. Zeit.*, **82**, 323 (1958).
5. E. Stahl, *Arch. Pharm.*, **1959**, 411.
6. E. Stahl, *Pharm. Rundschau*, **1**, nr. 2 (1959).
7. E. Demole, *J. Chromatography*, **1**, 24 (1958) and **6**, 2 (1961).
8. A. Scher, *Fette, Seifen, Anstrichmittel*, **61**, 345 (1959).
9. E. G. Wollich, M. Schmall, and M. Hawrylyshyn, *Anal. Chem.*, **33**, 1138 (1961).
10. J. H. Russel, "Thin Layer Chromatography," *Revs. Pure and Appl. Chem.*, **13**, 15–29 (1963).
11. J. M. Bobbitt, *Thin-Layer Chromatography*, Reinhold Publishing Co., New York, 1963.
12. E. Stahl, *Dünnschicht Chromatographie, Ein Laboratoriumhandbuch*, Springer Verlag, Berlin, 1962.
13. E. Stahl, *Z. anal. Chem.*, **181**, 303–312 (1961).
14. E. Demole, "Recent Progress in Thin-Layer Chromatography" in *Chrom. Rev.*, M. Lederer, ed., Elsevier Publishing Co., 1962, Vol. 4, p. 26.

6

Paper chromatography

6-1 Introduction

Paper chromatography is a special case of partition chromatography. Filter paper acts as the carrier for the stationary phase (usually water). Sometimes adsorption on the paper occurs. Very small quantities (<1 mg.) of substance can be separated by this method. In order to prevent evaporation of the solvents from the paper, the entire developing process must be carried out in a closed container, saturated with the solvent vapors.

6-2 Methods

Depending upon the object of the analysis, either sheets, strips, or circular disks of filter paper are used. The developing solvent can move under the influence of gravity (*descending method*) or under the influence of capillary forces (*ascending method* and *circular paper chromatography*).

The most important procedures are the following:

(*a*) *One-dimensional descending paper chromatography*, suitable for the separation of simple mixtures and for the identification of compounds.

(*b*) *One-dimensional ascending paper chromatography*, also suitable for simple mixtures.

(*c*) *Two-dimensional paper chromatography*, which involves a succession of two procedures with different solvent systems at right angles to one another. This method is important for the separation of complex mixtures of closely related substances.

(*d*) *Circular paper chromatography*. This method may be used to advantage when somewhat larger quantities must be separated.

(*e*) *Column paper chromatography*. When still larger quantities have to be separated, normal partition chromatography may be used, filling a column with filter paper or cellulose powder.

6-3 General Procedure

Filter paper (Whatman 1) is cut to the appropriate size. The direction of solvent flow should coincide with the direction in which the paper has been rolled (this

48

is the same as the long axis of the ellipse obtained by wetting the paper with a drop of liquid). Take care that the paper does not become soiled; touch it as little as possible with the fingers, and cover the working area with either another sheet of paper or a piece of clean cardboard.

A starting line is drawn on the paper and then a number of circles having a diameter of 5–10 mm. (see directions under examples in § 6-4). It is necessary to provide the paper with a fringe (2–3 cm. cut-ins) when, using descending chromatography, the elution process takes a long time.

An amount of substance just sufficient to wet one circle is put on the paper. This is called a "spot." If necessary, repeat this process until sufficient material has been applied; dry the paper between these applications. Always practice applying the spots and making them visible with the aid of test strips!

Suspend the paper in a chromatography trough. In order to prevent evaporation the container should close tightly; apply Vaseline to the glass plate and the ground edges. Clean the trough and holders with water. When changing solvents blow air through the trough for some time.

In order to allow the paper to equilibrate, hang it in the saturated vapor before elution. After elution remove the paper from the container and dry it in a vertical position (usually uppermost part down). Immediately indicate the solvent front with pencil and dry. The spots are made visible by spraying with a suitable reagent (*caution:* do not wet the paper too much) or by using ultraviolet light. Trace the circumference of the spots.

The R_F-value of a substance is the ratio:

$$\frac{\text{distance traveled by substance}}{\text{distance traveled by solvent front}}$$

This value is a characteristic constant for each substance (using a specific solvent system at a specified temperature). The R_F-value can be used for identification

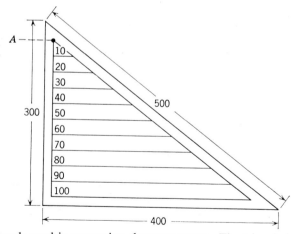

Fig. 6-1. Triangle used in measuring chromatograms. The triangle is made from transparent material and provided with 100 divisions. A pointed screw is placed at *A*.

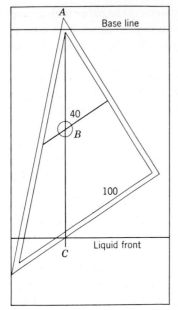

Fig. 6-2. Use of the triangle.

purposes; it is recommended that this value be determined for several solvent systems.

The triangle shown in Figs. 6-1 and 6-2 can be used to measure the chromatograms. Starting at point A, draw a line ABC perpendicular on the base line. This line intersects the solvent front C. Now place the triangle on the chromatogram in such a manner that its sharp angle A coincides with the center of the starting spot (A) while point C lies on the 100 line of the triangle. The center of the spot on the chromatogram (B) now coincides with another line of the triangle.

Read off the number belonging to this line (or if necessary interpolate and divide by 100). This is the R_F-value. In the example shown in Fig. 6-2, $R_F = 0.40$.

$$R_x = \frac{\text{distance traveled by substance}}{\text{distance traveled by standard}}$$

By determining the R_F-value of the standard in a separate experiment, R_x can be converted into R_F.

6-4   Examples

6-4a   DICARBOXYLIC ACIDS (Ascending one-dimensional)

Setup.   As in Fig. 6-5. Two chromatograms can be developed simultaneously.

Mixture.   Four acids, chosen from the following list, are used for the unknown:

1. Oxalic acid.	5. Succinic acid.	8. Glycollic acid.
2. Malonic acid.	6. Fumaric acid.	9. Azelaic acid.
3. Tartaric acid.	7. Adipic acid.	10. Sebacic acid.
4. Malic acid.		

Using solvent system A (see below) the R_F-values increase from 1 to 10; the order with system B is 1, 3, 4, 8, 2, 5, 6, 7, (9–10) ($R_F = 1$ for the last two).

Application.   Draw a horizontal pencil line about 5 cm. from the bottom of the paper (Whatman 1). Draw circles on this line (1 cm. diameter, 2–3 cm. apart). The unknown is applied to one of the circles, and one or more of the reference compounds are placed in the other circles. This is accomplished by touching the center of the circle with the solution (1 g. of acid in 100 ml.) on a capillary or glass rod, so that just a 1 cm. diameter circle is wetted. Approximately 10^{-5} g. is applied in this manner. Dry the paper in a current of hot air. The entire procedure is repeated once (2×10^{-5} g.) for acids 7, 9, and 10. Only one half of the quantities are needed with solvent system B.

Solvent Systems. A: 5 ml. of 25% ammonia, 15 ml. of water, and 80 ml. of ethanol. B: 78 ml. of ether, 18 ml. of glacial acetic acid, and 6 ml. of water.

Developing with A. Pour the solvent mixture into the trough. Suspend the paper in such a manner that the base line is 3–4 cm. above the surface of the liquid. Start the experiment toward evening, allow to develop for 16 hr., mark the solvent front the next day, dry the paper for 3 hr. in air, and spray with (*a*) bromocresol green (50 mg. in 50 ml. ethanol; use spray bottle as shown in Fig. 6–3); dry in stream of hot air; (*b*) lead acetate (2.5% in water).
The acids appear as yellow-green spots on a purple background.

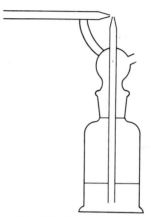

Developing with B. Start the experiment in the morning, develop for 6 hr., allow the paper to hang overnight, and spray the next morning with bromocresol green (40 mg. in 100 ml. of 95% ethanol, titrated to blue-green with KOH). The acids appear as yellow spots on blue background. Trace the outlines and jot down the R_F-values next to the spots.

Fig. 6-3. Spray bottle.

6-4b CARBOHYDRATES (Descending one-dimensional)

Setup. According to Fig. 6-4. Develop two strips simultaneously.

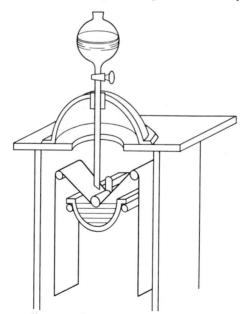

Fig. 6-4. Descending one-dimensional paper chromatography.

Mixture. The mixture is composed of

1. Xylose.	4. Lactose.
2. Glucose.	5. Fructose.
3. Arabinose.	6. Saccharose.

Application. Mark the base line about 8 cm. from the top of the paper (Whatman 1) and draw circles (5 mm. in diameter, 2 cm. apart). Cut a fringe (2–3 cm. cut-in) at the bottom of the paper. The reference solutions are 2.5% of each of the carbohydrates except saccharose, which is a 5% solution. When the surface of one circle is wetted with these solutions, approximately 0.01 ml. = 2.5 × 10^{-4} g. (5×10^{-4} in the case of saccharose) has been applied. Use one "spot" of carbohydrates 1, 2, and 3; four spots of 4; and five spots of 5 and 6 (dry between each application). Use two spots of the unknown.

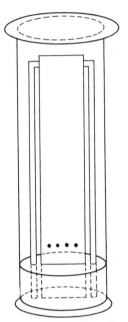

Fig. 6-5. Ascending one-dimensional paper chromatography.

Solvent System. Shake distilled water (50 ml.), butanol (40 ml.), and glacial acetic acid (10 ml.) together in a separatory funnel. Separate the layers. Use the top layer to develop the chromatogram and the bottom layer to equilibrate the system.

Developing. Suspend the paper in the trough, place an evaporating dish filled with the equilibration solvents on the bottom (adding some cotton aids evaporation), and allow to stand overnight. Carefully (do not spatter) pour the developing solvents into the appropriate part of the container the next morning. Check regularly whether enough solvent is present. Elute for a period of 28 hr. Remove the paper from the trough, dry for 1 hr. (fringe up), and spray with 0.01 molar anilinephthalate (1.66 g. of phthalic acid and 0.93 g. of aniline, freshly distilled from zinc, is dissolved in 100 ml. of water saturated with butanol; heat if necessary).

Dry the paper at once in a horizontal position for 10 min. at 100° in an oven. Red and brown spots appear; carbohydrates 5 and 6 are poorly visible at times; a fluorescent lamp improves visibility. Trace the spots and write the R_x-values (using xylose as reference) next to the spots.

6-4c PHENOLS (Descending one-dimensional)

Setup. As in § 6-4b.

Mixture. The mixture is composed of

1. Caffeic acid.	5. Pyrogallol.
2. Gentisic acid.	6. Catechol.
3. β-Resorcylic acid.	7. Gallic acid.
4. Salicylic Acid.	

Application. Draw base line 8 cm. from the top of the paper (Whatman 1), and draw circles of 7–8 mm., 2.5 cm. apart. The reference solutions are 1% (except caffeic acid, which is 5%). Apply one "spot" of each of the reference solutions (compare § 6-4b), and two spots of the unknown as well as of the caffeic acid.

Solvent System. As in § 6.4b.

Developing. Equilibrate as described in § 6-4b, develop for 16 hr., mark solvent front, dry the paper, and spray with a 1% aqueous ferric chloride solution. Green, brown, gray, and purple spots appear. Observe the chromatogram under fluorescent light also. The R_F-values of phenols 1 and 2 are nearly identical; they can be distinguished, however, because of their difference under fluorescent light. Trace the spots and mark down their R_F-values.

6-4d   AROMATIC AMINES (Descending one-dimensional)

Setup. As in § 6-4b.

Mixture. The mixture is composed of some of the following substances:
1. Orthanilic acid.
2. Sulfanilic acid.
3. *p*-Aminobenzoic acid.
4. 3-Amino-5-sulfobenzoic acid.
5. 4-Aminotoluene-2-sulfonic acid.
6. 4-Aminotoluene-3-sulfonic acid.

The test solutions contain 1.6 g./l.; the *p*-aminobenzoic acid 1 g./l.

Application. Mark base line and circles (6–8 mm. diameter, 2 cm. apart) on suitable Whatman 1 paper. Apply one "spot" of each substance (see § 6-4b).

Solvent System. Methanol (15.4 ml.), *n*-pentanol (7.5 ml.), benzene (23 ml.), and distilled water (4 ml.).

Reagents Used to Spray Paper. A: A *freshly* prepared solution of 200 mg. of sodium nitrite and 3 ml. of dilute hydrochloric acid in 100 ml. of distilled water. B: A solution containing 0.2% α-naphthylamine in ethanol. Purify the α-naphthylamine by vacuum distillation.

Developing. Suspend the paper in the container, place dish containing 20 ml. of the solvent system in the bottom, and allow to equilibrate overnight. Pour the solvents carefully into the container, using a separatory funnel. Elute for 6–8 hr. Remove the paper and *rapidly* mark the solvent front. Suspend the paper (bottom part up) and dry in a current of cold air. The spots are made visible by diazotization, followed by coupling with α-naphthylamine. Spray with reagent A until the paper has been moistened evenly all over, dry partially with *cold* air, and then spray with a little of reagent B. The spots (red-violet) appear fairly rapidly, except that of 4-aminotoluene-3-sulfonic acid, which does not become visible for some time. Observe under fluorescent light also. Trace spots and mark down R_F-values.

6-4e AMINO ACIDS (Descending one-dimensional)

Setup. As in § 6-4b. Place an evaporating dish containing 10 g. of phenol (saturated with water) in the bottom of the container (or 10 g. of solvent system B, also saturated with water).

Mixture. The mixture is composed of several amino acids listed in Table 6-1. (See also Fig. 6-8.)

Table 6-1

Acid	Minimum Quantity (μg) [Lederer, 5]	No. of Drops of 0.003M Solution	Color of Spot (Ninhydrine)
1. Asparagine	1	3	Brown-yellow
2. Aspartic acid	0.4	1	Blue
3. Phenylalanine	5	10	Gray-brown
4. β-Alanine	0.2	1	Blue
5. Glutamic acid	0.1	1	Purple
6. α-Aminoisobutyric acid	0.2	1	Purple
7. Glycine	0.1	1	Pink-purple
8. Serine	0.3	1*	Brown-red
9. Leucine	0.5	2	Purple
10. Proline	1	3	Yellow
11. Valine	0.2	1	Purple
12. Alanine	0.2	1	Purple

* 0.01M solution.

Application. Draw base line 8 cm. from tip of paper (Whatman 1) and draw circles 10 mm. in diameter 2.5 cm. apart, 1.5–2 cm. from edge of paper. The test solutions are 0.003M. Apply appropriate number of drops for each substance, using Table 6-1 as reference. Use one drop of the unknown.

Solvent Systems. A: A mixture of 30 g. of phenol and 10 ml. of distilled water. The phenol should be freshly distilled over zinc dust. B: A mixture containing 100 ml. of freshly distilled butanol, 45 ml. of glacial acetic acid, and 16 ml. of water.

Developing. Place the evaporating dish containing phenol saturated with water on the bottom of the container and suspend the paper. Add a small amount (about 100 mg.) of potassium cyanide to the evaporating dish and a cotton plug containing a few drops of concentrated ammonia just before closing the container. These precautions are taken to prevent the forming of brown spots on the paper, caused by reaction of phenol with traces of metal. Allow to equilibrate overnight. Add a sufficient quantity of the solvent system from a separatory funnel the next morning. Check regularly whether sufficient solvent is present. Develop for 24 hr.

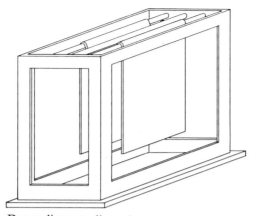

Fig. 6-6. Descending two-dimensional paper chromatography.

Remove the paper from the container, mark the solvent front, and dry upside down at room temperature. Although warm air may be used, caution is necessary (no oven!) since several amino acids are heat-sensitive.

For the identification of the amino acids, spray, and thus slightly moisten, the paper with 0.1–0.2% ninhydrine in butanol solution. Dry for 5 min. at 100–105° in an oven. Trace the spots at once (some fade) and write down the R_F-values.

6-4f AMINO ACIDS (Two-dimensional). See Fig. 6-6.

Setup. Use the large chromatography box (Fig. 6-6). Take a 46 × 57.5 cm. sheet of Whatman 1 paper, and draw a circle having a diameter of 1 cm. in one corner, 10 cm. from each side. Apply 1 or 2 "spots" of the mixture. Suspend the paper in such a fashion that the flow direction of solvent A is across the paper.

Equilibrate with phenol (saturated with water) overnight, as in example 6-4e, and develop with solvent A (example 6-4e) for 18–26 hr. Mark the solvent front and dry the paper well. Draw a current of warm air through the box until all the phenol vapor has disappeared; then place in the box an evaporating dish containing the next eluent. The box can become saturated with its vapor while the paper is drying.

Suspend the paper in the box again (turned 90°), equilibrate overnight with solvent B saturated with water vapor, and develop with solvent B (12–16 hr.). Dry the paper and spray as in example 6-4e. Trace the spots and determine R_F-values as shown in Fig. 6-7.

6-4g AMINO ACIDS [7, 8] (Circular)

Introduction. In addition to its use in separating small quantities this method is also suitable for separating several hundred milligrams of substance (as much as 1 g./component is possible in favorable cases). Horizontal circular filter paper disks are used, the liquid moving from the center outward. The following

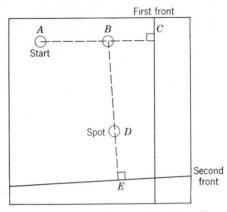

Fig. 6-7. Determination of both R_F-values, using two-dimensional paper chromatography.

simple relationship exists between the *circular* and the linear methods:

$$R_F \text{ circular} = (R_F \text{ linear})^{\frac{1}{2}}$$

Setup. (Fig. 6-9). Two flat glass plates (32 × 32 cm., thickness 5.5 mm.) rest on a Petri dish (diameter 17.5 cm., height 4 cm.). A hole of 6 mm. diameter is drilled in the bottom plate. Inside the large dish a smaller one (diameter 6.5 cm., height 3 cm.) is placed. The elution solvent is placed in the smaller dish.

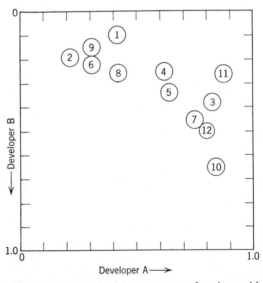

Fig. 6-8. Two-dimensional paper chromatogram of amino acids. For numbers see Table 6-1.

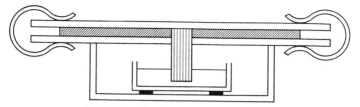

Fig. 6-9. Circular paper chromatography.

Mixture.   The mixture is composed of

1. β-Alanine.	4. Glycine	7. Methionine
2. Cystine	5. Leucine.	
3. Glutamic acid.	6. Proline.	

The test solutions are 0.01*M*; solvent is isopropyl alcohol-water (1:10); add conc. ammonia if necessary in order to bring everything into solution. A fairly large amount of ammonia is required in the case of cystine.

Application.   Cut out two circular disks (diameter 22 cm.) from Whatman 3 paper and mark the grain direction with pencil. Draw a concentric circle having a diameter of 4 cm. on each disk. Divide the circumference into eight equal sections, and draw eight 6-mm. circles (Fig. 6-10) on it. In the center of the paper drill a hole having the same diameter as the hole in the glass plate. Apply five "spots" of the test solutions to circles 1, 3, 5, and 7 and one spot to circles 2, 4, 6, and 8. Apply the spots to the second disk in such a manner that the grain directions are at right angles to one another (see Fig. 6-10).

Solvent System.   Shake *n*-butanol (30 ml.), glacial acetic acid (8 ml.), and water (38 ml.) together. Separate the layers and use the top layer as the developing solvent system.

Developing.   Make a cylinder from Whatman 1 paper of several centimeters length (not too stiff) and pass it through the hole in the glass plate. Cut off the top squarely with a razor blade, and place the paper disks around the cylinder in the proper position. Carefully push down on the cylinder with the second glass plate until the disks are fixed in place. Add the developing solvent to the

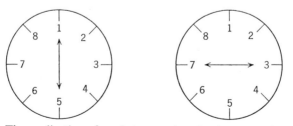

Fig. 6-10. The application of a substance using circular paper chromatography; the arrows indicate the grain direction of the paper.

small disk and place the glass plates horizontally on the large disk in such a way that the cylinder dips into the solvent.

Develop until the solvent front nears the edge of the paper (4–6 hr.).

Mark off the solvent front, dry the disks at 100° in the oven, spray (while horizontal) with 0.1% ninhydrine solution in butanol, and dry at 100° again. Calculate the (circular) R_F-values, write them next to the spots, and then calculate the linear R_F-values.

6-4h   AMINO ACIDS (Semipreparative circular)

Setup.   As in § 6-4g.

Mixture.   Dissolve 0.5 g. of glycerine and 0.5 g. of phenylalanine in 9 ml. of water and 1 ml. of 38% hydrochloric acid.

Application.   Cut five disks of 12 cm. diameter from Whatman 3 paper. Mark the grain direction with pencil. Draw two concentric circles, diameters 2 and 1.5 cm., on each paper disk and draw dots on the inner circles at 6-mm. intervals. Using a 1-ml. pipette, apply a sufficient amount of the amino acid solution to each dot so that the circumference of every spot touches the outer circle. Dry each spot in a current of *cold* air before going on to the next. Continue this process until a total of 1 ml. of solution has been applied to each disk.

Again drill a hole in the center of the disks. Provide it with a stiffly rolled cylinder made out of Whatman 1 paper (see § 6-4g). Place the disks on top of one another in such a manner that the grain directions alternate 90°. Finally cut out a small corner from each disk in order to be able later to ascertain the starting positions easily.

Solvent System.   The upper layer of a mixture of 40 ml. of butanol, 10 ml. of glacial acetic acid, and 50 ml. of distilled water.

Developing.   Develop until the solvent front is about $\frac{1}{2}$ cm. from the edge of the paper. This should take at least 10 hr. and can be accomplished only if the paper cylinder has been rolled tightly. Dry the disks and inspect them under ultraviolet light.

The separation can be improved by developing several times. To this end the disks are returned to their original positions and the developing repeated. The central cylinder may be rolled less tightly this time, since a 4-hr. developing period suffices. If necessary the process can be repeated a third time.

The amino acid rings are traced under ultraviolet light. Cut three small sectors out of one disk. Spray with a solution containing 0.1% ninhydrine in butanol, dry, and heat for 5 min. at 100° in an oven. The colored circles extend beyond the region usually visible under ultraviolet light. When cutting out the circles remember this difference. Extract the amino acids after cutting out the circles.

Glycine.   Cut the glycine rings into small bits, shake the paper with three 30-ml. portions of water, remove the paper by filtration, wash with a little water, and make up the volume of the filtrate to 100 ml. Determine the glycine content of an aliquot colorimetrically (see § 18-4).

Remove the solvent under reduced pressure on a steambath (appr. 50°), weigh the residue, determine the melting point, and compare it with the melting point of the starting material.

Phenylalanine. Cut the paper, reflux 3 times for 30 min. with 30 ml. of 80% ethanol. Filter; wash with 80% ethanol. Make up to 100 ml. and determine the amino acid content colorimetrically (§ 18-4).

Remove the solvent, weigh the residue, take the melting point, and compare.

Reporting. Hand in the amino acids isolated, and report yields and melting points.

6-4i   2,4-DINITROPHENYLHYDRAZONES (Descending one dimensional; reversed phase)

A. *Propylene glycol* as stationary phase.

Setup. According to Fig. 6-4.

Mixture. The mixture consists of 2,4-dinitrophenylhydrazones of the following carbonyl compounds:

1. Formaldehyde.	4. Acetone.	7. Benzaldehyde.
2. Acetaldehyde.	5. Butanone.	8. Crotonaldehyde.
3. Butyraldehyde.	6. Pentanone-2.	

Elution Solvent. Prepare a mixture of 96 vol.% petroleum ether (80–100°) and 4 vol.% absolute methanol.

Pretreatment of Paper. A base line is marked on a suitable-size sheet of Whatman 3 paper, about 8 cm. from the top, on which a number of starting points (2–2.5 cm. apart) are drawn. A second line, 5 mm. from the first, is drawn parallel to it.

Pour a solution containing 20% propylene glycol and 80% methanol on a porcelain plate and briefly soak the paper in this solution. Suspend the paper and allow to dry for 1 hr.

Application. About 5 mg. of each hydrazone is dissolved in 20 ml. of carbon tetrachloride ($\pm 600\ \mu$moles/l.). Two drops of this mixture are placed on the base line in such a way that the spot just touches the second line. Use a clean dropper or pipette each time.

Developing. The evaporating dish containing the solvent system is placed at the bottom of the tank. The paper is suspended in the tank. The cover of the tank is greased with Vaseline, and the developing solvent is carefully poured into the trough from a separatory funnel. Develop for 2 hr. Mark the solvent front and allow the paper to dry. The yellow spots are easily visible. Trace the outlines of the spots and calculate the R_F-values.

B. *Vaseline* (petroleum jelly) as stationary phase.

Setup.   As in A.

Mixtures.   The mixtures are composed of 2,4-dinitrophenylhydrazones of the following carbonyl compounds:

1. Butyraldehyde, heptaldehyde, octanal, nonanal, and decanal.
2. Butanone, hexanone-2, crotonaldehyde, and benzaldehyde.
3. Heptanone-2 and octanone-2.

Developing Solvent.   Mix 89 ml. of absolute methanol with 11 ml. of water.

Pretreatment of Paper.   For base lines and starting points see A. Soak the paper briefly in a 7 wt.% solution of colorless petroleum jelly in petroleum ether (60–80°). Allow the paper to dry for 15 min.

Application.   Exactly as in A.

Developing.   Place solvent in tank. Suspend paper, cover well, and allow paper to equilibrate overnight. Pour the eluting solvent (developer) in trough and develop for 7–8 hr. Mark solvent front and allow the paper to dry. Trace spots and calculate R_F-values.

Solvents.
    (*a*) CARBON TETRACHLORIDE. Heat 1 l. of CCl_4 under reflux for 30 min. with 5 g. of 2,4-dinitrophenylhydrazine and 1 g. of trichloroacetic acid and distill.
    (*b*) PROPYLENE GLYCOL. Technical.
    (*c*) METHANOL. Distill from NaOH after 30 min. refluxing.
    (*d*) PETROLEUM ETHER. Heat 1 l. of petroleum ether under reflux for 30 min. with 5 g. of 2,4-dinitrophenylhydrazine and 1 g. of trichloroacetic acid. Distill and collect the appropriate fractions (60–80°, 80–95°, 95–100°).

6-4j   SATURATED FATTY ACIDS (Circular; reversed phase)

Setup.   As in § 6-4g.

Mixture.   The mixture is composed of three of the following acids:

1. Stearic acid.	4. Lauric acid.
2. Palmitic acid.	5. Capric acid.
3. Myristic acid.	

The R_F-values increase from 1 to 5. The test solutions contain 20 mg. of fatty acid in 1 ml. of benzene.

Developing Solvent.   Shake 50 ml. of acetic acid and 5.5 ml. of water with paraffin oil. Allow to stand in separatory funnel overnight and use bottom layer.

Pretreatment of Paper.   Cut two disks (diameter 23 cm.) from Whatman 3 paper and mark the grain direction with pencil. Draw two concentric circles of 15

and 17 mm. radii on each disk. Draw eight dots on the smallest circle equi-
distant from one another as indicated in Fig. 6-10. Drill a hole in the center
with a corkborer (same diameter as hole in glass plate).

The disks are readied by submerging for 3 min. in a bath containing 15%
paraffin oil in benzene. Dry the disks by suspending them in air (marked grain
directions vertical). Submerge again for 2 min. and dry (turned 180°).

Application. The unknown is applied to spots 1, 3, 5, and 7, and the test
solutions to 2, 4, 6, and 8 (one spot for each solution; if necessary, two solutions
on a mark).

Apply the spots to the second disk in such a manner that the grain directions
of the two disks are at right angles during chromatography (Fig. 6-10).

Developing. Exactly as described in § 6-4g. Develop for 4–6 hr. Dry overnight
in air.

Coloring. The dried disks are treated separately. The paper is soaked for
20 min. in a 2% lead acetate solution, followed, for at least 30 min., by washing
with water to which initially a few drops of acetic acid have been added. The
disks should not be allowed to stick together. Take care the paper does not
crease or tear. The paper is then soaked in a solution containing 2 ml. of
$(NH_4)_2S_x$ (yellow ammonium sulfide) in 100 ml. of water. Dry the paper.
Calculate R_F-circular and R_F-linear. Mark values next to spots.

6-4k   EQUIPMENT

Pair of compasses	Hot plate
Triangle	2 Graduate cylinders (100 ml.)
4 Rulers	Graduate cylinder (25 ml.)
2 Pairs of scissors	Graduate cylinder (5 or 10 ml.)
Clothespins	2 Beakers (100 ml.)
Adapters	2 Evaporating dishes (6 cm.)
16 Metal clamps	Evaporating dish (8 cm.)
7 Jars (21 cm.)	Evaporating dish (10 cm.)
4 Short weighted bars	Evaporating dish (18 cm.)
5 Long weighted bars	Petri dish (14 cm.)
2 Sets of glass plates for circ.	2 Petri dishes (17 cm.)
chromatography	Erlenmeyer (300 ml.)
12 Pipettes	Erlenmeyer (100 ml.)
Hairdryer	Funnel (8 cm.)
2 Corkborers	Separatory funnel (250 ml.)
Hot plate	Distilling flask (100 ml.)
Flask (250 ml.)	

4 Thermometers (360°)
5 Chromatography jars with separatory funnels
Chromatography box with trough and separatory funnel
4 Cylinders (15 cm.)

6-5   References

1. J. N. Balston and B. E. Talbot, *A Guide to Filter Paper and Cellulose Powder Chromatography*, London, 1952.
2. R. J. Block, E. L. Durrum, and G. Zweig, *A Manual of Paper Chromatography and Paper Electrophoresis*, Academic Press, New York, 1956.
3. F. Cramer, *Papierchromatografie*, Verlag Chemie, Weinheim, 1952, 1958.
4. H. G. Cassidy, *Adsorption and Chromatography*, Vol. V in *Technique of Organic Chemistry*, A. Weissberger, ed., Interscience Publishers, New York, 1951.
5. E. Lederer and M. Lederer, *Chromatography*, Elsevier Publishing Co., Amsterdam, 1954.
6. R. C. Brimley and F. C. Barrett, *Practical Chromatography*, Chapman and Hall, London, 1956.
7. N. C. Ganguli, *Anal. Chim. Acta*, **21,** 335 (1955).
8. K. V. Giri, *J. Indian Inst. Sci.*, **37A,** 1 (1955).
9. R. Ellis and A. M. Gaddis, *Anal. Chem.*, **30,** 475 (1958); R. Ellis, A. M. Gaddis, and G. T. Currie, *ibid.*, **31,** 870 (1959).
10. I. Smith, *Chromatographic and Electrophoretic Techniques*, Vol. I, London, 1960.
11. I. M. Hais and K. Macek, *Handbuch der Papierchromatographie*, Band I, *Grundlagen und Technik*, G. Fischer Verlag, Jena, 1958, and Band II, *Bibliographie und Anwendungen*, 1960.

7

Gas-liquid chromatography

7-1 Introduction

Gas chromatography uses a gaseous moving phase. When the stationary phase is a solid, the term gas-solid chromatography (G.S.C.) is applied. The separation is achieved by the difference in the amount of adsorption of the components of the mixture on the solid phase.

When the stationary phase is a liquid (an inert solid, acting merely as a support, is usually impregnated with this liquid), the term gas-liquid chromatography (G.L.C.) is used.

This method is particularly suitable for the separation of mixtures of volatile components. Its most important advantages are:

(*a*) Larger separating (resolving) power is achieved; thus benzene (b.p. 80.1°C.) and cyclohexane (b.p. 81.4°C.) can be separated readily.

(*b*) The method possesses great sensitivity; quantities of the order of 10^{-5} to 10^{-6} g. of substance can still be analyzed.

(c) Quantitative determination of the components is possible.

(d) The method is rapid and lends itself to automation.

7-2 Principles

A small quantity of the mixture to be analyzed is introduced into a stream of inert gas (the carrier gas) in which it is vaporized rapidly. The mixture then passes through a column filled with the stationary phase. The components are carried through the column with different velocities, depending on their partition coefficients. A separation is achieved in this manner. The components leave the column one after the other and are quantitatively analyzed by a suitable detector.

At present two sets of detection systems can be distinguished:

1. *Differential detectors.* These give a signal whose magnitude is proportional to the concentration of the component in the detector (concentration-sensitive detector) or to the mass of the component which passes through the detector per unit time (mass-sensitive detector).

2. *Integral detectors.* These give a signal whose magnitude is proportional to the total quantity of a component which has passed through the detector.

63

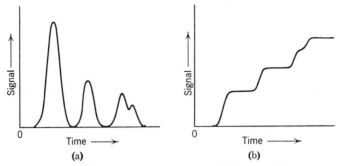

Fig. 7-1. (*a*) Differential chromatogram. (*b*) Integral chromatogram.

The graph which depicts the signal as a function of time is called the (gas) chromatogram. The chromatogram of a differential detector consists of a number of peaks (Fig. 7-1a), while that of an integral detector consists of a series of steps (Fig. 7-1b).

Some important differential detectors are:

(*a*) The thermal conductivity cell or katharometer. The katharometer consists of a thin wire which is part of a Wheatstone bridge circuit. The wire is heated electrically. Variations in the thermal conductivity of the surrounding gas cause variations in the equilibrium temperature of the wire and consequently also in its resistance.

(*b*) The gas density balance of Martin. This is a very ingenious device in which the density of the column effluent (gas leaving the column) is continually compared to that of the pure carrier gas. The sensitivity is high, and the construction somewhat complicated.

(*c*) The flame detector of Scott (Fig. 7-4). The carrier gas (hydrogen) is burned at the end of the column. The flame lengthens and its temperature increases as organic components leave the column. The temperature is measured just above the flame by means of a thermocouple.

(*d*) The ionization detector. The organic components in the carrier gas are ionized by β-rays discharged from a radioactive source (Sr^{90}, for instance). An ionization current is thus produced between two electrodes in the gas. A constant potential is maintained across these electrodes, and the ionization current is amplified and measured. Ionization can also be brought about by means of excited rare gases, as in the argon detector. Argon is used as the carrier gas in this case.

(*e*) The flame ionization detector. Combustion in a (hydrogen) flame causes ionization. The conducting gases cause a current to flow between two electrodes which are maintained at a constant potential. If a non-flammable carrier gas is used (nitrogen, helium), an appropriate quantity of hydrogen gas for the combustion in the detector must be added. The flame ionization detector and the argon detector are among the most sensitive detectors.

The oldest example of an integral detector is the titration cell, in which effluent fatty acids were titrated in aqueous medium [5]. A universal titration method is based on the oxidation of the organic compounds in a stream of oxygen or over cupric oxide and subsequent titration of the carbon dioxide [6]. The gas burette can also be used as an integral detector (see Chapter 8).

7-3 Theory

The characteristics of gas-liquid chromatography are as follows:

(*a*) The distribution isotherm is linear; thus symmetrical peaks are obtained in the chromatogram (see Fig. 7-1).

(*b*) A reasonable column length corresponds to a large number of theoretical plates.

The theoretical considerations of § 2-3 are applicable in this case.

The *retention volume* (V_{max}) is the quantity of gas which has passed through the column when the maximum of the elution curve breaks through. Formula 2-3 expresses this relationship:

$$V_{max} = \frac{V}{p}$$

where p = fraction of component in mobile phase. When a substance is insoluble in the stationary phase ($K \gg 1$),

$$V'_{max} = V$$

When the retention volumes are divided by the velocity of the carrier gas, the *retention times* are obtained. Denoting the latter by t_{max} and t'_{max},

$$\frac{t_{max}}{t'_{max}} = \frac{1}{p} = 1 + \frac{1}{\alpha K}$$

where α is equal to the ratio of the volumes of gas and liquid in the column, and K is the partition coefficient of the component.

In order to determine the *number of theoretical plates* of a column, formula 2-4 or 2-5 can be used. These formulas are transformed as follows:

Method 1 (see Fig. 7-2).   The inflection tangent is drawn and the intersection with the horizontal axis determined. The *peak width y* thus obtained is defined as:

$$y = 4\gamma(R)^{\frac{1}{2}}$$

where γ is a proportionality constant.

Since the distance between the starting point and the peak maximum is defined by

$$x = \gamma R$$

it follows that

$$R = 16\left(\frac{x}{y}\right)^2$$

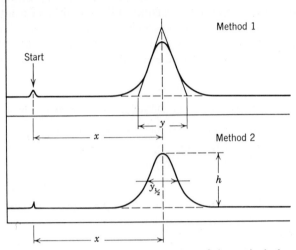

Fig. 7-2. Determination of the number of theoretical plates.

Method 2 (see Fig. 7-2).   The peak width at half height can also be determined.
It is equal to

$$y_{1/2} = y(5.54R)^{1/2}$$

so that

$$R = 5.54\left(\frac{x}{y_{1/2}}\right)^2$$

7-4 Applications

Qualitative Analysis. The retention volume depends upon the nature of the
stationary phase, the temperature, and the velocity of the carrier gas. When these
factors are kept constant the retention volume (or the retention time) is a characteristic which can be used for the identification of the components of a mixture.

Quantitative Analysis. If the detector signal is proportional to the concentration
of a component in the carrier gas ("linear detector"), then the area under the peak
is proportional to the quantity of the substance. Instead of the area, the peak
height multiplied by the width at half the peak height is frequently used. It can
be shown that for a Gaussian curve

$$hy_{1/2} = 0.93 \times \text{area}$$

Preparative Gas Chromatography.   The components of the mixture can be collected
in separate cooled gas traps after they leave the column. On a small scale (0.01–1.0
ml.) the separated components can be identified with the aid of infrared or mass
spectrometry, for instance. Columns of 10 mm. diameter suffice for this purpose.
Columns up to 10 cm. in diameter are used for large-scale preparative purposes
(5–20 ml.).

Capillary Columns. If instead of an inert solid as stationary phase support a 0.1–0.4 mm. tube of 20–300 m. length is used, the term capillary column is employed. These columns, made of metal, glass, or plastic, are characterized by a very large number of theoretical plates and are useful when highly complex mixtures (petroleum fractions, essential oils, tobacco smoke) are investigated.

7-5 Practical Hints

7-5a CHOICE OF THE STATIONARY PHASE

The stationary phase must be chosen in such a manner that not only the solubilities of the components of the mixture, but also the differences in the

Table 7-1 Stationary Phases for Gas Chromatography

Stationary Phase	Maximum Temperature in °C	Applicability
Di-(3,3,5-trimethylhexyl) phthalate ($\equiv$ "dinonyl phthalate")	125	General applicability, no pronounced selectivity; many compounds separated roughly according to volatility.
Diisodecylphthalate	175	
Silicone oil DC 550	200	
Apiezon L	250	
Dimethylformamide	0	Higher molecular weight hydrocarbons. The retention times of the olefins are longer than those of the corresponding alkanes.
Dimethylsulfolane	40	
2-Methylpiperazinediformamide	100	
Polyethylene glycol (1500)	160	Polar compounds such as alcohols, aldehydes, ketones, amines.
Tricresylphosphate	120	Chlorinated hydrocarbons.
2,4,7-Trinitrofluorenone	200	Aromatic and cyclic hydrocarbons, alcohols, ketones.

partition coefficients, are sufficiently large. As a rule of thumb the principle "like attracts like" can be used. Table 7-1 lists some commonly used stationary phases.

When the column temperature is raised, the quantity of the stationary phase which is carried from the column with the carrier gas increases. The lifetime (L) of a column depends on the absolute temperature:

$$\text{Log } L \sim \frac{1}{T}$$

7-5b   PREPARATION OF THE COLUMN PACKING

As support for the stationary phase a porous material is used with a specific area of 2–5 m.²/g. Suitable materials are Chromosorb and crushed firebrick (C22, Johns-Manville). Uniform particle size, for instance 80–100 mesh, is desirable for an efficient column.

A column packing usually contains from 5 to 30 parts/100 (wt./wt.) of the stationary phase. This liquid must be applied to the support as uniformly as possible by dissolving a weighed amount in a volume of a volatile liquid (i.e., pentane, ether, acetone) sufficient to cover the support material entirely. The solvent is then evaporated by carefully warming and stirring under nitrogen. Vibration of the column during the filling is advisable in order to achieve a uniform packing. A vibrator can be used, or the column can be held against a flattened part of the rotating axle of an electric motor. A funnel is connected to the top of the column with a piece of tubing. The addition should be done slowly and in small portions.

7-5c   HAMILTON SYRINGES

1. Use Hamilton syringes for injecting liquids or solutions.

2. Insert needle in liquid, draw some liquid into the syringe, and by tapping on top of the plunger empty the syringe. Repeat this process until all air bubbles are removed.

3. Draw required amount into syringe and clean the outside of the needle carefully, using lens paper.

4. Insert needle into rubber of injection block all the way.

5. Empty needle *rapidly* by tapping on the plunger.

6. Withdraw the syringe and clean it by inserting it into a rubber cap attached to a vacuum line.

7. Avoid bending of the needle.

7-6   Simple Gas Chromatograph with Flame Detector

7-6a   APPARATUS

The apparatus (Fig. 7-3) consists of a column filled with crushed firebrick C22 to which appr. 20 wt. % of a stationary phase has been added. The column is surrounded by a vapor jacket. Hydrogen is used as the carrier gas. Its inlet pressure (p_i) is regulated with the aid of a needle valve A. To suppress pressure variations a heavy-walled capillary (length 25 cm., inside diameter 0.5 mm.) is placed behind the needle valve. The velocity of the gas is measured with a flowmeter B. A tube D at the side is closed off with a rubber cap; the mixture to be analyzed is injected through the cap with a hypodermic needle (Hamilton). This tube is wrapped with a heating coil in order to facilitate rapid evaporation.

The gas leaves the column at F and is ignited at the end of the capillary (0.2 mm. inside diameter). To prevent condensation the outlet tube and the capillary are also provided with a heating coil. A coil in glass fiber having a resistance of 7 ohms/m. is suitable for this purpose.

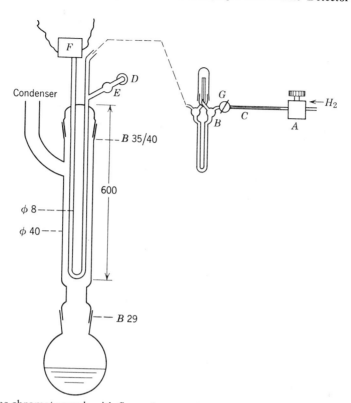

Fig. 7-3. Gas chromatograph with flame detector (dimensions in millimeters). *A.* Needle valve. *B.* Flowmeter. *C.* Capillary. *D.* Rubber serum cap. *E.* Evaporation chamber. *F.* Flame detector. *G.* Valve.

The microflame is aimed at a platinum-platinum-rhodium thermocouple. The junction of the latter is placed about 4.5 mm. above the outlet opening of the capillary. This distance, as well as the gas velocity, is chosen in such a manner that the tip of the flame remains just short of the junction (even during combustion of organic components).

The e.m.f. of the thermocouple is compensated for with a 4-volt dry cell using a potentiometric circuit (Fig. 7-5). At constant gas velocity the galvanometer* shows no deflection. When one of the components of the mixture leaves the column together with the carrier gas, the length and temperature of the flame change; the e.m.f. of the thermocouple is no longer fully compensated, resulting in a deflection of the galvanometer.

The detector is surrounded by a metal screen preventing a draft and allowing

* A galvanometer appropriate for this purpose has the following characteristics:

Full period undamped = 1.5 sec.
Internal resistance = 100 ohms.
External resistance = 100–2000 ohms.
Current sensitivity = appr. 10^{-8} amp./mm.
Voltage sensitivity = appr. 10^{-5} volt/mm.

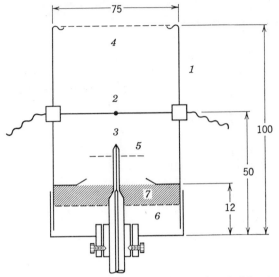

Fig. 7-4. Flame detector (dimensions in millimeters). *1*. Metal screen. *2*. Pt/Pt-Rh thermocouple. *3*. Capillary. *4, 5, 6*. Brass gauze (80 mesh). *7*. Glass fiber.

steady burning of the flame. The screen (Fig. 7-4, *4, 5*, and *6*) made of fine brass gauze and the glass fiber covering (*7*) serve the same purpose.

7-6b PROCEDURE

When working above room temperature, connect the reflux condenser and bring the heating liquid to a boil. Adjust the rate of boiling so that the liquid returns from the reflux condenser almost in a thin stream. Adjust the current through the heating wires around the inlet and outlet tubes of the column with a variac so that the temperature of these tubes is about 20° above that of the column. Open the hydrogen gas cylinder and turn the reducing valve until the pressure on the (closed) needle valve reads 14 p.s.i. Open valve *A* (Fig. 7-3), allowing a barely noticeable gas flow through capillary *C*. Connect *C* to the column. Open *G* and carefully open the needle valve further until the flowmeter *B* shows the proper gas velocity (40 ml./min.). The flowmeter can be calibrated beforehand by attaching a soap film meter at the outlet of the column.

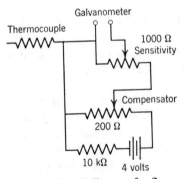

Fig. 7-5. Circuit diagram for flame detector.

Ignite the hydrogen at the outlet, connect the galvanometer (adjusted to lowest sensitivity), and adjust the resistance to compensate the voltage across the thermocouple. Carefully increase the sensitivity of the galvanometer.

Read the galvanometer every 30 sec. Record first a base line until a constant reading is obtained for approximately 10 min. Injection can now be carried out by pushing the injection needle through D so that the point of the needle rests inside a small ball of quartz fiber in the evaporation chamber E.

Inject the desired quantity (1–5 μl.). Read the galvanometer during the appearance of the peak every 15 sec. and record the maximum galvanometer reading for each component. Record the base line for 10 min. after the maximum of the last peak has passed.

Return the galvanometer setting to its least sensitive position when the experiment is finished. Close the reducing valve of the cylinder and finally close the needle valve. When the flowmeter reading is zero, close valve G. Disengage C. Close the main valve of the gas cylinder.

7-6c   QUALITATIVE ANALYSIS (Identification of an unknown peak in a chromatogram)

(a) Record the chromatogram of an unknown mixture and plot the results on a graph as in Fig. 7-6 (1 scale division of the galvanometer = 10 mm., 1 min. = 2 mm.). Take two recordings (A and B) and check whether they are equivalent.

(b) Usually some assumptions as to the nature of the components can be made on the basis of the origin of the mixture and other information. These assumptions can be checked as follows.

(c) Prepare a mixture of the unknown liquid (say 6 drops) and the component assumed to be present (3 drops). Record the chromatogram (C). If chromatogram C shows a relatively strong increase of one of the peaks as compared to that peak in A, there is a good chance that the expected component was indeed part of the original unknown. If the unknown did not contain the component, C should have one more peak than A.

(d) A, B, and C can now be drawn on one piece of graph paper in order to make a direct comparison.

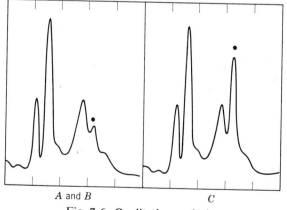

A and B   C

Fig. 7-6. Qualitative analysis.

Examples. Examples (column temperature, 77°; heating liquid, carbon tetrachloride) are as follows:

1. Petroleum ether, 60–80°.
2. Petroleum ether, 80–100°.
3. Ether–acetone–benzene–toluene.
4. Benzene–toluene–*m*-xylene.
5. Cyclohexane–*n*-heptane–acetone–diethylketone.
6. Methanol–ethanol–*n*-propanol.
7. Ethanol–acetone.
8. *n*-Heptane–acetone.
9. *n*-Propanol–toluene.
10. Benzene–cyclohexane.
11. Toluene–chlorobenzene.
12. *n*-Hexane–*n*-heptane.

7-6d QUANTITATIVE ANALYSIS (Binary mixture)

Prepare a number of calibration curves of both components (varying the ratio, e.g., from 1:4 to 4:1) and take two chromatograms of the mixture. Record the results graphically (10 mm. deflection = 10 mm., 1 min. = 4 mm.). Record the results as shown in Form 7-1.

The peak height (still better, the peak height times the half-height width) is proportional to the amount of substance. Prepare calibration curves of relative peak height and of relative peak surface vs. the mole ratio of the components in the calibration mixture. Determine finally the composition of an unknown with the aid of these data.

Examples. The mixtures indicated under 7-6c can be used as examples.

Form 7-1

Name: Date: Column temperature:		Quantity injected: Gas velocity:			μl. ml./min.				
Sample No.	Substance	Retention Time (min.)	Volume Ratio	Mol Ratio	Peak Height Ratio	Peak Area Ratio	Plate No. (Method 1)	Plate No. (Method 2)	

7-6e EFFECT OF FLOW RATE

Figure 7-7 shows the effect of flow rate on resolution, peak height, and shape.

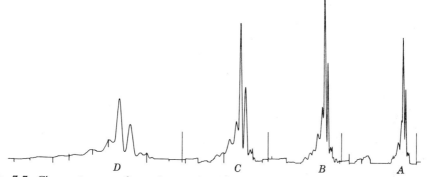

Fig. 7-7. Chromatogram of petroleum ether (b.p. 140–160°), showing effect of flow rate.
A = 8 lb./in.^{2} (115 ml./min.); B = 6 lb./in.^{2} (83 ml./min.); C = 4 lb./in.^{2} (48 ml./min.);
D = 2 lb./in.^{2} (18 ml./min.).

7-6f EQUIPMENT

Hamilton injection syringe
10 Small test tubes in rack
Calibration curve for flowmeter

7-7 Simple Gas Chromatograph with Titration Detector

7-7a APPARATUS

A very simple method has been developed by Blom *et al.* [6, 7] which allows exact quantitative analysis. The components leaving the column are burned completely with the aid of oxygen and copper oxide, and the carbon dioxide formed is determined by means of a titration.

The apparatus used is shown in Fig. 7-8.

7-7b PROCEDURE

The quartz tube, filled with copper oxide, is connected to the column at L, the oven temperature is raised to 800°, and the titration vessel S is connected to the quartz tube with a piece of rubber tubing. Nitrogen and oxygen are passed through C and M, respectively, at appropriate velocities.

Put approximately 15 ml. of pyridine and 1 drop of thymol blue solution into the titration vessel. Neutralize with a solution of sodium methoxide until the liquid just turns blue, and start the stopwatch immediately while recording the burette reading. Keep the color of the liquid blue by addition of sodium methoxide solution. Record the burette reading after 10 min. When 0.005 ml. or less of $0.1N$ sodium methoxide has been added, the apparatus is ready for use.

An appropriate amount (1 mg.) of sample is weighed in a thin-walled glass tube one end of which is provided with a capillary tip. The end of the capillary is closed by fusing after the sample has been placed in the glass tube.

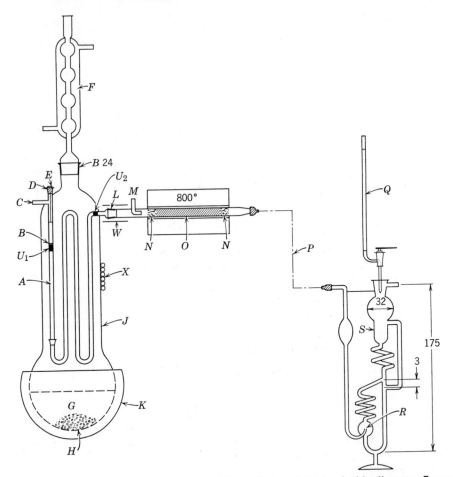

Fig. 7-8. Apparatus for gas chromatographic analysis. *A*. Tube, inside diameter 7 mm. (may be spiral shape). *B*. Glass filter disk, thickness 2 mm. *C*. N_2 inlet. *D*. Inlet closed with rubber stopper. *E*. Metal rod, provided with sieve plate. *F*. Condenser. *G*. Reflux liquid. *H*. Boiling stones. *J*. Container. *K*. Electric heating mantle. *L*. Exit tube. *M*. O_2 inlet. *N*. Asbestos. *O*. Copper oxide rods. *P*. Rubber tube, inside diameter 2 mm. *Q*. Burette, 10 ml. *R*. Inlet, inside diameter of exit, 0.5 mm. *S*. Titration vessel. U_1, U_2. Asbestos plug. *W*. Copper strips wound with asbestos cord at column temperature > 80°. *X*. Asbestos cord at column temperature > 80°.

This tube is put on the filter plate *B via D*, which is then closed with the rubber stopper. Nitrogen is passed through *C*, and oxygen through the quartz tube *M*.

Approximately 15 ml. of pyridine and 1 drop of thymol blue solution are added to the titration flask *S*, and the solution is neutralized exactly with the sodium methoxide solution. During the entire analysis the solution should remain blue. Using the metal rod *E*, break the glass tube and start the stopwatch simultaneously. Record the burette reading every 30 sec. and prepare the appropriate graph. The retention times of the components expected in the mixture are determined in a comparative experiment by carrying out an analysis on the pure compounds in a similar manner.

7-7c CALCULATION

Let t_1 be the time when a component is just leaving the column, and t_2 the time when the component has just passed through the column completely. Then the amount of this component in per cent is given by

$$[(V_2 - V_1) - (t_2 - t_1)V_0]t \frac{M}{p} \frac{100}{a}$$

where V_2 = burette reading (ml.) at time t_2;
  V_1 = burette reading (ml.) at time t_1;
  $t_2 - t_1$ = duration (min.) of titration of this component;
  V_0 = sodium methoxide blank (ml./min.);
  M = molecular weight of the component;
  p = number of carbon atoms per molecule;
  a = weight of the sample (mg.).

7-7d REAGENTS

0.1N Sodium Methoxide.   Add about 2.5 g. of sodium to 1 l. of methanol (containing $< 0.1\%$ water).

0.02N Sodium Methoxide.   Neutralize 800 ml. of pyridine with $0.1N$ sodium methoxide (using thymol blue as indicator), add another 200 ml. of $0.1N$ sodium methoxide, and stir.

Indicator Solution.   Use a solution containing 375 mg. of thymol blue in 100 ml. of pyridine.

Pyridine.   To 1 l. of pyridine add 50 g. of activated charcoal which has been dried at 105°. Boil under reflux for 1 hr. Allow the charcoal to settle and siphon the liquid into a distillation flask *via* a coarse glass filter. Distill, discarding the pyridine-water azeotrope and collecting the pure pyridine. (The water content of the pyridine should be less than 0.5 mg./ml.)

Copper Oxide.   Sticks, 0.5–0.7 mm. in diameter, 5 mm. in length (Merck).

7-8 Procedure Using Perkin-Elmer Model Fractometer Gas Chromatograph
  (Figs. 7-9 and 7-10)

7-8a USE WITH THERMAL CONDUCTIVITY DETECTOR

  1. Open carrier gas tank and adjust the reducing valve to a pressure of 4 atm.
  2. Adjust the flow by turning knob *1* until a pressure of 0.6 atm. is indicated on the flowmeter *b*.

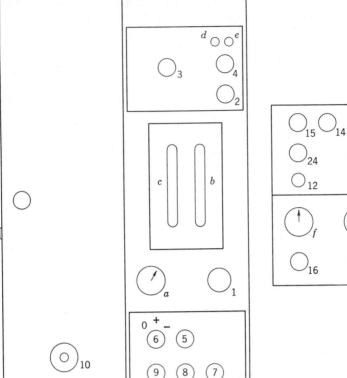

Fig. 7-9. Oven and thermal conductivity detector of Perkin-Elmer Fractometer Gas Chromatograph.

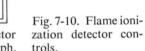

Fig. 7-10. Flame ionization detector controls.

1. Pressure. *2.* Thermostat (coarse). *3.* Heating. *4.* Thermostat (fine). *5.* Bridge current. *6.* Polarity switch. *7.* Attenuator. *8.* Base-line adjustment (coarse). *9.* Base-line adjustment (fine). *10.* Injection block. *11.* Injection block heater switch (now in position *on*). *12.* On-off switch. *13.* Attenuator. *14.* Base-line adjustment. *15.* Base-line adjustment. *16.* Air pressure. *17.* H_2 pressure.

3. Adjust knob *2* to the desired temperature, using knob *3* to regulate the heating element according to the chart provided by the assistant.

4. Knob *4* is a more accurate thermostat control knob. When knobs *2, 3,* and *4* are properly adjusted as indicated on the thermometer *c*, the light bulb *e* will automatically light and go out for equal periods.

5. The bridge current is now switched on by using knob *5*. Use setting "6" for helium and "2" for nitrogen. (*Caution:* Be sure that the carrier gas flows before the bridge current is turned on.)

6. Switch on recorder by turning knobs marked *main* and *recorder*. The knob at the back of the recorder should point to "H," and the thermal conductivity

detector knob should be on "1." When helium is used as the carrier gas, knob *6* should be on "t," for nitrogen on "—."

7. Knob *7* (attenuator) is switched from "K" to "512."

8. Measure the flow again, using a separate (soap film) flowmeter. When the correct column temperature has been reached, adjust the flow (knob *1*) to about 60 ml./min.

9. Switch the recorder and chart on by using the knob marked "rec. chart."

10. Adjust the base line, using knobs *8* (fine) and *9* (coarse). During this adjustment the attenuator knob should be in desired ("1," "2," or "4") position.

11. Inject sample (see § 7-5c) at (*10*). The injection block may be heated by turning on knob *11*. This should never be done longer than 10 min. Turn off knob *11* *before* injection. When knob *3* is in position "10," maximum heating of the injection block is obtained. *Note:* Never open oven door during an experiment.

12. Switch off apparatus as follows:
  a. Turn recorder off.
  b. Turn knobs *2*, *3*, and *4* to zero.
  c. Turn knob *5* to "1."
  d. Turn attenuator *7* to "K."
  e. Close the tank valve of the carrier gas. Wait until the gauge reads zero and then turn knob *1* counterclockwise.

7-8b   USE WITH FLAME IONIZATION DETECTOR

1. Use instructions under § 7-8a for temperature adjustment.
2. Be sure apparatus has been switched to use with the flame ionization detector.
3. Open air and hydrogen tanks to a pressure of 2–3 atm. (reducing valve).
4. Turn knob *12* to setting "."
5. Turn on recorder.
6. Turn attenuator *13* to "1."
7. Adjust base line with knobs *14* and *15*.
8. Knob *24* should be on position "2."
9. Turn air regulator knob *16* (clockwise) until a pressure of 1.1 atm. shows on *f*.
10. Turn the hydrogen regulator knob *17* until a pressure of 0.6 atm. shows on *9*.
11. Ignite the flame by pushing knob *18* for 30–60 sec. The ignition of the gas can be determined by watching the movement of the recorder pen.
12. Inject the substance.

Turning off the instrument

1. Turn off recorder and detach pen from paper.
2. Turn temperature controls to zero.
3. Turn attenuator to "K."
4. Turn knob *12* to zero.
5. Close gas (hydrogen) cylinders, wait until gauges read zero, and turn out reducing valve.
6. Finally do the same for the air cylinder.

7-9   References

1. A. I. M. Keulemans in *Gas Chromatography*, C. G. Verver, ed., Reinhold Publishing Co., New York, 1959, 2nd pr. 1960.
2. C. Phillips, *Gas Chromatography*, Butterworths Scientific Publications, London, 1956.
3. R. Kaiser, *Chromatographie in der Gasphase*, Bibliographisches Institut, Mannheim, 1960–1961.
4. S. Dal Nogare and R. S. Juvet, Jr., *Gas-Liquid Chromatography*, Interscience Publishers, a division of John Wiley and Sons, New York, 1962.
5. A. T. James and A. J. P. Martin, *Biochem. J.*, **50,** 679 (1952).
6. L. Blom, L. Edelhausen, and T. Smeets, *Z. anal. Chem.*, **189,** 91 (1962).
7. L. Blom and L. Edelhausen, *Anal. Chim. Acta*, **13,** 120 (1955), and **15,** 559 (1956).
8. A. B. Littlewood, *Gas Chromatography, Techniques and Applications*, Academic Press, New York, 1962.
9. H. Purnell, *Gas Chromatography*, John Wiley and Sons, New York, 1962.
10. R. Kaiser, *Gas Phase Chromatography*, Butterworths Scientific Publications, London, 1963.

8

Gas-solid chromatography

8-1 Principles

The analysis of gases of low molecular weight (CO, N_2, H_2, lower alkanes and alkenes) can be carried out elegantly with the aid of gas adsorption chromatography. Janák [1] developed a method using carbon dioxide as the carrier gas. The gases are measured in a gas burette after removal of the carrier gas by absorption in alkali.

A difference from gas-liquid chromatography consists in the fact that gas-solid chromatography deals with a system having a non-linear partition isotherm (see Fig. 8-1).

Activated charcoal or silica gel is used as adsorbent.

8-2 Apparatus (Fig. 8-2)

Carbon dioxide of 99.8% purity (Matheson) should be used. The CO_2 flow is regulated with a needle valve. A constant inlet pressure is maintained with regulator A. A (small) portion of the gas escapes *via* the tube (provided with the fine glass filter) in the right-hand portion of the pressure regulator. As the pressure increases, the mercury in the right leg descends, a larger portion of the glass filter plate is uncovered, and more gas can escape. By means of a vertical motion of the left leg of the apparatus the pressure can be adjusted.

The gas then passes through the capillary of the flowmeter C. The pressure drop in this capillary is a measure of the gas velocity; it is determined by means of a liquid manometer filled with paraffin oil (bottom of C). The gas pressure is measured with the liquid manometer D, which is also filled with paraffin oil.

The volume (about 1 ml.) of the gas inlet system H at the opening of the column E should be known accurately. In this manner an exact amount of the unknown gas mixture can be measured before its passage through the column. The eluent gas passes into the microburette F, which is provided with a 45% KOH solution and is calibrated to 0.01 ml. (smallest scale division).

8-3   Procedure

(*a*) Empty gas burette *F*, rinse with water, and fill with distilled water.

(*b*) Opening the carbon dioxide cylinder to an inlet pressure of about 10 cm. (Hg) should result in a steady CO_2 flow through the apparatus. In about 2 hr. all air will have been displaced from the apparatus. Slow down the CO_2 flow and carefully (watch flowmeter *C*) lower the leveling bulb of the gas burette. Replace the distilled water in the gas burette by the 45% KOH. The amount of KOH in the gas burette suffices for about 5 hr. Raise the leveling bulb, close the stopcock of the gas burette, and adjust the CO_2 flow so that with an inlet pressure of about 10 cm. (Hg) a velocity of 40 ml./min. is obtained. Very small air bubbles will now be seen to rise in the gas burette. For careful work no more than 0.004 ml. of air 1 min. is an average value for the blank.

(*c*) Turn the stopcocks of the inlet system *H* to position 2 and rinse *H* with the gas mixture which is to be analyzed. Close the connection with the reservoir with *H* and turn the stopcock of *H* to position 1. Inside *H* there now is a quantity of gas whose volume is known accurately at atmospheric pressure. Record the temperature and the barometer reading.

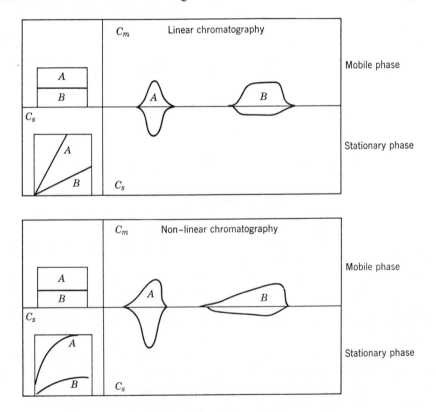

Fig. 8-1. Linear and non-linear chromatography.

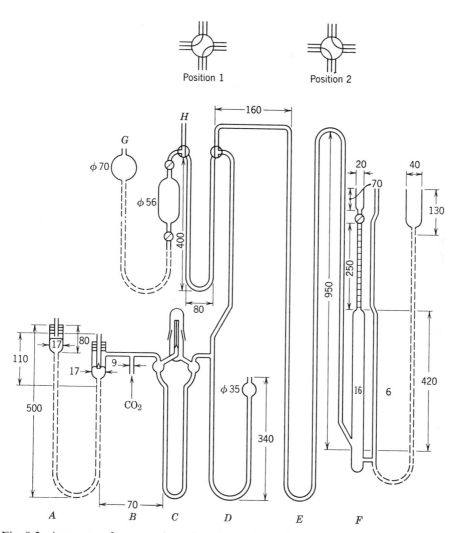

Fig. 8-2. Apparatus for gas adsorption chromatography (dimensions in millimeters), according to Janák. See text for explanation of letters.

(*d*) Adjust the gas burette until the level of the liquid in the burette is slightly above the 0.100 reading while the level of the meniscus in the leveling tube is exactly equal to the 0.100 reading. Check and record pressure and velocity of the carrier gas.

(*e*) As soon as the meniscus in the burette reaches the 0.100 reading, the analysis is started. Turn the stopcock at *H* to position 1 and simultaneously start a stopwatch.

(*f*) Record the gas burette reading every 15 sec. After the analysis is finished, record the blank readings for some time and use these readings to correct the burette readings. Finally, lower the leveling bulb until the levels of the liquid in the burette and in the comparison tube are equal and record this burette reading.

(*g*) If no further analyses are to be done, empty the gas burette and then fill it with a small amount of distilled water. Close the CO_2 valve and undo the cylinder.

(*h*) Activated carbon can be used as column packing (particle size, 0.25–0.9 mm.). First dry the activated carbon at 120°C. Fill the column by adding small portions through a funnel while constantly tapping the column. Close both ends with glass wool.

8-4   Calculations and Report

Make a graph of the burette readings vs. the time (0.1 ml. = 2 cm., 1 min. = 1 cm.). Determine the volume of the components that is correct for the pressure in the gas burette during the analysis, and calculate the composition of the gas mixture.

Make a graph of the increase in volume (every 15 sec.) vs. the time, and determine the retention times and retention volumes of the components. Record on the graph your name, origin of the mixture examined, date, barometer reading, temperature, value of the blank, inlet pressure, and velocity of the carrier gas.

8-5   Examples

        1. Illuminating gas.
        2. Illuminating gas–CO_2 (1 : 4; scale of the graph, 0.1 ml. = 5 cm.).
        3. Propane gas.
        4. Butane gas.

8-6   Reference

1. J. Janák, *Collection Czechoslov. Chem. Commun.*, **19**, 684, 700 (1954).

9

Ion-exchange resin

9-1 Introduction

High polymeric organic compounds, containing basic (*anion-exchange*) and acidic (*cation-exchange*) functional groups, are used as ion-exchange substances.

A satisfactory cation-exchange resin can be obtained, for instance, by the copolymerization of styrene and a small amount of divinylbenzene, followed by sulfonation of the polymer:

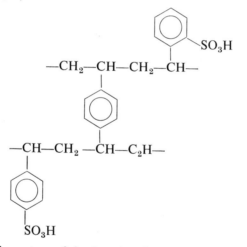

Depending upon the nature of the functional group, we distinguish:

Strongly acidic cation-exchange resins: for instance, $(R)SO_3^{\ominus}$; at every pH the polymer network contains negative charges. Weakly acidic cation-exchange resins; for instance, $(R)COOH$; at a pH of 0–3 no charge is present on the polymer (acid not dissociated); at a pH > 7 the polymer is negatively charged. Strongly basic cation-exchange resins: for instance, $(R)NH_3^{\oplus}$; at every pH there is a positive charge on the polymer. Weakly basic cation-exchange resins: for instance, $(R)NH_2$ and $(R)NR_2$; at pH < 3 there is a positive charge on the polymer, at pH 7–10 no charge.

Table 9-1 contains a list of some common ion-exchange materials.

83

Table 9-1

Resins	Functional Group	Backbone	Moisture Content (g.water/g. dry resin)	Capacity (meq./g. dry resin)	Packing Density of Moist Resin (g./ml.)	Regenerate with	Trademarks	Manufacturer*
Cation exchangers Strong acid	—SO$_3$H	Polystyrene	0.7	4	0.8	Excess strong acid	Zeokarb-225 Amberlite IR-120 Dowex-50 Imac C-12, C-22	P R D I
Weak acid	—COOH	Polymethacrylic acid	1	9–10	0.7	Acid	Zeokarb-226 Amberlite IRC-50 Imac Z-5	P R I
Anion exchangers Strong acid	—NR$_3^{\oplus}$	Polystyrene	1	4	0.7	Excess strong alkali	De-Acidite FF Amberlite IRA-400, 410 Dowex-1 Dowex-2 Imac S-4	P R D D I
Weak base	—NR$_2$ —NHR	Polystyrene	0.3	4	0.7	Sodium carbonate	De-Acidite G Amberlite IR-45 Imac A-13, A-17 A-19, A-21	P R I

* P = Permutit Co.; R = Rohm and Haas; D = Dow Chemical Co.; I = Industriele Maatschappy Activitit, Amsterdam.

9-2   Theory

9-2a   SELECTIVITY

The exchange reaction is an equilibrium.

$$(R)^\ominus A^\oplus + B_{aq}{}^\oplus \rightleftharpoons (R)^\ominus B^\oplus + A_{aq}{}^\oplus$$

By using an excess of $B_{aq}{}^\oplus$, the resin may be transformed into the "B-form." The position of the equilibrium depends not only on the concentration of the components but also on the equilibrium constant. The latter may differ for various ions. If the concentration of ions in the resin grains is indicated with a star *, then

$$K_A{}^B = \frac{(B^\oplus *)(A^\oplus)}{(A^\oplus *)(B^\oplus)}$$

When $K_A^B < 1$, then the resin will absorb A from a solution containing A and B (see Table 9-2).

Table 9-2   Selectivity of Ion Exchangers

	Ion A	Ion B	K_A^B
I. Sulfonated polystyrene	H	Li	0.8
(containing 8–10%	H	K	3
divinylbenzene)	H	Ag	18
	H	Ca	42
	Na	K	1.8
II. Benzyldimethyl-	Cl	F	0.1
ammoniumpolystyrene	Cl	Br	2.5
(containing about	Cl	I	18
8% divinylbenzene)	Cl	OH	0.5
	Cl	NO$_3$	3

9-2b   TITRATION CURVES

The affinity for $H^\oplus$ and $Na^\oplus$ (or $Li^\oplus$) will not differ much if a strongly acidic resin is used. Similar affinities for $OH^\ominus$ and $Cl^\ominus$ will be found with a strongly basic resin.

Weakly acidic resins are dissociated only slightly in strongly acid medium. Therefore they display a large affinity for $H^\oplus$, whereas cations are bound only at high pH (low $H^\oplus$ concentration).

The titration curve of a normal carboxylic acid (acetic acid) shows virtually no salt effect.

$$CH_3COOH + OH^\ominus = CH_3COO^\ominus + H_2O$$

A large effect may be noticed with weakly acidic ion-exchange resins (Fig. 9-1).

$$(R)COOH + Na^\oplus + OH^\ominus = (R)COO^\ominus Na^\oplus + H_2O$$

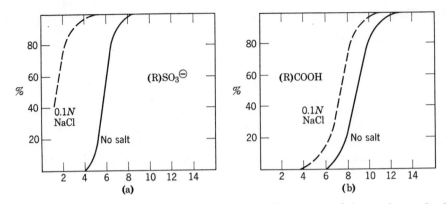

Fig. 9-1. Titration curves of cation-exchange resin. Percentage of the total capacity is plotted against the pH of the solution. (a) Strongly acidic resin. (b) Weakly acidic resin.

The grains of the resin first absorb the $Na^{\oplus}$ and $OH^{\ominus}$. The pH at which half of the acid has been neutralized depends, in the case of a weakly acidic resin, upon the base employed. It may be pH = 9 for KOH and pH = 8 for $Ba(OH)_2$. The apparent affinity of the resin for $Ba^{\oplus\oplus}$ is greater in this case than for $K^{\oplus}$. The titration curve (see Fig. 9-2) can therefore be used to supply information about the relative affinities of the resin for many ions.

9-2c   EXCHANGE VELOCITY

In order to make optimum use of the ion-exchange resin a knowledge of the exchange velocity is important. This velocity may be determined by mixing resin and solution and by following the decrease in concentration of the ions.

The exchange velocity is mainly diffusion controlled, decreasing with (a) lowering of the temperature; (b) lowering of the concentration of the solution; (c) increasing

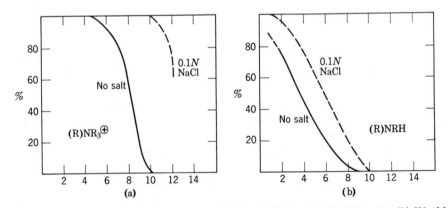

Fig. 9-2. Titration curves of anion-exchange resins. (a) Strongly basic resin. (b) Weakly basic resin.

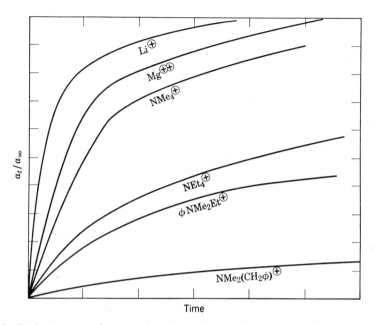

Fig. 9-3. Exchange rate of a strongly acidic cation-exchange resin with cations of various sizes.

the size of the resin grains; (*d*) increasing the size of the ions (see Fig. 9-3); (*e*) increasing the amount of cross linking of the resin.

9-3 Applications

Ion-exchange resins may be used in two ways:

1. The resin is stirred in a solution. An equilibrium is reached, and the resin is removed by filtration. Here the resin serves as an insoluble acid, salt, or base.

2. A solution is percolated through a column containing the resin. Its capacity is used to a greater extent in this manner.

A few of the more important applications follow.

(*a*) *Water Softening.* $Ca^{\oplus\oplus}$ and $Mg^{\oplus\oplus}$ ions in hard water may be exchanged for $Na^{\oplus}$ by percolating the water through the column containing a cation-exchange resin in the Na-form.

$$(R)-SO_3^{\ominus}Na^{\oplus} + \tfrac{1}{2}Ca^{\oplus\oplus} \rightleftharpoons (R)-SO_3^{\ominus} \cdot \tfrac{1}{2}Ca^{\oplus\oplus} + Na^{\oplus}$$

The resin can be regenerated with a concentrated NaCl solution.

(*b*) *Demineralization.* When a dilute salt solution is percolated through a cation-exchange resin in the H-form, all cations are replaced by $H^{\oplus}$. An anion-exchange resin is used next, replacing all anions by $OH^{\ominus}$. The regeneration of the resin is accomplished with HCl or NaOH. This demineralization produces conductivity water.

It is most economical to remove strong acids first, using a weakly basic anion-exchange resin, (R)NH$_2$, which can be fully regenerated with NaOH. A strongly basic resin then removes the weak acids.

(c) *Mixed-Bed Columns.*   The demineralization may also be carried out with one column, containing a mixture of cation- and anion-exchange resins. Here the advantage lies in the great efficiency, the disadvantage in the fact that the resins must be regenerated separately. Differences in density are used for this purpose, anion resins usually floating upon treatment with water.

(d) *Catalysis* [6].   A strongly acidic ion-exchange resin (H-form) may serve to catalyze chemical reactions such as esterification. The catalyst is removed by filtration. Acetaldehyde can be converted to aldol in the presence of a strongly basic resin (in OH-form).

(e) *Ion Exclusion* [7].   The resin particles are swollen and contain, say, 50% water. The resin particles of a cation-exchange resin (Na-form) having a capacity of 2000 meq./l. may therefore be compared to a $2N$ salt solution. The salt concentration is zero in the liquid between the particles.

When an NaCl solution is allowed to percolate through the column, the electrolyte tends to diffuse in such a manner that its concentration is the same everywhere. In other words, the NaCl will be found mainly in the liquid between the resin particles and not inside the resin. A non-electrolyte behaves differently. It tends to diffuse equally inside the particles as well as outside; because of adsorption its concentration may even be larger inside the particles than outside. As a result, the electrolyte will move more rapidly than the non-electrolyte upon elution. A separation may be achieved in this fashion.

Table 9-3 shows some of the separations which can be achieved.

> *Examples.*
> 1. NaCl-ethylene glycol.
> 2. HCl-acetic acid.

(See §9-5g, h, i.)

(f) *Ion Retardation.*   A porous strongly basic resin, (R)—NR$_3$$^{\oplus}$, is allowed to swell up in an acrylic acid solution. The acrylic acid is then polymerized. The resulting polymer, called a "snake cage resin," is imprisoned in the three-dimensional structure of the anion-exchange resin.

When a salt solution is mixed with this resin, the Cl$^{\ominus}$ ions are attracted by the —NR$_3$$^{\oplus}$ groups, while the Na$^{\oplus}$ ions are retarded by the —COO$^{\ominus}$ groups. When eluting with water, the NaCl leaves the column. The same phenomena are observed with an NaOH solution. Since the Cl$^{\ominus}$ ions are attracted more strongly by the NR$_3$$^{\oplus}$ group than the OH$^{\ominus}$ ions, the NaOH is eluted faster than the salt. Two electrolytes can be separated in this manner (Fig. 9-4).

(g) *Electrodialysis* (see Fig. 9-5).   A foil made of cation-exchange resin is similar to a negatively charged frame. Positive but not negative ions will pass through this frame. Conversely, positive ions will not pass through an anion-exchange

Table 9-3 Separation by Ion Exclusion

Acid	Dissociation Constant K	Degree of Ionization (0.25N sol.)	Separation Possible with 0.25N Solution on Dowex-50				
			HCl	CCl₃COOH	CHCl₂COOH	CH₂ClCOOH	CH₃COOH
Hydrochloric acid	—	100%	—	+	+++	+++	+++
Trichloroacetic acid	2×10^{-1}	58%	+	—	++	++	++
Monochloroacetic acid	1.4×10^{-3}	7%	+++	++	+	—	—
Acetic acid	1.75×10^{-5}	0.8%	+++	++	+	—	—
Dichloroacetic acid	5×10^{-2}	36%	+++	++	—	+	+

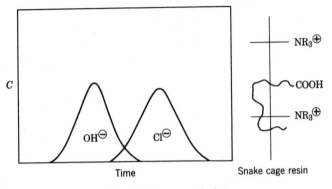

Fig. 9-4. Ion retardation.

resin. These foils are used successfully in electrodialysis; the yield is increased, since ion transport can take place in the desired direction only.

(h) *Applications in Organic Chemistry* [see also (i)]. Ion-exchange resins permit the separation of (weak) acids and bases from their salts in an elegant fashion. If a strongly acidic resin (in the H-form) is used,

$$(R)SO_3{}^{\ominus}H^{\oplus} + R'{-}COO^{\ominus} + Na^{\oplus} \rightarrow (R)SO_3{}^{\ominus}Na^{\oplus} + R'{-}COOH$$

With a strongly basic resin (in OH-form), free organic bases (for instance, alkaloids) may be prepared from their salts.

Another interesting application is the treatment of aldehydes with anion-exchange resins (as bisulfite salts):

$$(R)NR_3{}^{\oplus}SO_3H^{\ominus} + RCHO \rightarrow (R)NR_3{}^{\oplus}R{-}\overset{\overset{\displaystyle H}{|}}{\underset{\underset{\displaystyle SO_3{}^{\ominus}}{|}}{C}}{-}OH$$

Washing with alkali liberates the aldehyde.

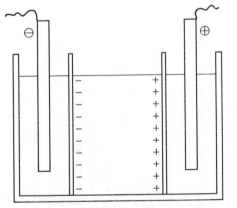

Fig. 9-5. Electrodialysis.

(*i*) *Chromatography Using Ion-Exchange Resins*. Excellent results are obtained when certain classes of organic compounds (amino acids, peptides, and nucleic acids) are chromatographed over an ion-exchange resin. Usually a combination of adsorption and electrostatic forces is brought into play. To understand the nature of these forces a few examples will be discussed.

Organic anions (for instance, $RCOO^{\ominus}$) are bound to a weakly basic resin $(RNR_2H^{\oplus}Cl^{\ominus})$. By eluting with base (NaOH), the resin is discharged, and the carboxylate ion leaves the column. By elution with a strong acid (HCl) the carboxylate ion is transformed into the weakly dissociated carboxylic acid. This carries no charge and is no longer attracted to the column.

A very weak organic acid (for instance, phenol) may be bound by a strong cation-exchange resin (hydrogen bonding). Elution with alkali transforms the phenol to the phenolate ion, which is repelled by the negative charges on the cation-exchange resin. Thus the phenol is eluted.

An amino acid is bound to a strongly acidic cation-exchange resin. Elution with a strong acid achieves nothing except perhaps binding the amino acid more strongly:

$$(R)SO_3^{\ominus} + {}^{\oplus}H_3N-CH_2COO^{\ominus} \xrightarrow{HCl} (R)SO_3^{\ominus} + {}^{\oplus}H_3N-CH_2COOH$$

Elution with alkali causes a reversal of charges on the amino acid, and it can leave the resin:

$$(R)SO_3^{\oplus} + {}^{\oplus}H_3NCH_2COO^{\ominus} \xrightarrow{NaOH} (R)SO_3^{\ominus} + H_2NCH_2COO^{\ominus}$$

The three usual techniques may be employed (see also § 2-2).

i. *Frontal analysis*. The "breakthrough" point for each component in the mixture is determined.

ii. *Displacement analysis*. Elution takes place with a solution containing an ion which is more strongly adsorbed than the ions in the mixture. An advantage of this method is the fact that "self-sharpening" of the bands increases the elution velocity and the capacity of the column (by as much as 50%) over those of elution analysis.

iii. *Elution analysis*. Elution takes place with a solution containing ions less strongly absorbed than the components of the mixture. Movement of the liquid is slow (<0.5 ml./min.), and column capacity small (5–10% for preparative purposes; <1% for analytical purposes).

> *Example*. One typical example follows. When a mixture of organic bases is subjected to frontal analysis over a strongly acidic resin (in H-form), the weakest bases move fastest. A buffer solution is used preferentially when employing elution analysis. In displacement analysis water is percolated through the column after the mixture has been put on the column; the displacement is carried out with a base stronger (lower pK) than the bases in the mixture (for instance, 0.1–0.5N ammonia or NaOH). The stronger bases are absorbed more strongly. As a consequence the components of the mixture leave the column in

the order of their increasing basicity. The concentration of the bases in the eluate will be identical to that in the solution used for the displacement analysis.

The theory of chromatography with ion-exchange resins is identical to that treated in Chapter 2.

9-4 Determination of the Capacity of the Ion-exchange Resin

The total capacity of an ion-exchange resin is equal to the number of active groups per milliliter of resin. The capacity is expressed in milliequivalents per milliliter, since the resins must be kept moist (swollen). A normal ion-exchange resin contains 1000–2000 meq./ml. of resin, comparable to 1–$2N$ acid or base.

The total capacity is determined by changing the resin into its H-form (using HCl). The resin is washed with water until the eluant is neutral and an NaCl solution is percolated through the column, changing the resin into its Na-form. The HCl liberated is determined by titration.

The "breakthrough" capacity is another concept of considerable practical value. Washing a cation-exchange resin (in its H-form) with a salt solution (concentration C_0) transforms the resin into its Na-form:

$$(R)SO_3H + NaCl \rightarrow (R)SO_3Na + HCl$$

This transformation starts at the top of the column, the "sodium-front" moving downward until finally the first $Na^{\oplus}$ ions leave the column. When the sodium concentration (C_1) in the eluate is determined and C_1/C_0 is plotted against the number of milliequivalents of $Na^{\oplus}$ which entered the column (= the number of milliliters of liquid leaving the column times C_0), a graph is obtained as shown in Fig. 9-6. The breakthrough capacity and, provided that the curve is symmetrical, the total capacity can be read from the graph.

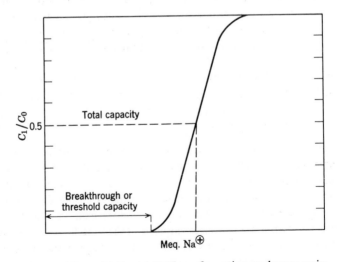

Fig. 9-6. Capacity determination of a cation-exchange resin.

Eluting with NaOH allows determination of the breakthrough of hydroxyl ions.

$$(R)SO_3H + NaOH \rightarrow (R)SO_3Na + H_2O$$

In addition to the total capacity, the breakthrough capacity depends also on the NaCl (or NaOH) concentration, the percolation velocity, the temperature, the dimensions of the column, and the grain size of the resin. These variables should be recorded on the graph.

9-5 Examples

9-5a BREAKTHROUGH CAPACITY OF AMBERLITE IR-120 (OR DOWEX-50) (Cation-exchange resin, sulfonated polystyrene)

Soak about 50 ml. of Amberlite IR-120 in a beaker for $\frac{1}{2}$ hr; change the water several times. Rinse 20 ml. into a column (length 40 cm., diameter 2 cm.) and remove very tiny particles by pumping water into the bottom of the column.

Change the resin into its H-form by displacing the water with 6% HCl; repeat after 15 min. Rinse with distilled water until the eluate is free of Cl ions. Allow measured 15- to 20-ml. portions of 0.1N NaOH solution to percolate through the column until the presence of OH ions becomes evident (phenolphthalein). Change receivers, rinse the column with distilled water, and titrate the eluate with 0.1N HCl. The result is subtracted from the NaOH added originally; the answer shows the amount of NaOH on the column at the moment of the breakthrough. Calculate the breakthrough capacity in milliequivalent per milliliter. A suitable percolation velocity is 100 ml./hr.

9-5b CAPACITY OF AMBERLITE IR-120

Another 50 ml. of Amberlite IR-120 is soaked in water for $\frac{1}{2}$ hr.; change the water several times. Rinse 20 ml. into a column exactly as in § 9-5a. Change into H-form as above. Allow a 0.1N NaOH solution to flow through the column at a rate of 2 ml./min. and collect 20 ml. fractions. Add a drop of phenolphthalein to each fraction and titrate, using 0.1N HCl (microburette).

Continue the experiment until the concentrations of the eluate and that of the alkali put on the column are equal. Plot the results as shown in Fig. 9-6 and calculate breakthrough capacity and total capacity from the graph. Record on the graph all other pertinent parameters.

9-5c TOTAL CAPACITY OF AMBERLITE IR-120

The total capacity can also be determined as follows. Bring 10 ml. of the resin into its H-form by stirring for 15 min. with 6% HCl. Renew the HCl and stir again for 15 min. Wash with distilled water until free of chloride.

Then add a known volume of 0.5N NaOH (calculate the quantity needed from the results of example 9-5a and use 10% excess), stir for 15 min. in a closed flask to prevent CO_2 absorption, remove the resin by filtration, stir several times with distilled water, and titrate. Filtrate and wash liquids with 0.1N HCl. Calculate the total capacity and compare with the results of § 9-5a.

9-5d CAPACITY OF AMBERLITE AR-45 (Anion-exchange resin, polymer containing primary, secondary, and tertiary amino as well as quaternary ammonium groups)

Follow § 9-5a. Use 7% NaOH to change the resin into its OH-form. Use HCl to determine capacity. Acidify fractions with HNO_3 and titrate, using the method of Volhardt or potentiometry (see § 22-3).

9-5e DETERMINATION OF CONCENTRATION OF SODIUM ACETATE

Change 20 ml. of Amberlite IR-120 into its H-form. Dissolve 1 g. of sodium acetate in 50 ml. of water and percolate this solution through the resin in about 45 min. Wash with distilled water until neutral and titrate with $0.1N$ KOH.

9-5f DEMINERALIZATION

The experiment is performed using a finely powdered mixture of sodium chloride and glucose (1:20, wt./wt.). Dissolve about 10 g. of this mixture in 100 ml. of water. Measure the optical rotation. Allow 25 ml. of this solution to percolate through a column containing 25 ml. of Amberlite IR-120 (H-form).

Wash with three 25-ml. portions of water (the second and third portions may be allowed to percolate more rapidly). Repeat the operations, using Amberlite IR-45 (OH-form). Combine the eluates and make up to 250 ml. Measure the rotation and check for $Na^{\oplus}$ and $Cl^{\ominus}$.

9-5g SEPARATION OF HYDROCHLORIC ACID FROM ACETIC ACID (ION EXCLUSION) [7]

A column (diameter 1.5 cm.) is filled with Amberlite IR-120 to a height of 60 cm. (H-form, 50-100 mesh). Mix together 7 ml. of $0.5N$ HCl and 7 ml. of $0.5N$ acetic acid and allow to percolate through the column at a rate of 1 ml./min. Elute with distilled water at the same rate, collecting about thirty 5-ml. fractions. Titrate these with $0.1N$ NaOH. Plot the milliliters of alkali against the number of the fraction.

9-5h SEPARATION OF ETHANOL FROM SODIUM CHLORIDE BY MEANS OF ION EXCLUSION

Amberlite IRA-400, converted to the Cl-form with 6% HCl, is placed in a column (diameter 1.7 cm., height 50 cm). Add 15 ml. of a solution containing 1 g. of NaCl and 6 ml. of ethanol in 100 ml. of water (CO_2 free). Water (free of CO_2) is used for elution (2 ml./min.), and 5-ml. fractions are collected. The refractive index (n_D^{25}) is determined and plotted against the number of the fraction.

9-5i SEPARATION OF PHENOL FROM HYDROCHLORIC ACID BY MEANS OF ION EXCLUSION

A column (diameter 1.7 cm., length 65 cm.) is filled with Amberlite IR-120 (50-100 mesh) to a height of 50 cm. Convert the resin to its H-form with 6% HCl and carefully wash with water.

Add 15 ml. of a solution containing 2 g. of phenol and 1.7 ml. of 38% HCl in 100 ml. of water to the column. Elute with water at a rate of 1.5 ml./min. and collect 10-ml. fractions. Titrate these fractions using 0.1N KOH, until they are acid to litmus. The phenol content in fractions 13–40 is determined spectrophotometrically (at 270 mm.). Plot the results.

9-5j   SEPARATION OF GLUCOSE, FRUCTOSE, AND SACCHAROSE

A 1-cm. column is filled over a length of 11 cm. with a strongly basic resin (for instance, Dowex-1, Cl 10% crosslinked). Small resin particles must be removed, however. To this end equal volumes of water and resin are shaken (10 times) together in a graduate cylinder and allowed to settle for 30 min.; then the water is decanted. Repeat until the water layer is virtually clear.

The resin is washed with 1N HCl. A 0.1M potassium tetraborate solution is then passed through the column until the eluate is free of Cl ions. Wash with water. Wash column with a 0.005M potassium tetraborate solution before use.

About 25 mg. of partially hydrolyzed saccharose (or a mixture of equal parts of saccharose, glucose, and fructose) is used in this experiment by dissolving it in 6 ml. of 0.005M potassium tetraborate.

Elute with:

> 0.005M potassium tetraborate (saccharose)
> 0.02M potassium tetraborate (fructose)
> 0.03M potassium tetraborate (glucose)

at a rate of 1 ml./min.; collect 25-ml. fractions and determine the optical rotation. A total of 100 fractions is collected.

9-5k   SEPARATION OF AMINO ACIDS [9]

Amberlite IR-120, finely ground and screened to 100 mesh, is used. The resin (100 ml.) is placed in a simple column and washed consecutively with 200 ml. of 6% HCl, 500 ml. of 7% NaOH, and 200 ml. of 0.2N NaOH. The pH of the resin is brought to 3.2, using a citrate buffer (105 g. of citric acid monohydrate, 42 g. of NaOH, and 58 ml. of conc. HCl diluted to 5 l. with water; check pH with pH meter).

Transfer the resin to a column consisting of three parts with diameters of 1.7 cm., 1.2 cm., and 0.8 cm. Small polyethylene disks are placed on top of the resin. The three parts are joined, and the horizontal tubes closed off by means of rubber hose and glass rods. Above each resin a liquid layer should remain. The column should not run dry.

Dissolve 10 mg. of glycine and 40 mg. of asparagine in 100 ml. of citrate buffer of pH = 2.2 (21 g. of citric acid monohydrate, 8.4 g. of NaOH, and 16 ml. of HCl, diluted to 1 l.). Add 5 ml. of the buffer solution to the column. Rinse the amino acids into the column, using two 0.3-ml. portions of the citrate buffer (pH = 2.2). Place a separatory funnel containing citrate buffer of pH 3.2 on top of the column and elute, using a fraction collector; collect 2-3 ml. fractions.

Place 2 drops of every fraction on a piece of Whatman 1 paper, dry, and spray with a solution of 0.5% ninhydrine in ethanol. Warm the strips of paper at 100–120° for 5 min.

The amino acid content may also be determined colorimetrically (see § 18-4a) and the result plotted as usual.

9-5l   DECOMPOSITION OF PICRATES [10]

A strongly basic resin (for instance, Amberite IRA-400) is used in its bicarbonate form. Put 20 ml. of the resin (200–400 mesh) on a 1-cm. column and wash with 300–400 ml. of 10% $NaHCO_3$ solution until the eluate is free of Cl ions (check with $AgNO_3$ after acidification), and briefly boil. Wash with 500 ml. of distilled water followed by 100 ml. of acetone-water (9:1, vol./vol.).

The picrate [0.5 g. dissolved in 100 ml. of acetone-water (9:1, vol./vol.)] is added. Elute with 100 ml. of solvent, after absorption of the picrate solution at a rate of 0.5–1 ml./min. Combine the eluates, and remove the acetone under reduced pressure and the water by freeze-drying (see § 13-5). Determine the yield of the base.

Upon completion of the experiment convert the resin into its Cl-form at once by washing with a mixture of conc. HCl and acetone (1:4, vol./vol.) until the eluate is colorlesss.

Examples.   Some examples are as follows:
1. Codeine: m.p. base 154–157°;   m.p. picrate 196–197°.
2. Cinchonine: 261–262°;   222–225°.
3. Cinchonidine: 205–206°;   208–209°.

9-5m   SEPARATION OF GLUTAMIC ACID FROM PYRROLIDONE-CARBOXYLIC ACID

A column (diameter 1 cm.) is filled with Dowex-50 cation-ion exchanger to a height of 15 cm. Wash successively with 200 ml. of $2M$ NaCl solution, 500 ml. of water, 100 ml. of $4N$ HCl solution, and finally with water until the elute is neutral.

Dissolve the mixture of amino acids in 25 ml. of water, if necessary by addition of some ammonia, and pour the solution into the column. Glutamic acid and ammonia are held by the column.

Elute the pyrrolidone carboxylic acid with 250 ml. of water. Boil the eluate for 5 min. to remove CO_2; cool and titrate with $0.5N$ NaOH to methyl red. Elute the glutamic acid with 200 ml. of $2N$ ammonia. Add 50 ml. of $0.1N$ NaOH to the eluate, boil to remove all the ammonia, add 50 ml. of $0.1N$ HCl, boil again to remove CO_2. Cool and titrate with $0.1N$ NaOH to methyl red.

Calculate the composition of the original mixture.

9-5n   EQUIPMENT

2 Beakers (250 ml.)
Separatory funnel (500 ml.)

2 Graduate cylinders (100 ml., 250 ml.)
Thermometer (200°)
Funnel
Three-stage column, standard taper joints and separatory funnel
4 Chromatography columns (40 × 2 cm.)
2 Erlenmeyers (500 ml.)
4 Erlenmeyers (300 ml.)
2 Pipettes (20 ml.)
Weighing bottle
2 Stirring rods
7% NaOH
6% HCl
Universal indicator

9-6 References

1. G. H. Osborn, *Synthetic Ion Exchangers*, Chapman and Hall, London, 1955.
2. O. Samuelson, *Ion Exchanger Separations in Analytical Chemistry*, John Wiley and Sons, New York, 1963.
3. H. G. Cassidy, *Adsorption and Chromatography*, Vol. V in *Technique of Organic Chemistry*, A. Weissberger, ed., Interscience Publishers, New York, 1951, Ch. IX, p. 267.
4. R. Griessbach and G. Naumann, in *Methoden der organischen Chemie*, Houben-Weyl ed., G. Thieme Verlag, Stuttgart, 1958, Band 1/1, p. 521.
5. C. Calmon and T. R. E. Kressman, *Ion Exchangers in Organic and Biochemistry*, Interscience Publishers, New York, 1957.
6. F. Helfferich, *Angew. Chem.*, **66**, 241 (1954).
7. R. M. Wheaton and W. C. Bauman, *Ind. Eng. Chem.*, **45**, 228 (1953).
8. J. X. Khym and L. P. Zill, *J. Am. Chem. Soc.*, **74**, 2090 (1952).
9. S. Moore and W. H. Stein, *J. Biol. Chem.*, **192**, 663 (1951) and **211**, 893 (1954).
10. J. M. Bobbit, *J. Org. Chem.*, **22**, 1729 (1957).
11. F. G. Nelfferich, *Ion Exchange*, McGraw-Hill Book Co., New York, 1962.

IO

Paper electrophoresis

10-1 Introduction

Electrophoresis is a method of separation based upon the difference in velocities of charged particles in an electric field. To make certain that convection does not prevent a successful separation, use is made of gels (agar, for instance). In another frequently used method, the liquid phase is applied to paper (paper electrophoresis).

The method is of importance for the separation of amino acids, peptides, proteins, nucleic acids, sugars, and alkaloids.

10-2 Principle

The electrophoresis is carried out on a strip of paper soaked in a buffer. The ends of the paper strip dip into two jars containing the buffer solution and connected to the electrodes. A small quantity of the mixture is placed on the paper, and a stabilized d-c voltage applied across the paper. The charged particles move in the electric field.

10-3 Theory

10-3a ION MOBILITY

The force f exerted on a particle of charge q by a field strength F at infinite dilution is equal to

$$f = Fq$$

The particle is accelerated until an equilibrium is established due to the friction f'. According to Stokes' law,

$$f' = 6\pi r \eta v$$

for a spherical particle if v = velocity of particle;
r = radius of particle;
η = viscosity of medium.

A constant velocity equal to

$$v = \frac{Fq}{6\pi r \eta}$$

98

is thus achieved by the particle. The mobility of the particle, i.e., the velocity per unit of field strength, is

$$u = \frac{q}{6\pi r \eta}$$

In practice infinite dilution is never achieved. A retardation, caused by an (opposite) ion cloud, will increase with increasing ionic strength.

The separation of two kinds of ions (A and B) is facilitated when their mobilities (u_A and u_B) differ widely. After t minutes the difference in the distance traveled is equal to

$$\boxed{d_A - d_B = (u_A - u_B)Ft} \tag{10-1}$$

10-3b MIGRATION VELOCITY OF WEAK ELECTROLYTES

A weak acid is only partly ionized in solution.

$$A\!-\!H \underset{}{\overset{K_A}{\rightleftharpoons}} A^{\ominus} + H^{\oplus}$$

At a certain pH:

$$pH = pK + \log \frac{[A^{\ominus}]}{[AH]}$$

Since this is a dynamic equilibrium, each particular particle will be present as an ion only part of the time. The larger the degree of ionization, the longer each particle will be present as an ion. Thus the apparent mobility (U_A) of the weak acid A will depend not only on the mobility of the anion (u_A) but also on the degree of dissociation.

$$U_A = \frac{u_A[A^{\ominus}]}{[HA] + [A^{\ominus}]} = \frac{u_A K_A}{[H^{\oplus}] + K_A} \tag{10-2}$$

The extent to which two acids A and B may be separated depends on the difference in apparent mobilities.

$$U_A - U_B = \frac{u_A K_A}{[H^{\oplus}] + K_A} - \frac{u_B K_B}{[H^{\oplus}] + K_B}$$

The difference [4] is at a maximum when

$$[H^{\oplus}] = \frac{(u_A/u_B)^{\frac{1}{2}} - (K_A/K_B)^{\frac{1}{2}}}{1 - (u_A K_A)^{\frac{1}{2}}(u_B K_B)^{-\frac{1}{2}}} \cdot (K_A K_B)^{\frac{1}{2}}$$

or

$$\boxed{pH = \frac{pK_A + pK_B}{2} - \log \frac{u_A{}^{\frac{1}{2}} u_B{}^{-\frac{1}{2}} - K_A{}^{\frac{1}{2}} K_B{}^{-\frac{1}{2}}}{1 - (u_A K_A)^{\frac{1}{2}}(u_B K_B)^{-\frac{1}{2}}}} \tag{10-3}$$

Some results are shown in Table 10-1.

Table 10-1

Mixture	Optimum pH
Lysine and histidine	6.6
Glutamic acid and aspartic acid	7
Glycine and serine	9.2

10-3c DIFFUSION

Diffusion during electrophoresis causes broadening of bands. This broadening increases with time, concentration, and temperature and hinders separation. Thus an increase in field strength resulting in a shortening of the required time (see formula 10-1) may be advantageous. A large field strength increases the amount of heat released because of an increase in current density. Thus improved cooling is needed.

10-3d ELECTRO-OSMOSIS

A number of negatively charged functional groups ($-COO^{\ominus}$) are present in filter paper. These may give rise to an electric double layer between the paper fibers and the solution when the paper is soaked in an electrolyte. When an electric field is applied, the liquid will flow toward the cathode (electro-osmosis). Naturally this flow influences the displacement of the ions. The effect increases with increasing ionic strength.

Because of the nature of paper, the particles sometimes tend to follow its grain direction instead of a straight path. Adsorption phenomena may also play a role.

10-4 Apparatus

The horizontal paper electrophoresis tank (Shandon Scientific Company, London) is used in combination with a stabilized 1000 volt (*danger!*) power supply (Shandon type 2523 MK II).

The electrophoresis tank (Figs. 10-1 and 10-2) consists of a Lucite container, with the two electrode compartments and a bridge for the paper. The electrode

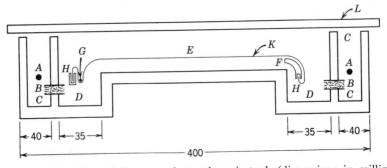

Fig. 10-1. Shandon horizontal paper electrophoresis tank (dimensions in millimeters). *A*. Electrodes. *B*. Glass tube containing cotton plug. *C*. Electrode compartment. *D*. Buffer compartment. *E*. Paper strip. *F*. Paper supports. *G*. Glass rod. *H*. Slit to fasten paper. *K*. Base line. *L*. Cover.

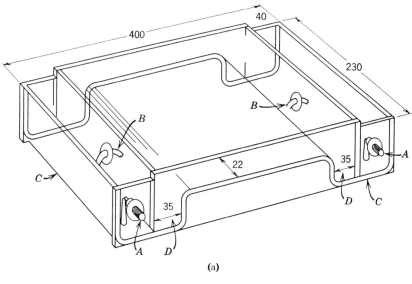

(a)

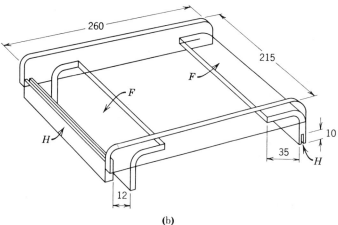

(b)

Fig. 10-2. Electrophoresis tank (a) and paper bridge (b).

compartments are connected to the buffer solution compartments by means of a tube (containing a cotton plug). The ends of the paper strips dip into the latter compartments.

10-5 Procedure

Whatman paper 1, 4, 3, or 31 is used, depending on the need for high or low resistance. On each of four strips (4 × 33 cm.) draw a base line, 10 cm. from one end. Soak the strips in the buffer solution before use. Submerge the strips one by one in the solution, hold them between two pieces of filter paper, and place them on top of a glass plate. Squeeze them out by using a rubber roller. Attach the strips to the holder, fastening the ends in the appropriate slits (use a strip of heavy filter paper if necessary). (See Fig. 10-1.)

The paper can be lightened by pushing the glass rod *g*. Place the bridge in the tray, and fill the compartments to a height of 2 cm. with equal volumes of the upper solution. About 750 ml. of solution is needed. The tray should be placed horizontally, and the liquid levels should be equally high on either side; otherwise the liquid will be siphoned out *via* the paper.

The electrodes are connected to the connecting clamps of the apparatus. Check whether the connections are made in such a way that the substances will move in the proper direction.

Turn on the desired voltage and allow to equilibrate for 15 min. Turn off the current. *Do not touch the tank while the current is on.*

After the current is turned off, the mixture can be applied to the paper. A folded piece of filter paper is dipped into the solution, clamped between two glass plates, and carefully pressed to the paper at the base line in such a manner that the paper is moistened over its entire width.

The bridge is covered with a separate glass plate to prevent moisture condensing on the cover from falling on the paper. If necessary, a thin glass rod can be placed underneath the paper strips in the middle of the bridge to prevent them from sagging.

Turning on the Current

1. The *"range"* knob is placed in the desired position: I = 20–300 volts; II = 300–500 volts; III = 500–750 volts; IV = 750–1000 volts.

2. The *"voltage"* knob is turned as far counterclockwise as possible.

3. Check all connections, making sure that no live wires or parts can be touched while the current is on.

4. Turn on the current.

5. After a few moments the voltmeter oscillates sharply. After this oscillation wait a few minutes.

6. Read the voltmeter (lower scale) and adjust if necessary with the "voltage" knob.

10-6 Examples

10-6a SEPARATION OF AMINES

Mixture. The mixture is composed of some of the following amines:

1. Methylamine.	4. Trimethylamine.
2. Ethylamine.	5. Lysine.
3. Propylamine.	6. Glycine.

The mobility decreases in this order: $1 > 2 > 4 > 3 > 5 > 6$. The test solutions contain 10 mmoles of amine for every liter of buffer solution except glycine, whose concentration is 5 mmoles/l.

Buffer Solution. Citric acid (10.5 g.) and NaOH (2.0 g.) in 450 ml. of water; adjust pH to 3.8 by careful addition of 2–3 ml. 1N NaOH and make up to 500 ml. with distilled water.

Reagent. 0.1% ninhydrine in butanol.

Separation. Prepare four strips of Whatman 1 paper as described in § 10-5. Apply the mixture to one strip and the test solution to the three other strips (combined two by two). Separate at 300 volts for 2.5 hr. The base line should be at the anode side.

Turn off the current, take the bridge out of the tank, and immediately cut off the ends of the strips which have hung in the buffer solution. Dry the paper with a commercial hair dryer, spray with ninhydrine reagent, and allow to dry at 110° for 10 min. Trace the outlines of the spots with pencil and measure the distance the amines have traveled; compared to glycine. Since the isoelectric point of glycine is at a pH of 3.8, the movement of glycine under the conditions described is due to end–osmosis.

Record the variation in current during the experiment.

10-6b   SEPARATION OF AMINO ACIDS

Mixture. The mixture is composed of a number of the following amino acids:

1. Lysine.	4. Methionine.
2. Glycine.	5. Proline.
3. Leucine.	6. Aspartic acid.

The mobility of the ions decreases in order from 1 to 6. The solutions of glycine, proline, and methionine are 0.02 mole/l., those containing leucine, aspartic acid, and lysine, 0.04 mole/l.

Buffer Solution. 0.25N acetic acid solution (15 ml. of acetic acid made up to 1 l.); pH = 2.75.

Reagent. 0.1% ninhydrine in butanol.

Separation. Prepare four strips of Whatman 1 paper as before. Apply the mixture to one strip, the test solutions to the other three strips. Combine the test solutions two by two. Separate by applying 800 volts for 2 hr. The base line should be at the anode side. Follow directions as in § 10-6a.

Figure 10-3 shows a diagram of a vertical electrophoresis tank (Shandon, England).

10-6c   EQUIPMENT

Electrophoresis tank	Ninhydrine
Whatman paper	Butanol
Amines	Hair dryer
Buffer solution	Amino acids

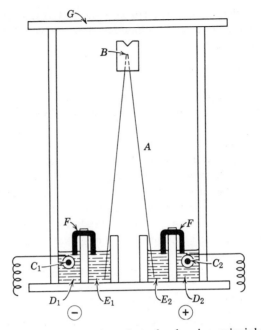

Fig. 10-3. Diagram of vertical electrophoresis tank, showing principle of construction. *A.* Filter paper strip. *B.* Nylon string for paper suspension. C_1, C_2. Platinum-coated electrodes. D_1, D_2. Electrode buffer compartments. E_1, E_2. Buffer compartments for the paper strips. *F.* Wicks connecting compartments *D* and *E*. *G.* Removable glass lid.

10-7 References

1. M. Lederer, *An Introduction to Paper Electrophoresis and Related Methods*, Elsevier Publishing Co., Amsterdam, 1955.
2. R. J. Block, E. L. Durrum, and G. Zweig, *A Manual of Paper Chromatography and Paper Electrophoresis*, Academic Press, New York, 1958.
3. W. Grassmann and K. Hannig, "Präparative Elektrophorese" in *Methoden der organischen Chemie*, Houben-Weyl, ed., G. Thieme Verlag, Stuttgart, 1958, Band 1/1, p. 681.
4. R. Consden, A. H. Gordon, and A. J. P. Martin, *Biochem. J.*, **40**, 33 (1946).
5. L. P. Ribeiro, E. Mitidieri, and O. R. Affonso, *Paper Electrophoresis*, Elsevier Publishing Co., Amsterdam, 1961.
6. M. Bier, *Electrophoresis—Theory, Methods, and Applications*, Academic Press, New York, 1959.

II

Distillation,
crystallization,
sublimation

II

Distillation

A ATMOSPHERIC PRESSURE DISTILLATION

11-1 Introduction

Distillation is a method of separation which makes use of the fact that in most cases the vapor in equilibrium with a liquid mixture is richer in the more volatile component(s).

11-2 Theory

11-2a TEMPERATURE–COMPOSITION DIAGRAM

For a binary system, a graphical representation can be made of the boiling point (at constant pressure) at the start, as a function of the composition (T, x-curve, boiling point curve). The vapor in equilibrium with the liquid has a different composition at every temperature; thus a second curve is obtained (T, X-curve, vapor composition curve). Figure 11-1 shows such a diagram for an ideal binary system. The compositions of the liquid (x) and the vapor (X) are expressed in terms of the mole fraction of the most volatile component (A).

A liquid mixture of composition x will start boiling at temperature T_K; the escaping vapor has the composition X.

11-2b RELATIVE VOLATILITY

The volatility of component A (in a mixture of A and B) is

$$V_A = \frac{\text{concentration in the vapor}}{\text{concentration in the liquid}} = \frac{X}{x}$$

For component B the relationship is

$$V_B = \frac{1 - X}{1 - x}$$

The relative volatility α is defined as

$$\boxed{\alpha = \frac{V_A}{V_B} = \frac{X(1 - x)}{x(1 - X)}} \qquad (11\text{-}1)$$

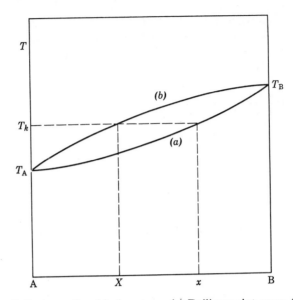

Fig. 11-1. T, x, X-diagram of an ideal system. (*a*) Boiling point curve (T, x). (*b*) Vapor composition curve (T, X).

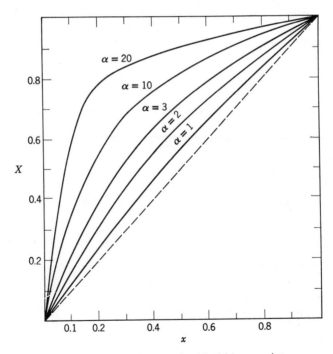

Fig. 11-2. xX-diagram for ideal binary mixtures.

This relationship is a measure of the degree to which it is possible to separate a mixture by distillation. When $\alpha = 1$, the compositions of vapor and liquid are equal and no separation is possible. The larger α, the easier is the separation.

Raoult's law for an ideal system is

$$\pi_A = xP_A$$

when π_A is the partial pressure of component A, and P_A the vapor pressure of A at the temperature of the system. Similarly, for component B

$$\pi_B = (1 - x)P_B$$

Total pressure is therefore

$$P = xP_A + (1 - x)P_B$$

According to Dalton's law,

$$X = \frac{\pi_a}{P} \quad \text{and} \quad (1 - X) = \frac{\pi_B}{P}$$

also

$$V_A = \frac{X}{x} = \frac{P_A}{P} \quad \text{and} \quad V_B = \frac{1 - X}{1 - x} = \frac{P_B}{P}$$

$$\boxed{\alpha = \frac{P_A}{P_B}}$$

Using the integrated equation of Clapeyron,

$$\ln P_A = -\frac{\Delta H_A}{RT} + C$$

and Trouton's rule (non-polar liquids obey this rule reasonably well)

$$\Delta H = 20.5 T_K$$

we find that

$$\boxed{\log \alpha = \frac{8.9 \times \Delta t}{T_A + T_B}} \tag{11-2}$$

where T_A and T_B = boiling points of A and B in °K, 760 mm.

$$\Delta t = |T_A - T_B|$$

11-2c THE xX-DIAGRAM

In order to calculate distillation processes an xX-diagram is frequently used. For an ideal system where α is constant it may be calculated readily. From formula 11-1 it follows at once that

$$X = \frac{\alpha x}{1 + (\alpha - 1)x}$$

The result for several values of α is shown in Fig. 11-2.

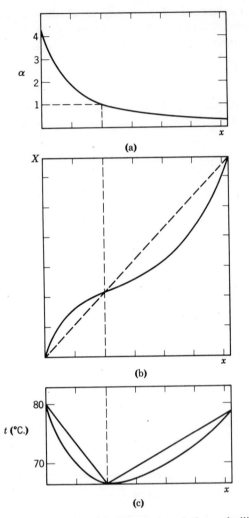

Fig. 11-3. Ethanol-benzene system. (a) Change in relative volatility. (b) Xx diagram. (c) tx diagram.

Examples. Two ideal systems are the following:

1. Benzene + toluene.
2. *n*-Heptane + methylcyclohexane.

11-2d NON-IDEAL SYSTEMS, AZEOTROPES

Most binary systems deviate from ideal behavior. The relative volatility α becomes dependent upon the composition of the mixture. The course of the distillation can then be calculated only from an xX-diagram which has been determined experimentally.

Azeotropy is an extreme case of non-ideal behavior. For a certain ratio of the components, the compositions of the liquid and vapor are equal. The equilibrium line will dissect the diagonal of the xX. The T, x- and T, X-curves show a maximum or a minimum. Figure 11-3 shows an example of a minimum azeotrope. Details about azeotropes may be found in Horsley [5].

11-2e   SIMPLE DISTILLATION

The course of a simple distillation can be read from Fig. 11-1. At temperature T_k, the mixture (composition x) starts boiling; the vapor escaping has the composition X. In the course of the distillation the composition of the residue changes from x to B; the composition of the vapor at any instant varies from X to B. The result is shown in Fig. 11-4.

A simple distillation will effect a satisfactory separation for large values of α only, as in the removal of volatile solvents from solids and polymeric impurities. In all other cases fractional distillation is indicated.

11-2f   PRINCIPLE OF FRACTIONAL DISTILLATION

A vertical column, filled with chips or beads to increase its surface area, is placed between the flask and the condenser. The rising vapor comes in close contact with the descending liquid. Thus an effect is achieved similar to a series of evaporation and condensing units.

The efficiency of a fractional distillation column depends upon these factors:

(*a*) *The number of theoretical plates*, the number of simple evaporation and condensation processes necessary in achieving the same separation as with the designated column.

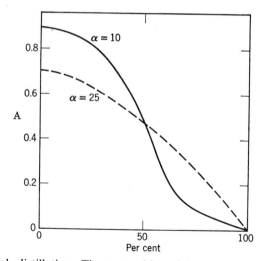

Fig. 11-4. A simple distillation. The composition of the vapor at any moment (expressed in mole fractions of A) is plotted as a function of the amount of liquid distilled (mole per cent starting mixture).

(b) *The holdup of the column*, the amount of liquid in the column during the distillation.

(c) *The pressure drop*, the difference in pressure between the top and the bottom of the column. This depends upon column diameter, kind of packing, and throughput (vapor flow rate).

11-3   Apparatus

The columns used in the laboratory are usually designed so that liquid-vapor contact occurs over the entire column length. Other columns may have "plates" spaced at regular intervals along the column. These plates are designed to increase the contact between liquid and vapor and are used frequently in industry.

Let n be the number of theoretical plates of a column of length l. Then l/n is called the H.E.T.P. (height equivalent to one theoretical plate), which is a measure of the efficiency of the column or its packing. It is to be noted, however, that a column need not have a fixed number of theoretical plates. The number may vary, depending on the nature of the mixture, the initial concentration of components the pressure, the load, the reflux ratio, etc.

11-3a   NUMBER OF PLATES NEEDED TO EFFECT SEPARATION

Formula 11-1 shows the vapor equilibrium in the pot:

$$\frac{X_0}{1 - X_0} = \alpha \frac{x_0}{1 - x_0}$$

For the "first plate" similarly:

$$\frac{X_1}{1 - X_1} = \alpha \frac{x_1}{1 - x_1}$$

Since the vapor from the pot condenses on the first plate,

$$X_0 = x_1$$

and

$$\frac{X_1}{1 - X_1} = \alpha^2 \frac{x_0}{1 - x_0}$$

After n plates (at total reflux)

$$\frac{x_d}{1 - x_d} = \frac{X_n}{1 - X_n} = \alpha^{n+1} \frac{x_0}{1 - x_0}$$

where x_d is the concentration of component A at the top of the column, and x_0 the initial concentration in the pot.

$$\boxed{n + 1 = \log \frac{x_d(1 - x_0)}{x_0(1 - x_d)} \Big/ \log \alpha}$$ (the Fenske equation)   (11-3)

Calculations. Initial mixture: 50 mole % benzene + 50 mole % toluene ($\alpha = 2.47$).

Result desired: composition at top of column (at total reflux), 99.5 mole % benzene.

Number of plates needed:

$$n = \left[\left(\log \frac{0.995}{0.500} \times \frac{0.500}{0.005} \right) \middle/ \log 2.47 \right] - 1 = 4.9$$

Upon collection of the distillate, the composition in the pot, and consequently that in the distillate, changes slowly.

11-4 Determination of the Separating Capacity of a Column

Using a binary system whose xX-diagram is known accurately, we can determine the separating capacity of a column. It is expressed in terms of the number of theoretical plates (to the nearest whole number). In addition, the mixture used, the pressure, and the load applied (distillation velocity, ml./hr.) should be mentioned. Unless specified otherwise, the number of theoretical plates is taken at infinite reflux ratio.

Mixtures. Test mixtures used frequently are:

1. Benzene–carbon tetrachloride, for columns of 0–20 theoretical plates.
2. *n*-Heptane–cyclohexane, for columns of 20–100 theoretical plates.
3. Chlorobenzene-ethylbenzene, useful at 1 atm. up to 60 theoretical plates. May be used at reduced pressures.

A discussion about the determination of the number of theoretical plates, using the first test mixture, follows. See Sigwart [4] for details on the other systems.

The following points are of importance in determining the number of theoretical plates:

(*a*) The purity of the test liquids.
(*b*) Exactly vertical arrangement of the column.
(*c*) Proper wetting of the packing; by briefly flooding the column at the start of the experiment wetting may be achieved.
(*d*) Proper equilibration of the column.
(*e*) As small a quantity of liquid taken off the top as possible; in any case not more than 1% of the initial charge.

The equation of Fenske may be used to determine the number of plates from the composition of the top and the bottom. However, α varies with composition for the test mixture benzene–carbon tetrachloride. It is necessary, therefore, to use the xX-diagram determined experimentally. The composition of the mixture is determined by means of the refractive index. Table 11-1 shows the relationship between refractive index and number of theoretical plates. The numbers found for the top and the bottom must be subtracted from one another. A 2:1 (vol./vol.)

Table 11-1   Determination of Number of Plates of Benzene–Carbon Tetrachloride

n_D^{25}	Number of Plates	n_D^{25}	Number of Plates	n_D^{25}	Number of Plates
		1.4700	21.9	1.4800	13.7
		10	20.8	10	13.0
		20	19.8	20	12.4
		30	19.0	30	11.7
		40	18.1	40	11.0
1.4650	29.5	50	17.3	50	10.4
60	27.5	60	16.5	60	9.8
70	25.9	70	15.8	70	9.1
80	24.3	80	15.1	80	8.4
90	23.1	90	14.4	90	7.7

ratio of benzene–carbon tetrachloride is used for columns with about ten theoretical plates.

11-5   Some Practical Hints

Choice of Column.   Some types of columns used frequently in the laboratory are listed in Table 11-2.

Vigreux columns (Fig. 11-5) have no packing. They are usually available in several sizes. Although ordinarily the number of theoretical plates is small, their versatility in terms of capacity and pressure variation makes them very useful.

The *Podbielniak* (Heligrid) column (Fig. 11-6) is filled with a spiral of thin metal wire. Its sturdy construction, considerable separating power, and capacity make it a useful column.

Table 11-2   Column Types

Type	Diameter (mm.)	Length (cm.)	No. of Plates at Total Reflux	Remarks
Vigreux	8	50	5–6	10–50 ml. liquid
Vigreux	10	150–200	15–20	For analytical distillation of 100–300 mm. and for distillation at reduced pressure (10–760 mm.)
Podbielniak (Heligrid)	17	100	30–50	150–600 ml. liquid
Fenske	12	265		For substances which corrode chrome wire (e.g., halogen compounds)
Spiral band	5	60	20–50	20–200 ml. small holdup

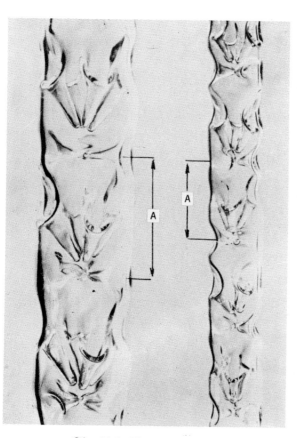

Fig. 11-5. Vigreux columns.

When compounds have to be distilled which react with metal, a *Fenske* column (Fig. 11-7) may be used. This column is filled with glass rings. A disadvantage of this column is the tendency to flood and foam unless all the glass rings are unbroken. Its holdup may also be considerable.

The *spiral* or *rotating band* column attempts to combine large numbers of theoretical plates with relatively small size. Its capacity is limited.

Number of Plates. The number of plates required may be calculated by means of equation 11-3. In practice the number of plates used rarely exceeds $n = 3.5/\log \alpha$.

Reflux Ratio. The reflux ratio (R) is the amount of condensate returning to the column divided by the amount taken off. The minimum reflux ratio permissible is given by Fenske [7].

$$\frac{R_{\min}}{1 - R_{\min}} = \frac{x_d - \dfrac{\alpha x_0}{1 + (\alpha - 1)x_0}}{x_d - x_0}$$

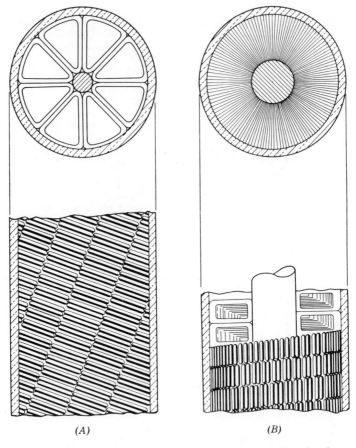

(A)   (B)

Fig. 11-6a. Heligrid packings: (A) assembly of sector-section coils twisted around central core; (B) staircase assembly of rectangular section coils around central core.

The reflux ratio should equal or better the number of theoretical plates in order to use the separating capacity of a column to its fullest extent.

Holdup.   The holdup should always be less than 10% of the initial amount of liquid. The relationship and the equation discussed above are valid only when the holdup is small compared to the total starting mixture.

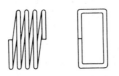

Fig. 11-6b. Podbielniak (Heligrid).

Fig. 11-7. Fenske helices.

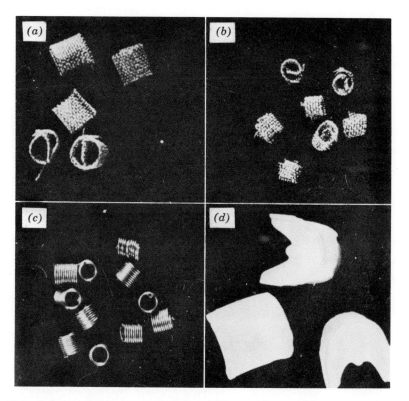

Fig. 11-8. Column packings. (*a, b*) Dixon filling. (*c*) Wendeln. (*d*) Berl saddels.

Time Required.   The time needed to reach a steady state increases with increasing number of plates. As a rule of thumb, 1.5 hr. for every ten plates is a reasonable estimate. This time increases further when the load decreases.

Last Fraction.   There is always the danger of heating the pot to dryness toward the end of a distillation. To prevent this, a stable high-boiling liquid (e.g., decaline, b.p. 190°) is often added so that even the least volatile component of the original mixture can be distilled in good yield.

Note.   Rose and Johnson [8] may be consulted for calculations involving most cases of discontinuous fractional distillation.

11-6 Analytical Distillation

11-6a SEPARATING A MIXTURE BY USE OF AN ANALYTICAL COLUMN

The column shown in Fig. 11-9 is useful for analytical purposes. The column packing consists of double spiral Nichrome wire.

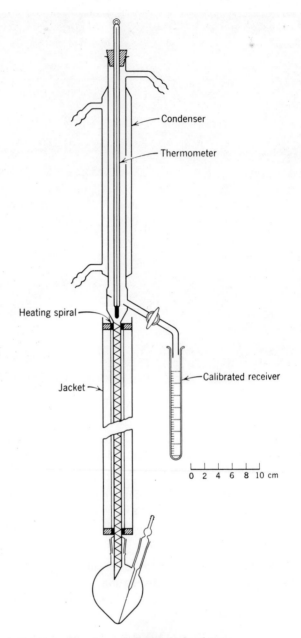

Fig. 11-9. Simple analytical spiral column.

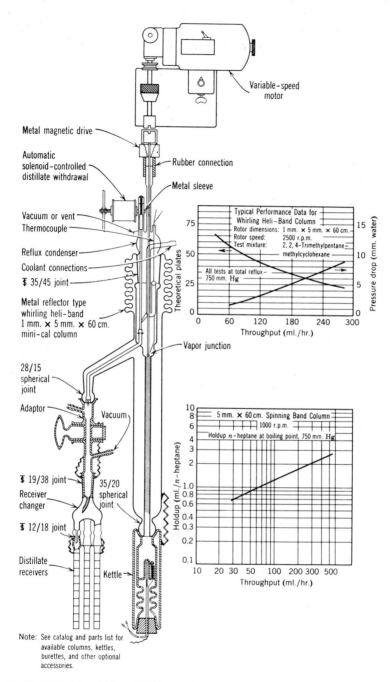

Fig. 11-10. Podbielniak whirling Heli-band (magnetic-type vacuumtight drive) Mini-Cal column. (Reproduced with permission from Podbielniak, Inc., 341 E. Ohio St., Chicago, Ill.)

Cleaning the Apparatus. Add acetone to the still pot and heat under reflux for at least 15 min. Remove the pot and draw air through the warm column until dry. Use *no silicone grease* on any joints, since it prevents wetting of glass and packing.

Operating Procedure. Use 70 ml. of a mixture containing 40 ml. of the least volatile component. Collect twelve 5-ml. fractions (reflux ratio about 15). Record the boiling point after 3 and 5 ml. of distillate have been collected for each of the first and last four fractions. Record the boiling point after every milliliter of fractions 5–8. The refractive indices (n_D^{25}) of all the fractions as well as of the pure components are determined.

Calculations and Report

(*a*) Calculate α, using equation 11-2, and calculate the composition to be expected of the first fraction by means of formula 11-3.

(*b*) Record the data as indicated in Form 11-1.

	Name: Date: Column type:					Sample: Initial amount: Reflux ratio: $\alpha =$					
No. of fraction	Weight of fraction			Head temp.	Column temp.	Bath temp.	Pressure	Time	n_D^{25}	Remarks
	Total weight	Fare	Wt. of liquid							

(*c*) Determine the composition of the fractions by means of the refractive index, using the calibration curve obtained by plotting 0, 25, 50, 75, and 100 vol. % of one of the constituents against n_D^{25} on large coordinate paper.

(*d*) Prepare the following graphs:

i. T_k (see § 11-2a) vs. the number of milliliters of distillate.
ii. n_D^{25} vs. milliliters of distillate.
iii. The composition found in (*c*), in mole per cent for both components, vs. milliliters of distillate.

11-6b EQUIPMENT

Distillation column with thermometer (200°)	Pipette
Thermometer (370°)	Three-way plug
Cow with 12 graduated receivers	Test tube rack
Oil bath, hot plate, thermostat	Calcium chloride tube
Manometer, manostat, variac	Boiling stick
Graduated cylinder (100 ml.)	4 Test tubes (5 mm.)
Funnel	

B VACUUM DISTILLATION

11-7 Introduction

Since many organic compounds are thermally unstable, distillation under reduced pressure is frequently necessary. In addition to lowering the boiling point, vacuum distillation often changes the relative volatility of the components. The water–ethanol system is an example of a mixture which forms an azeotrope at 760 mm. When the pressure is reduced to 70 mm. Hg or less, the components can, however, be separated completely.

According to the Clapeyron equation,

$$\ln P = -\frac{\Delta H}{RT} + C \quad \text{and} \quad \log_{10}\frac{P_1}{P_2} = \frac{\Delta H}{2.3R}\frac{T_2 - T_1}{T_2 T_1} \tag{11-4}$$

Since the heat of vaporization may vary somewhat with the temperature, the following (empirical) equation (Antoine) is more satisfactory:

$$\log P = \frac{a}{t + b} + c \tag{11-5}$$

where t = temperature in degrees C.;
    a, b, c = constants determined empirically.

11-8 Distillation Rate

Equations 11-4 and 11-5 indicate that the boiling point of a substance may be decreased to any temperature desired merely by reducing the pressure sufficiently. However, in practice certain limitations must be recognized. With the normal vacuum distillation apparatus a reduction of the pressure (as measured behind the condenser) below 1 mm. has little or no effect on the boiling point. The reason for this anomaly is the large pressure drop of several millimeters of mercury between still pot and condenser. Although it may thus seem that a small pressure drop is desirable, Table 11-3 illustrates that the distillation rate would decrease too much.

Table 11-3   Distillation Rate of a Particular Still as a Function of the Pressure Drop

Pressure Drop (mm.)	Time Required to Distill 1 g. of Substance
10	0.5 min.
1	1 hr.
10^{-1}	1 week
10^{-2}	2 years
10^{-3}	40 years

The only way then to accomplish a distillation at a reasonable rate when the required pressure is very low is to take care that only a short wide path exists between pot and condenser (see Chapter 12), thus reducing the resistance to the transport of the vapor.

Since the amount of vapor in the column is much smaller under reduced pressure than at atmospheric pressure, the heat capacity (of the column) is likewise much lower. To reduce heat losses the insulation needs to be improved considerably.

The pressure should therefore never be lower than necessary.

11-9   Apparatus

Table 11-4 can serve as a guide in the choice of the appropriate apparatus. The apparatus for a normal vacuum distillation consists of the following:

(a) *Pump*. Aspirator (to about 10 mm.) or oil pump (10 to 0.1 mm.).

(b) *Trap*. The oil pump is protected by means of a trap placed in a Dewar flask filled with Dry Ice–acetone (alcohol).

(c) *Pressure regulator*. Constant pressure is maintained with the aid of a pressure regulator of the types shown in Fig. 11-12. Type (a) can be used to regulate pressures between 10 and 710 mm. Below 50 mm. type (b) may be used also. With type (b),

Table 11-4

Normal "vacuum" distillation	Used for compounds which distill at temperatures lower than 250° at atmospheric pressures.
Molecular distillation (see Chapter 12)	For substances of molecular weight up to 1200. With a centrifugal type of apparatus, substances of low thermal stability may be distilled, since their exposure time to high temperatures is reduced to a fraction of a second.
Brush-type still (Fig. 11-11)	For substances of molecular weight 250–900. The separation achieved is better than that obtained with a molecular still.

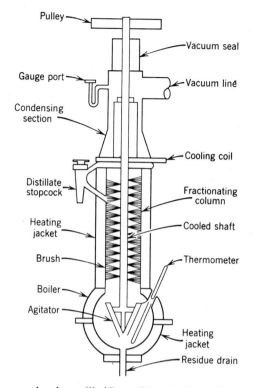

Fig. 11-11. Brush-type molecular still (Consolidated Electrodynamics Corp.). (Used with permission from K. B. Wiberg, *Laboratory Technique in Organic Chemistry*, McGraw-Hill Book Co., New York, 1960)

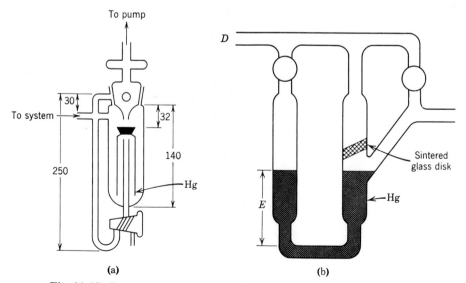

(a) (b)

Fig. 11-12. Pressure regulators. (*a*) Cartesian manostat. (*b*) Manostat.

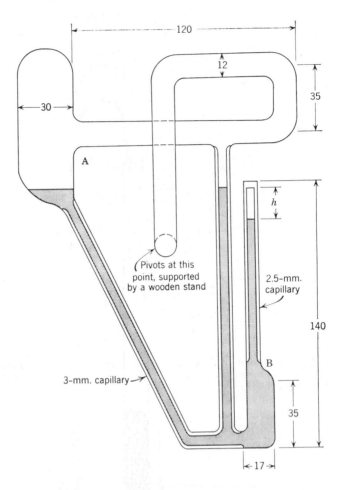

Fig. 11-13. McLeod gauge. (Used with permission from K. B. Wiberg, *Laboratory Technique in Organic Chemistry*, McGraw-Hill Book Co., New York, 1960)

the pressure in the apparatus can never exceed the sum of the pressures in the pump and the height of the mercury level *E*. When the pressure rises, gas is evacuated *via D*. Merely by tilting the manostat, the pressure can be maintained at various values without changing the amount of mercury. However, at pressures below 10 mm. these types of manostats become inaccurate. A very simple way of maintaining some pressure regulation is to place a ballast tank (essentially a round-bottom flask of 5- to 10-l. volume) between the column and the pump and to allow air to trickle into the system through a small needle valve.

(*d*) *Manometer*. Down to 5 mm. pressure a closed mercury manometer suffices. At lower pressures a tilting McLeod gauge (Fig. 11-13) is used.

11-10   Rotary Vacuum Evaporator

A recurring operation in a laboratory is the concentration of dilute solutions. Since α is usually very large, the apparatus need not be designed for its ability to achieve good separations.   Figure 11-14 shows a rotary evaporator designed

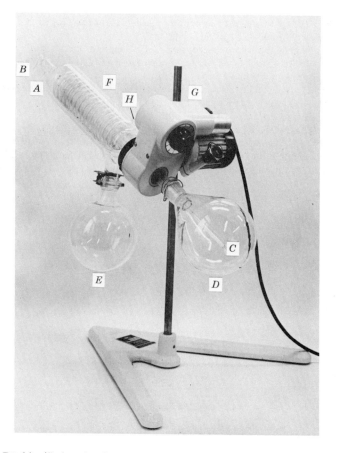

Fig. 11-14. Büchi (Switzerland) rotary vacuum evaporator (Swissco Instruments, Greenville, Ill.).

for batch as well as continuous operation.   Many variations of this basic type are known.   The solution is allowed to enter flask D through tube C whose upper end A is connected *via* a stopcock B to the reservoir.   Usually a glass rod dipping into the solution to be concentrated is connected to A with a rubber tube.   The receiver D may be warmed with a steam or water bath.   The distillate collects in flask E, which may be cooled in ice.   Evacuation is achieved *via* H.   The flask D is continuously rotated by motor G.

11-11 References

1. J. Verheus and F. J. Zuiderweg, *Destillatie Handleiding*, H. J. Paris, Amsterdam, 1954.
2. T. P. Carney, *Laboratory Fractional Distillation*, The Macmillan Company, New York, 1949.
3. A. and E. Rose *et al.*, Vol. IV in *Technique of Organic Chemistry*, A. Weissberger, ed., *Distillation*, Interscience Publishers, New York, 1951.
4. K. Sigwart in *Methoden der organischen Chemie*, Houben-Weyl, ed., G. Thieme Verlag, Stuttgart, 1958, Band I/1, p. 777–889.
5. L. H. Horsley, "Table of Azeotropes and Nonazeotropes," *Anal. Chem.*, **19,** 508 (1947) and **21,** 831 (1949). This has appeared also as a separate publication, *Azeotropic Data*, American Chemical Society, Washington, 1952.
6. R. Jäckel, "Vacuumdistillation," in *Methoden der organischen Chemie* (Houben-Weyl), Georg Thieme Verlag, Stuttgart, 1958, Band I/1, pp. 897.
7. M. R. Fenske, *Ind. Eng. Chem.*, **24,** 482 (1932).
8. A. R. Rose and R. C. Johnson, *Chem. Eng. Progr.*, **49,** 15 (1953).
9. A. Rose in *Treatise on Analytical Chemistry*, D. M. Kolthoff and P. J. Elving, eds., Interscience Publishers, New York, 1961, Part I, Vol. 2, Ch. 29, pp. 1235–1280.
10. A. E. Coulson and E. F. G. Herington, *Laboratory Distillation Practice*, London, 1958.

12

Molecular distillation

12-1 Introduction

Molecular distillation is a method used to purify thermally unstable high-boiling compounds. This method is of considerable importance in spite of the fact that the separations achieved are poor.

12-2 Principle

Molecular distillation consists of placing a cooled surface very close to the liquid to be distilled, heating the latter to 50–300°C. The mean free path of the molecules is given by the equation

$$\text{(cm.)} = \frac{1}{2^{\frac{1}{2}}\pi n(2a)^2} \tag{12-1}$$

where n = number of molecules per cubic centimeter;
a = molecular diameter.

Since the mean free path is inversely proportional to the number of molecules per unit volume, it is also inversely proportional to the pressure. This relationship is given in Table 12-1.

Table 12-1

Pressure (mm.)	Mean Free Path (cm.)
1.0	5.6×10^{-3}
10^{-1}	5.6×10^{-2}
10^{-2}	5.6×10^{-1}
10^{-3}	5.6

It is evident that the pressure must be about 10^{-3} mm. before the mean free path is increased to several centimeters. When this condition is obtained, part of the molecules escaping from the liquid surface reaches the cooled surface without colliding with another molecule. Thus the liquid distills without boiling.

It is of importance during the distillation of thermally unstable substances to minimize the time the liquid is in contact with the heated surface of the still pot. The molecular distillation described in this chapter does not satisfy this requirement. However, special apparatus (falling film still) exists which reduces this time to about a minute or even fractions of seconds (centrifugal still).

The course of a normal distillation is followed by noting the boiling point of the mixture. Since this is not feasible with a molecular distillation, a temperature range (of about 50°C.) is recorded during which the distillation occurs at a reasonable rate. Thus the rate of distillation at a specific temperature is the characteristic quantity (see § 12-4).

12-3 Theory

The evaporation rate of a substance in an absolute vacuum is determined by the equation derived by Langmuir:

$$n = \frac{p'N}{(2\pi MRT)^{\frac{1}{2}}} \tag{12-2}$$

where n = number of vaporizing molecules per second and per square centimeter of surface area;

N = Avogadro's number;

p' = saturated vapor pressure of the substance (dynes/cm.^{2});

R = gas constant (erg/mole/degree);

T = temperature (°K.);

M = molecular weight.

Rearranging, we obtain

$$\boxed{w = 5.83 \times 10^{-2} p \left(\frac{M}{T}\right)^{\frac{1}{2}}} \tag{12-3}$$

where w = number of grams of substance vaporizing per second per square centimeter of surface area;

p = pressure (mm. Hg).

The actual rate of distillation (i.e., the rate at which the material collects on the cooled surface) is somewhat less, since some collisions occur. The liquid does not boil; and since the evaporation process of this liquid at rest occurs at the surface only, the transport of the volatile component through the liquid may play a role.

The separation of a mixture of two components will now be treated. The more volatile component bears the subscript 1.

Let Q_1 = original weight of most volatile component in the mixture;

w_1 = weight evaporating in t seconds;

W_1 = weight (of most volatile component) remaining after t seconds.

After t seconds the mole fraction of the most volatile component in the residue is

$$\frac{W_1/M_1}{W_1/M_1 + W_2/M_2}$$

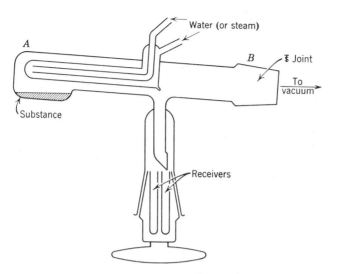

Fig. 12-1. Molecular distillation.

The rate of evaporation of component 1 is

$$-\frac{dW_1}{dt} = \frac{W_1/M_1}{W_1/M_1 + W_2/M_2} \cdot p_1\left(\frac{M_1}{2\pi RT}\right)^{\frac{1}{2}} \text{g./cm.}^2/\text{sec.}$$

A similar expression is derived for the second component. Dividing, we find

$$\frac{dW_1}{dW_2} = \frac{W_1}{W_2}\frac{p_1}{p_2}\left(\frac{M_2}{M_1}\right)^{\frac{1}{2}}$$

Integrating between the limits Q ($t = 0$) and W ($t = t$) gives

$$\log\frac{W_1}{Q_1} = \frac{p_1}{p_2}\frac{M_2}{M_1}\log\frac{W_2}{Q_2} = \alpha \log\frac{W_2}{Q_2}$$

where

$$\alpha = \frac{p_1}{p_2}\left(\frac{M_2}{M_1}\right)^{\frac{1}{2}} = \text{the relative volatility}$$

Since p_1/p_2 increases at lower temperatures, a better separation is achieved. However, equation 12-2 shows that the distillation rate is low.

12-4   Elimination Curve

The elimination rate is the rate of appearance of a substance in the receiver during a molecular distillation. At constant temperature this rate decreases with time, since the concentration of the substance in the residue decreases. At constant concentration this rate increases with the temperature.

An elimination curve is obtained by increasing the temperature step by step and determining the rate of elimination of a substance (i.e., its concentration in every fraction) at each temperature. The shape of this curve is shown in Fig. 12-2.

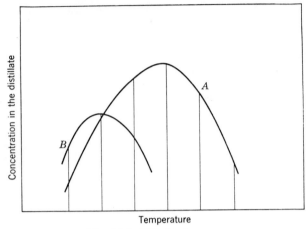

Fig. 12-2. Elimination curves.

It can be reproduced (especially at its maximum) to within 1°C, under standardized conditions.

When the time interval (the number of minutes a liquid is kept at a certain temperature) is increased, more of the substance distills in each fraction and the maximum moves to lower temperatures (curve *B*).

In order to compare elimination curves under different conditions, the elimination curve of a standard is measured during each determination. A dye is used in order to be able to determine the concentration colormetrically. Dyes used frequently are the substituted anthraquinones.

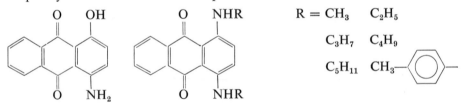

12-5 Apparatus (Figs. 12-1 and 12-3)

The desired vacuum is obtained by using an oil pump–mercury diffusion pump combination. Pressures of 10^{-5} mm. or lower are feasible. Use a McLeod manometer to measure the pressure (Fig. 11-13).

Follow the directions of § 29-2 for handling the manometer, joints, and stopcocks. Wear safety glasses at all times when working with high-vacuum systems.

A simple molecular still is shown in Figs. 12-1 and 12-3. Part *A* (Fig. 12-1), containing the substance to be distilled, can be heated by using any convenient type of electric oven. Part *B* is connected to the vacuum line by means of a standard taper joint with stopcock.

The still is filled with a long-stemmed funnel. For very viscous oils, it is most convenient to use a volatile solvent. The solution is carefully added through the

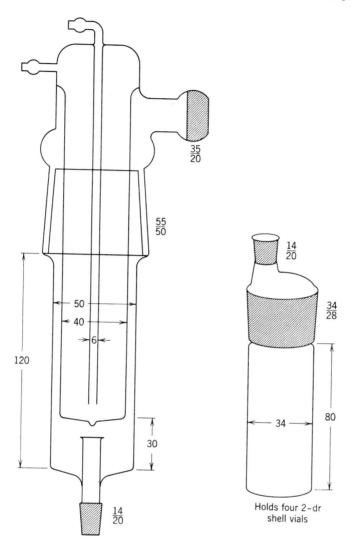

Fig. 12-3. Modified Hickman still [3]. (Used with permission from K. B. Wiberg, *Laboratory Technique in Organic Chemistry*, McGraw-Hill Book Co., 1960.)

funnel, and the solvent removed by evaporation at an aspirator. When all the solvent has been removed, it is advisable to warm the residue gently (water bath) under vacuum for about 30 min. before applying high vacuum.

12-6   Example

12-6a   CONCENTRATION OF VITAMIN A

About 5 ml. of cod-liver oil is added to the still through a long-stemmed funnel. The system is connected to the high-vacuum pump, and while the still is being evacuated the electric oven is swithced on. As the pressure drops to 10^{-5} mm., the temperature is allowed to rise to 80°. Steam is connected to the condensing system.

When the oven or jacket temperature reaches 240°, slow distillation starts. During the course of 3–4 hr. four 100-mg. fractions are collected in tared receiver tubes.

At the end of the distillation the oven is switched off, followed by the steam. Air is bled in gently, and the vacuum pump turned off when the pressures are equalized. Every fraction is dissolved in 25 ml. of ethanol-n-heptane (1:1 vol./vol.), and the absorptivity at 325 nm. is determined. Dilution by a factor of 5 is usually required for fraction 1. Calculate $E_{1 cm.}^{1\%}$ ($= x$).

Now dissolve about 100 mg. of cod-liver oil in 25 ml. of ethanol:n-heptane (1:1) and determine $E_{1 cm.}^{1\%}$ ($= y$). Calculate the enrichment of vitamin A. Determine the vitamin A content in cod-liver oil and in the distillate, using the data:

$$\text{Vitamin A} = C_{20}H_{29}OH; \quad \lambda_{max} = 325 \text{ nm. } (\epsilon = 51,400)$$

12-6b EQUIPMENT

Molecular still
Receiver tubes
Funnel
Cod-liver oil
Volumetric flasks (25 ml.)
Ethanol
n-Heptane

12-7 References

1. T. P. Carney *Laboratory Fractional Distillation*, The Macmillan Co., New York, 1949, Ch. 22.
2. A. and E. Rose *et al.*, Vol. IV, "Distillation," in *Technique of Organic Chemistry*, A. Weissberger, ed., Interscience Publishers, New York, 1951.
3. K. C. D. Hickman, *Chem. Recs.*, **34**, 51 (1944).
4. G. Burrows, *Molecular Distillation*, Clarendon Press, Oxford, 1960.

13

Vacuum sublimation

13-1 Principle

Sublimation is used for the purification of (volatile) solids. The process can be speeded up by working at reduced pressures.

13-2 Theory

A substance will pass directly from its solid phase to its vapor phase if evaporation is carried out below its triple point. The rate of evaporation which can be reached under optimum conditions (clean surface, absolute vacuum) is given by formula 12-3:

$$w = 5.83 \times 10^{-2} p \left(\frac{M}{T} \right)^{1/2} \text{ (g./cm.}^2\text{/sec.)}$$

As can be seen from this formula, the rate of sublimation is proportional to the surface area. It is therefore recommended that a substance be finely divided before sublimation. Furthermore, as with molecular distillation, the lower the pressure (closer to absolute vacuum), the closer the sublimation rate will approach the evaporation rate.

With increasing pressure, the transport rate in the gas phase becomes the limiting factor. This in turn depends upon the rate of diffusion. When use is made of gas flow, which carries along the substance from the evaporation surface, the rate of flow becomes the limiting factor.

13-3 Preparative Sublimation (Fig. 13-1)

Place approximately 15 g. of substance in the container at A, using a long-stemmed funnel. Use the end of the stem to spread out the material evenly.

Apply high-vacuum grease to the ℥-joints and attach a 100-ml. round-bottom flask E to the bottom of the apparatus. Fill the outside oil bath D with oil up to the level indicated. Carefully evacuate the apparatus and turn on the cooling water.

Carefully warm the oil bath to a temperature allowing a reasonable sublimation rate (but never higher than 30° *below* the melting point of the substance). The oil bath is heated by means of a 240-ohm heating coil C (12 m. Nichrome wire, 0.3 mm.

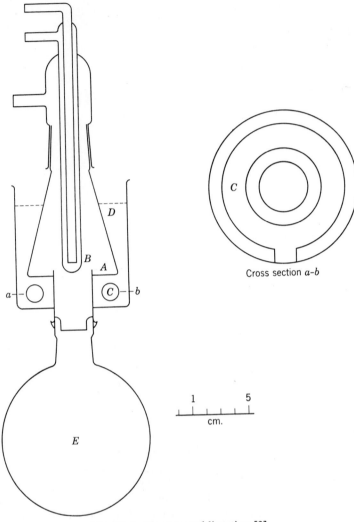

Fig. 13-1. Vacuum sublimation [3].

diameter), placed inside a glass tube, which extends through the wall of the oil bath at one point. A variac is used to regulate the current.

The substance condenses on the cooler B. By gently tapping on the cooler, it is possible to loosen the crystals which fall into the receiver E.

When the experiment has been completed, allow the oil bath to cool. Carefully break the vacuum. Determine the weights and melting points of the starting material and the product.

13-4   Microsublimation (Fig. 13-2)

Fill the boat C with about 100 mg. (finely powdered) of substance. Apply high-vacuum grease to $\bar{\text{S}}$-joints (see § 29-2 for tips on handling high-vacuum

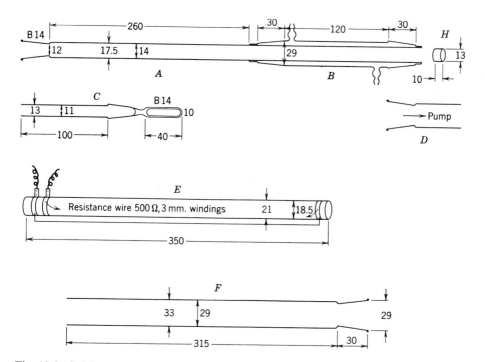

Fig. 13-2. Sublimation apparatus. The material to be sublimed is placed in the boat (C) which fits into the open end of the tube (A). This part of the tube (A) is surrounded by a heating coil (E), and a tube (F) is placed over coil (E). A number of rings (H) are placed inside section (B) of the sublimation tube and a connecting tube (D) fitted with a stopcock (not shown) is placed on the end of (B). The material sublimes onto the rings. The physical constants of the material (m.p., for instance) can be determined for several of these fractions.

equipment). Carefully evacuate the apparatus to about 10^{-5} mm., and warm in an oven (or oil bath) to a suitable temperature (at least 30° below the melting point). Record the temperature and pressure at which the sublimation occurs.

When sublimation is complete, first cool the apparatus, carefully break the vacuum, and free all joints from grease (use cotton moistened with benzene). Scrape the sublimate out of the receiver onto a watchglass, using a long spatula. Record the weight and melting point of the starting material. Put the product into a vial and label with recording temperature, pressure, yield, and melting points. Clean and dry the apparatus.

13-5   Freeze-drying

13-5a   PRINCIPLE

Freeze-drying is a method of drying heat-sensitive compounds by sublimation of water at 0° (or less) under vacuum. It is an important method in protein and enzyme chemistry.

Table 13-1   Sublimation Data (Jaeckel [1])

Compound	Melting Point (°C.)	Sublimation at 0.5–1 mm.		
		Bath Temp. (°C.)	Time (hr.)	Yield (%)
Naphthalene	79	50	0.5	86
Coumarine	68	40	2.8	100
Acetanilide	113	70	2.25	99.8
Iodoform	119	75	0.5	97
β-Naphthol	122	75	1.25	99.6
Benzoic acid	120	80	0.75	99.9
Phthalic anhydride	129	80	2.5	99.5
Cinnamic acid	132	90	2.25	99.7
Urea	132	95	3.25	99.2
Atropine	114	85	42	99.2
Anthracene	215	100	5	99.1
Acetylsalicylic acid	135	105	21	99.7
Isatin	200	110	10	99.7
Cholesterol	145	130	7	99.5
Saccharine	224	150	1.5	99.9
Alizarin	285	180	9	99.7

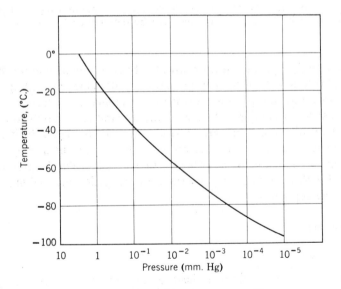

Fig. 13-3. Vapor pressure of ice.

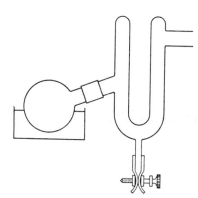

Fig. 13-4. Freeze drying.

13-5b THEORY

At $-18°$ the vapor pressure of ice is approximately 1 mm. (see Fig. 13-3). Formula 12-3 shows that the evaporation rate is 1 g./cm.²/min. at that pressure. This rapid evaporation rate causes further cooling of the ice, since heat cannot be supplied rapidly enough.

Success depends again upon a large evaporating surface; short, wide connections, especially a short path between the evaporating and condensing surfaces; and a low pressure.

Since the last trace of water is bound by adsorption, its equilibrium vapor pressure is much lower than that of ice at the same temperature. In practice freeze-drying can be achieved to a pressure of 10^{-2} mm., equivalent to ice at $-60°$.

13-5c SETUP

About 100 ml. of protein solution is added to a round-bottom flask (Fig. 13-4). Vacuum grease is put on the joint, and the flask is cooled by rotating it in a container with Dry Ice–acetone until a thin layer freezes on the inside wall. The flask is connected at once to the condenser, and the vacuum turned on immediately.

The dry protein powder is removed from the flask at the end of the experiment. It is weighed, bottled, labeled, and turned in. The condenser and trap must be cleaned and dried.

13-6   References

1. R. Jaeckel in *Methoden der organische Chemie*, Houben-Weyl, ed., G. Thieme Verlag, Stuttgart, 1958, Band I/1, p. 897.
2. G. Broughton in *Technique of Organic Chemistry*, A. Weissberger, ed., Interscience Publishers, New York, 1956, Vol. III, Part I, Ch. VI, p. 831.
3. A. Brandenburg and R. Visser, *Instrumentenbouw*, **8**, 94 (1960).
4. R. J. McCarter, "Improved Molecular Still and Sublimer for Vacuum Operation," *Rev. Sci. Instr.*, **33**, 388–389 (1962).

14

Zone melting

14-1 Introduction

Zone melting is a technique used to obtain substances of a high degree of purity. The impurities are carried along by a molten zone which moves slowly through a tube containing the solid. Thus the impurities are concentrated at the end of the tube.

Conversely the method may be used to obtain reasonable quantities of impurities present at very low concentrations. The operation itself is carried out automatically and must be repeated several times.

Originally zone melting was developed in order to purify metals (e.g., germanium). Impurities could be reduced to less than 1 part in 10^7–10^9.

14-2 Theory

14-2a SIMPLE CRYSTALLIZATION

Consider a liquid of which two thirds is allowed to crystallize. The crystals, removed by filtration, will be in a state of higher purity than the substance in the liquid phase. Let the concentration of the impurities in the solid and liquid phases be C_s and C_l, respectively. The distribution coefficient is $K = C_s/C_l$.

It is assumed that (a) the impurity does not diffuse into the solid phase; (b) complete mixing in the liquid phase is achieved; (c) melting does not cause volume changes (= changes in density); (d) the partition coefficient remains constant.

When a fraction y of the total has solidified, then

$$C_l = \frac{p}{V(1-y)}, \qquad C_s = K\frac{p}{V(1-y)}$$

where V = total volume of the substance;

p = total amount of impurity in the liquid phase;

$y = x/L$.

138

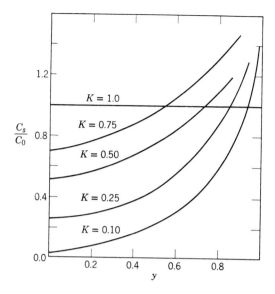

Fig. 14-1. Simple crystallization.

Suppose that a further quantity dy solidifies; then

$$C_s = -\frac{dp}{V\,dy} \rightarrow \frac{dp}{dy} = -K\frac{p}{1-y}$$

or

$$\frac{dp}{p} = -K\frac{dy}{1-y}$$

Integration between the limits p_0 (= total amount of impurity in the liquid phase at the start) and p, and 0 and y, respectively, yields

$$p = p_0(1-y)^K$$

When $p_0/V = C_0 =$ concentration of the impurity at the start,

$$\boxed{\frac{C_s}{C_0} = K(1-y)^{K-1}} \qquad (14\text{-}1)$$

Figure 14-1 shows C_s/C_0 as a function of y.

14-2b   ZONE MELTING

Assume that the concentration of the impurity $= C_0$ at the start of the experiment. Furthermore, the same conditions are assumed to hold as in § 14-2a. When the melt zone (see Fig. 14-2) has a length l and a diameter q, the amount of impurity in the melt zone $p = C_l l q$. A displacement of the zone over a distance dx causes melting of a volume $q\,dx$ while a similar quantity crystallizes out at the other end. This quantity which has crystallized contains an amount of impurity

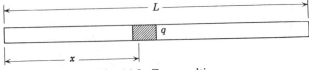

Fig. 14-2. Zone melting.

$dp' = C_s q\, dx = K C_l q\, dx$. The substance which melts contains an amount of impurity $dp'' = C_0 q\, dx$.

When $dp' \neq dp''$, the amount of impurity in the melt zone changes by an amount $dp = dp'' - dp' = (C_0 - K C_l) q\, dx$.

Since $p = C_l l q$ and $dp = q l\, dC_l$, then

$$l\, dC_l = (C_0 - K C_l)\, dx \tag{14-2}$$

Therefore

$$\frac{dC_l}{dx} + \frac{K}{l} C_l = \frac{C_0}{l}$$

where x goes from 0 to x and C_l from C_0 to C_s/K.

Upon integration

$$\frac{C_s}{C_0} = 1 - (1 - K)\, \text{exp}\left(-\frac{Kx}{l}\right) \tag{14-3}$$

This derivation and the equations obtained in this manner do not hold for the last piece (the last zone length) in the tube.

The change of concentration in the solid phase when a zone of length l has been passed is given by equation 14-3 (see Figs. 14-3 and 14-4).

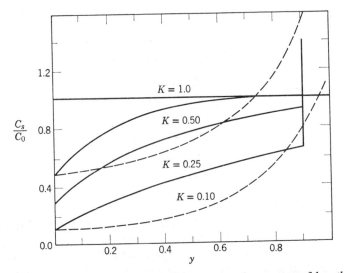

Fig. 14-3. Concentration distribution after passage of one zone of length $l/L = 0.10$ as a function of K. For comparison the result of a simple crystallization is given for two values of K.

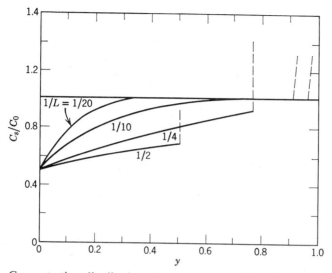

Fig. 14-4. Concentration distribution after passage of zones of different length ($K = \frac{1}{2}$).

Figure 14-3 also shows the effect of a simple crystallization. This process is more effective than zone melting, but (a) in zone melting repetition of the process can be carried out very simply; and (b) very little material is lost.

14-2c DETERMINATION OF THE PARTITION COEFFICIENT K

One zone of length l is passed through a tube of infinite length and diameter q. This zone contains an amount of impurity totaling $C_0 q l$ at $x = 0$. This amount increases with the displacement until it becomes $C_l = q l C_0 / K$. Thus the zone carries along $C_0 \left(\dfrac{1}{K} - 1 \right) q l$ amount of impurity.

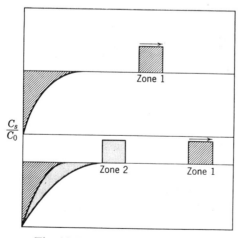

Fig. 14-5. Passage of several zones.

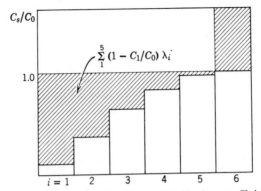

Fig. 14-6. Determination of distribution coefficient.

Each successive zone carries with it the maximum quantity $C_0\left(\dfrac{1}{K} - 1\right)q$ after it has traveled a sufficient distance. When m zones have passed, the quantity carried along is $mC_0\left(\dfrac{1}{K} - 1\right)lq$.

The result is a lowering of the concentration of the impurity at the starting point of the tube. If the tube is divided into n pieces, each λ_i long, and if the concentration of the impurity C_i is determined for each such piece, then

$$mC_0\left(\frac{1}{K} - 1\right)l = -\sum_{i=1}^{n}(C_i - C_0)\lambda_i$$

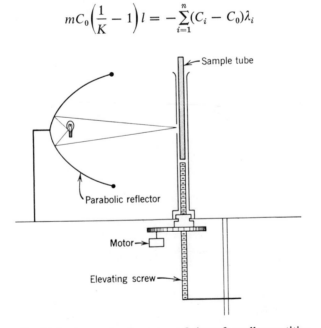

Fig. 14-7. Apparatus for zone refining of small quantities.

or

$$\frac{1}{K} = 1 + \sum_{i=1}^{n} \left(1 - \frac{C_i}{C_0}\right) \frac{\lambda_i}{lm}$$

In practice the length of the tube is not infinite. When several zones have passed and the tube has been divided into pieces, Fig. 14-6 gives an indication of the situation. We then total over all fractions for which $C_i/C_0 \leqslant 1$.

14-3 Apparatus

14-3a APPARATUS FOR SMALL QUANTITIES

An apparatus (Fig. 14-7) described by Handley and Herington [6] is suitable for the purification of small (50–150 mg.) quantities of solid. The sample tube rises slowly by means of a motor-driven threaded rod. The heat, supplied by a lamp, is focused on the sample by a parabolic reflector. The apparatus is simple to construct, using an automobile headlight [5, 6] and a large watchglass.

14-3b SEMIMICRO APPARATUS

A commercially available semimicro apparatus is shown in Fig. 14-8. Quantities of 0.15–10 g. can be purified. The sample is contained in a 15 cm. glass tube which is raised at a rate of 2.5 cm./hr. Heating is accomplished with a removable spiral Nichrome element.

14-4 Procedure

Use the longest tube suitable for the amount of substance available. By means of a funnel attached to the tube with plastic tubing, carefully add the finely powdered solid in small portions. Melt the contents after each addition, using a microburner. (Wear safety glasses, since the tubes may crack.) Starting at the closed end, remove air bubbles by tapping. As the filling proceeds, the material nearest the closed end will begin to crystallize. Now clean the glass tubes and determine their weight. Determine the weight of the six fractions. Weigh out an appropriate quantity of each sample (i.e., 30, 15, or 10 mg. of 2, 4, or 6% dye) and dissolve in alcohol. Use a 25-ml. volumetric flask for the five fractions and a 50-ml. flask for fraction 6. Determine the absorptivity in a colorimeter.

14-5 Example

14-5a ACETANILIDE–4-AMINOAZOBENZENE

Prepare a mixture containing 0.5–1.5% of 4-aminoazobenzene in acetanilide. Carry out three passes with the zone-melting apparatus. Divide into six fractions as described in § 14-3a. The amount of dye in each fraction is determined by measuring the absorptivity in a colorimeter and comparing the results to a graph obtained with known amounts. Plot the percentage of 4-aminoazobenzene against the fraction (1 cm. tube length = 1 cm., 1% = 1 cm.). Check the

Fig. 14-8. Semimicro zone-melting apparatus (catalog no. C14/5010, Baird & Tatlock, London; approx. $250).

material balance to determine whether any dye is lost. Fill the tube to within 1 cm. of the top and remove particles which have not melted.

Place the tube in the apparatus. Adjust the knob to place the top of the tube just above the lower edge of the little window. Switch on the lamp, and as soon as a molten zone appears, switch on the motor. Adjust the resistances. The tube should move at a rate of 25 mm./hr. When the tube has reached its uppermost position, return the knob to starting position and repeat the entire process.

If the apparatus is started early in the morning, a second pass can be started in the evening. The apparatus shuts off automatically. Repeat the operation five times.

Measure the length of the molten zone several times. When the experiment is completed, remove the tube from the apparatus and break it into six equal parts (use a file to scratch the tube). Weigh each piece and note its length. After melting the samples, pour them into a mortar, powder carefully, and place in numbered Erlenmeyers.

Form 14-1

Name:		Mixture:					
Date:		Avg. amount of dye: %					
No. of passes:							

(a) Fraction No.	(b) Length (cm.)	(c) Weight	(d) Weighed out (mg.)	(e) Absorptivity	(f) Amount of dye according to calibration graph	(g) % Dye in fraction	(h) (mg.) Dye in fraction	(i) Ratio to average percentage	

Reporting. (Letters refer to corresponding letters in columns of Form 14-1.)

(*f*) Use double the amount for fraction 6.

(*g*) Calculate, using (*d*) and (*f*).

(*h*) Calculate, using (*c*) and (*g*).

(*i*) The ratio of (*g*) to the original percentage, which is determined colorimetrically if necessary.

(*j*) Using (*c*) and (*g*), calculate the average percentage of dye and compare to the value originally determined.

(*k*) Determine material balance.

(*l*) Plot data in (*i*) vs. (*a*).

(*m*) Calculate partition coefficient from (*b*) and (*i*).

14-5b EQUIPMENT

Weighing bottle (30 ml.)   6 Weighing tubes
Mortar (6 cm.) and pestle   File
Zone-melting tubes   Calibration graph
Funnel (2.5 cm.)   Acetanilide
6 Erlenmeyers (stoppered)   4-Aminoazobenzene

14-6   References

1. R. S. Tipson in *Technique of Organic Chemistry*, A. Weissberger, ed., Interscience Publishers, New York, 1956, Vol. III, Part 1, p. 395.
2. A. Lüttringhaus in *Methoden der organischen Chemie*, Houben-Weyl, ed., G. Thieme Verlag, Stuttgart, 1958, Band I/1, pp. 341–391.
3. C. H. L. Goodman, *Research*, **7**, 168 (1954).
4. W. G. Pfann, *Zone Melting*, John Wiley and Sons, New York, 1958.
5. E. F. G. Herington, R. Handley, and A. J. Cook, *Chem. & Ind.*, 1956, 292.
6. R. Handley and E. F. G. Herington, *Chem. & Ind.*, 1956, 304.
7. G. Hesse and H. Schildknecht, *Angew. Chem.*, **68**, 641 (1956).
8. H. Röck, *Naturwiss.*, **43**, 81 (1956).
9. H. C. Wolf and H. P. Deutsch, *Naturwiss.*, **41**, 425 (1954).
10. W. R. Wilcox, R. Friedenberg, and N. Back, *Zone Melting of Organic Compounds*, *Chem. Revs.*, **64**, 187–220 (1964).

15

Inclusion compounds

15-1 Introduction

Some compounds crystallize in such a manner that regular spaces or channels appear in the crystal lattice. Molecules of other compounds may fit in these channels, provided certain steric requirements are met.

Urea, for instance, can crystallize in a tetragonal as well as in a hexagonal lattice. The latter permits the existence of long channels capable of enclosing a variety of straight-chain organic compounds: *n*-paraffins of more than six carbon atoms, as well as their derived alcohols, aldehydes, ethers, ketones, carboxylic acids, esters, etc. Since the branched-chain isomers cannot thus be "included," a simple separation between straight-chain and branched compounds is often possible.

Thiourea behaves similarly. Its larger channels permit many branched-chain compounds to be included.

15-2 Examples

15-2a NONANE-UREA ADDUCT

Two milliliters of *n*-nonane is carefully poured along the walls of a 100-ml. beaker containing about 30 ml. of a saturated urea-methanol solution. White needles of the adduct form at the interface. A white precipitate is formed by stirring the solution.

Warming the mother liquor to 40° allows recrystallization of the precipitate. Thus prismatic crystals up to 3 cm. long can be obtained. The nonane separates again upon decomposition of the adduct with water.

15-2b NONANE-CYCLOHEXANOL

Two milliliters of cyclohexanol is added with stirring to a saturated methanolic urea solution; no precipitate forms. Then 2 ml. of *n*-nonane is added. The precipitate thus obtained is recrystallized by dissolving it in the mother liquor (40°C).

Remove the adduct by filtration and decompose with water. Separate the nonane layer and dry it over sodium sulfate. Determine the refractive index

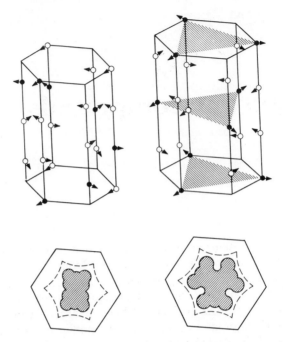

Fig. 15-1. Inclusion compounds. At the left the urea adduct crystal lattice is shown containing a linear alkane. At the right the lattice of a thiourea adduct enclosing a branched alkane is shown. [W. Schlenk, jr., *Ann.*, 573, 142 (1951)]

(n_D^{25}), and compare it to the n_D^{25} of pure nonane and of a 1:1 (vol./vol.) mixture of cyclohexanol-nonane.

15-2c LAURIC ACID-NAPHTHALENE

A solution consisting of 1 g. of naphthalene and 2 g. of lauric acid in 30 ml. of cyclohexane (or benzene, carbon tetrachloride, or ethylene chloride) is shaken for 4 hr. with 9 g. of finely powdered urea. Remove the adduct by filtration and decompose with warm water. The lauric acid is dried in a desiccator, and the yield and melting point are determined. (The yield is nearly quantitative.) The naphthalene is isolated from the cyclohexane filtrate and similarly treated.

15-2d CHLOROBENZENE–CARBON TETRABROMIDE

A mixture containing 25 g. of chlorobenzene and 3.5 g. of carbon tetra-bromide is shaken for at least 12 hr. (mechanically) with 8 g. of freshly powdered urea and 1 ml. of methanol. Remove the precipitate by filtration. Weigh the filtrate and determine its refractive index. The latter is used to determine its composition; the filtrate is about 98 % pure chlorobenzene.

The solid is decomposed with 60 ml. of hot water. About 3 g. of carbon tetrabromide separates. Wash with water, dry, and determine its melting point.

15-2e METHYL RICINOLEATE FROM RICINOLEIC OIL

About 85% of the fatty acids in ricinoleic oil consists of ricinoleic acid:

$$CH_3(CH_2)_5—CHOH—CH_2—CH=CH—(CH_2)_7—COOH$$

The ricinoleic oil is transesterified into a mixture of methyl esters. To this end a mixture of 100 g. of the oil is heated under reflux for 28 hr. with 250 ml. of absolute methanol containing 5 ml. of conc. sulfuric acid in a 500-ml. flask.

After the reaction mixture is cooled, an equal volume of saturated salt solution is added and the water layer is neutralized to methyl orange with sodium carbonate. The ester layer is separated, washed twice with water, and just made acidic to methyl orange by addition of a drop of hydrochloric acid. Finally, the esters are dried by heating in an open beaker, first for 10 min. at 90°, then for 20 min. at 110°. The yield is about 80 g. The mixture of esters is treated with boric acid. The hydroxyl group of ricinoleic acid reacts, preventing the ester from forming an inclusion compound. The remainders of the linear fatty acid esters are precipitated as their urea adducts. The filtrate is treated with water to decompose the borate. About 60 g. of pure methyl ricinoleate is obtained in this manner.

15-2f EQUIPMENT

2 Graduate cylinders (10 and 50 ml.)
4 Beakers (100 ml.)
Thermometer (100°)
Hirsch funnel (5 cm. diameter)
Büchner funnel (6 cm. diameter)
Filter flask (100 ml.)
Filter test tube
2 Alkaloid tubes
Pipette

Hot plate and thermostat
Beaker (600 ml.)
2 Evaporating dishes
2 Waterglasses
2 Stirring rods
Separatory funnel (50 ml.)
6 Test tubes + test tube holder
Desiccator
Mortar and pestle

15-3 References

1. F. Cramer, *Einschlussverbindungen*, Springer Verlag, Berlin, 1954.
2. W. Schlenk, Jr., in *Methoden der organische Chemie* (Houben-Weyl), Georg Thieme Verlag, Stuttgart, 1958, Band I/1, pp. 391–417.
3. Sister M. Hagan, *Clathrate Inclusion Compounds*, Reinhold Publishers, New York, 1962.
4. J. E. Mock, E. A. Trabant, and J. E. Myers, *Some Properties and Applications of the Rare-Gas Clathrate Compounds*, Purdue University Press, Lafayette, Ind., 1961.
5. M. M. Hagan, B.V.M., *J. Chem. Educ.*, **40**, 643 (1963).

III

Optical and spectroscopic methods

16

Refractometry

16-1 Introduction

The refractive index n of a substance is the ratio of the velocity of light in this substance to the velocity in a vacuum. The refractive index varies with the wavelength of the light used and with the temperature. In most cases the refractive index for liquids and solids is determined relative to air ($n^0_{5893\,\text{Å}}$ = refractive index at 0°C. and sodium D line = 1.000277). Light at the sodium D line (n_D) is usually chosen when measurements at one wavelength are made. For most liquids n_D decreases by about 0.0004 for every degree of increase in temperature.

16-2 Theory

According to Snell's law,

$$n_1 \sin \theta_1 = n_2 \sin \theta_2 \qquad (16\text{-}1)$$

where n_1 = medium 1;
$\quad n_2$ = medium 2;
and θ_1 and θ_2 = the incident angle and the angle of refraction, respectively (see Fig. 16-1).

In the usual measurement of liquids, n_1 is the refractive index of the liquid and

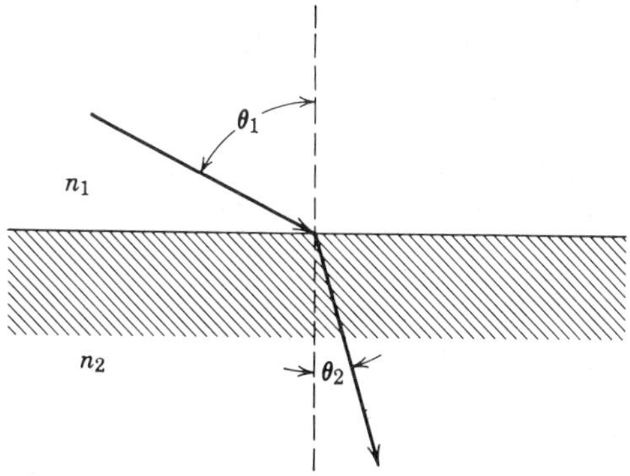

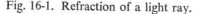

Fig. 16-1. Refraction of a light ray.

153

n_2 that of the second prism. If the second prism has a very high refractive index, $n_1 < n_2$, when the angle of incidence (θ_1) is increased to 90°, then $n_1 \sin 90° = n_1$ (sin 90° = 1), and formula 16-1 reduces to $n_1 = n_2 \sin \theta_2$. Conversely, if $n_1 > n_2$, $n_2 = n_1 \sin \theta_1$ when $\theta_2 = 90°$. The angle which the light makes with the normal to the boundary surface in the medium of higher index is called the *critical angle* of total reflection. The Abbe and Pulfrich refractometers are based on the so-called critical angle phenomenon.

The molar refraction M_{K_D} is a function of the refractive index n, the density d, and the molecular weight M and is given by the Lorentz-Lorenz formula:

$$M_{K_D} = \frac{n^2 - 1}{n^2 + 2} \frac{M}{d} \tag{16-2}$$

The molar refraction is essentially an additive property and can be calculated for many compounds by the addition of the atomic or group increments [1, p. 1163]. A selected set of increments is shown in Table 16-1.

Table 16-1   Atomic and Group Constants

C	2.418		Cl	5.967	
H	1.100		Br	8.865	
O	1.525	(OH)	C=C	1.733	
	2.211	(C=O)	C≡C	2.398	
	1.643	(OR)	N	2.45	(RNH_2 aliphatic)
S	7.97	(RSR)		3.21	(RNH_2 aromatic)

16-3   Applications

Refractive index measurements are used in the identification of substances, in the quantitative analysis of solutions, and in the determination of the purity of samples. The data can be of value in molecular structure determinations, since certain structural characteristics (such as conjugation of double bonds) reveal themselves by a deviation from molar refraction as determined by the addition of the atomic or group increments.

In principle it is possible to determine the optical rotation of asymmetric compounds by means of the refractive index. Little use has been made of this method, however, since the accuracy required is near the limits of the best refractometers.

16-4   The Abbe Refractometer

16-4a   APPARATUS (Fig. 16-2)

The Abbe refractometer has become the standard instrument for the determination of the refractive index of liquids. The path of the light rays in this refractometer is shown in Fig. 16-4 and Fig. 16-5. The light first passes the prism P_1, the upper

Fig. 16-2. Abbe refractometer.

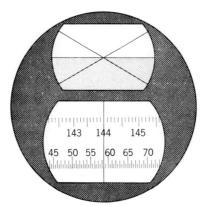

Fig. 16-3. Field of vision (above). Scale (below).

surface of which is a ground surface. Every point on this surface can be considered a light source from which light disperses in all directions. A part of the light passes through the liquid contained between both prisms and changes direction upon entering the second prism P_2.

The boundary between the light and dark fields (Fig. 16-3) is viewed through an eyepiece. The prisms are inclined by movement of the alidade (the arm on which the eyepiece is mounted) until the critical boundary exactly divides the cross hairs. The refractive index n_D can be read directly on the scale to three decimals. The fourth decimal must be estimated.

The refractometer gives the refractive index at 589 mμ (sodium D line) even when white light is used. The dispersion (the difference in n at 486 mμ and 656 mμ) can be determined by using a nomogram and a knowledge of the refractive index and the setting of the compensator [1, p. 1208].

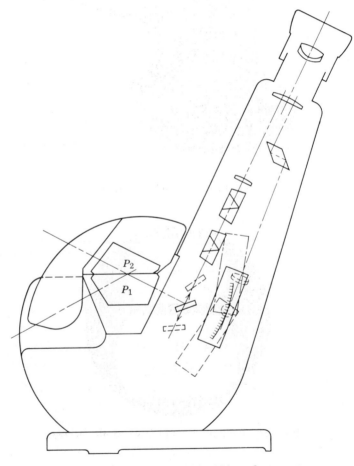

Fig. 16-4. Path of light rays in Abbe refractometer.

16-4b   CLEANING THE INSTRUMENT

Both prisms are cleaned carefully with lens tissue or cotton and a volatile solvent (alcohol, ether, acetone). The prisms are made of glass which has a high refractive index; this glass is very soft and scratches when care is not observed.

16-4c   PROCEDURE

For accurate work at one temperature (for instance, 20°) it is important that water from a properly controlled thermostat be passed through the instrument for at least 10 min. before measurements are made.

Open the prism block (Fig. 16-2, knob *4*), remove the lens tissue if present, clean both prisms (Fig. 16-4, P_1 and P_2), and place one drop of the liquid on the lower prism, using a carefully cleaned pipette. *Do not touch the prism with the pipette.* Close the prisms, open the cover (Fig. 16-2, *5*), and close the mirror *6*. Turn knob *3* until the division between the dark and the light field comes into view. When daylight is used as the source of light, the compensator knob *2* must be turned until no color is visible at the dark–light division.

Move the borderline (Fig. 16-3) (between the dark and light fields) exactly on the cross hairs (knob *3*), and read the refractive index on the top scale (Fig. 16-3) (estimate the fourth decimal). Repeat this process five times, in turn approaching the cross hairs with the borderline above and below. Average these five observations and record the temperature.

Turn off the thermostat and water supply. Clean the prisms. Place a piece of lens tissue on the lower prism and close the prism block. Close cover *5*. Clean the pipette, leaving the entire apparatus and auxiliary equipment clean and ready for use.

16-4d   ZERO-READING CHECK

Determine the refractive index of distilled water ($n_D^{20} = 1.3330$, $n_D^{25} = 1.3325$). The deviation should not be more than two in the last (fourth) decimal. The measurements can be corrected for small deviations. In case of large deviations (more than 0.0005) the instrument must be adjusted. Check with the assistant when this seems necessary.

16-5   Bellingham and Stanley Angle Refractometer

16-5a   INTRODUCTION

This refractometer is based upon the same principle as the Pulfrich refractometer. Monochromatic light passes through the sample and through the prism, which is in contact with the sample. The refractive index can be determined to an accuracy of $\pm 4 \times 10^{-5}$.

16-5b   PRINCIPLE

Let *n* be the refractive index of the sample, *N* that of the prism, and *A* the angle of the prism. Light entering parallel to the horizontal prism surface leaves again,

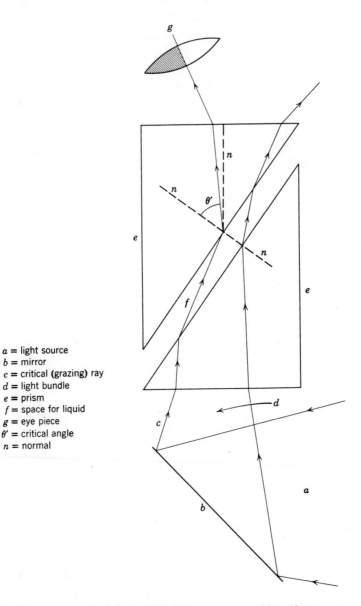

a = light source
b = mirror
c = critical (grazing) ray
d = light bundle
e = prism
f = space for liquid
g = eye piece
θ' = critical angle
n = normal

Fig. 16-5. Diagram showing path of light rays in Abbe refractometer.

making an angle B with the tangent of the second prism surface (Fig. 16-5). Depending on n, the light leaves according to (a) or (b). For

$$\text{For } (a): \quad n = \sin A (N^2 - \sin^2 B)^{\frac{1}{2}} + \cos A \sin B \qquad (16\text{-}3)$$

$$\text{For } (b): \quad n = \sin A (N^2 - \sin^2 B)^{\frac{1}{2}} - \cos A \sin B \qquad (16\text{-}4)$$

16-5c APPARATUS

The light path of the refractometer is shown schematically in Fig. 16-6. Light from a monochromatic source enters the surface via a condenser. The condenser consists of two lenses which have a total focal length of 3 cm. measured from the foremost lens; thus the light source should (if possible) be placed within a 3-cm. distance from this lens.

The prisms as well as the cell are water-jacketed in order to be able to thermostat the instrument. Beckman thermometers are placed in the water circuit at equal distances before and after the refractometer. The average of the two temperatures is taken as the temperature of the prism and sample.

The emerging ray is observed with a telescope consisting of an objective (movable), reflecting prism, cross hairs engraved on glass plate, and eyepiece. The telescope is connected to an engraved glass disk, graduated in 15' of arc (θ_n). The glass scale is read from both sides by means of an eyepiece; these results are averaged. The scale is read to an accuracy of 15'; on the micrometer screw (one division = 10″) the remaining minutes and seconds of arc are read (estimate to 1″).

The eyepieces contain lenses which can compensate possible parallax in the left-hand scale. The scale is illuminated by two 6-volt lamps and the cross hairs by a 3.5-volt lamp. The latter burns out rapidly and hence should be turned on only during the observation of the normal position. During all the other observations illumination of the cross hairs is unnecessary, since they contrast sharply against the background illumination passing through the prisms.

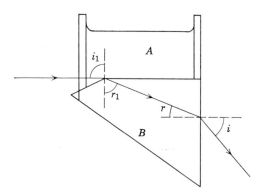

Fig. 16-6. Light path of critical angle refractometer.

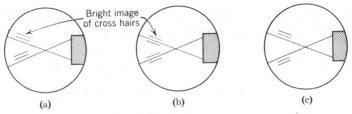

Fig. 16-7. (a)–(c). Field of view at or near zero point.

16-5d   OPTICAL AIMING OF THE INSTRUMENT

Condenser.   Theoretically the emerging rays should be parallel, but in practice the rays are best focused in the prism. Focus the (inverted) image of the light source on the slit with a piece of tissue paper. When the light is too intense a screen may be placed in front of the slit to act as a diaphragm.

Telescope.   The ring with the cross hairs should be clamped in such a position that it touches the eyepiece when the latter has been completely screwed in. Move the telescope until the reflected image of the illuminated cross hairs is visible in the ring. Adjust the objective lens until the cross hairs as well as their reflected image are sharp and without parallax. Tighten the objective with the screw. Place the elliptical diaphragm over the objective to sharpen the boundary.

Prism.   Using the three screws at the back of the water jacket (first loosen the clamp between the three screws somewhat; tighten it again after the adjustment has been made), turn the prism until the cross hairs and their reflected image look as is shown in Fig. 16-7a. Now move the telescope until the same image is obtained through reflection against the upper prism surface. The screws enable adjustment to be made until the two images are identical. In that case the second prism surface has assumed a position of 90° to the telescope.

Hydrogen Lamp.   For measurements of dispersion, three lines of the hydrogen spectrum are used (helium lines are sometimes used): H_α (red, 6563 Å), H_β (blue, 4861 Å), and H_γ (violet, 4341 Å). The lamp should be placed as close to the condenser as possible. Observe the condenser in order to obtain a sharp boundary *in the portion of the field* (light intensity is not at a maximum). Every movement of light source or condenser influences the sharpness and position of the boundary. Continuous checking is required.

When measurements are made using the violet hydrogen line, a large parallax is observed between the image of the boundary and the cross hairs. An extra negative lens is then necessary. In addition the proper position must be checked, using the refractive index of a standard.

16-5e   CLEANING THE INSTRUMENT

Check whether the lenses are clean; use special lens tissue for this purpose. Both prism surfaces must be clean; no color should be visible when light enters the prism at right angles.

16-5f PROCEDURE

The cylindrical cell is placed on the prism, using a *minimum* amount of silicon grease. The cover is placed over the cell (keep the immersion heater outside the cell), and only then is the heater inserted carefully. Before filling the cell, the heater is removed. Fill the cell with about 1.5 ml. of liquid. Wait several minutes in order to obtain the proper temperature.

Reading the Instrument. Adjust successively to the upper and lower ends of the cross hairs and take the average of these readings. The adjustment is made by turning the micrometer screw to 0′0″, and tightening the knob above the micrometer screw in order to fix the telescope in such a position that its borderline falls at the end of the lower cross hairs. By turning the micrometer, make the final adjustment to obtain the position shown in Fig. 16-7b. Read the micrometer. Repeat the operation five times and average the results (*b*). Now determine, by averaging five readings, the reading using the ends of the upper cross hairs (*c*) (the knob fixing the telescope position remains unchanged).

Now turn the micrometer until the first division of the glass scale falls just between the two markings at the right side of the telescope; again read five times and average (*d*). Record which scale division was observed. Repeat for the left scale (*f* and *g*). The proper position of the borderline is:

$$\tfrac{1}{2}(b + c) + e - d = r \quad \text{(right-hand scale)}$$
$$\tfrac{1}{2}(b + c) + g - f = r \quad \text{(left-hand scale)}$$

Determining the Normal. First arrest the telescope in such a position that the reflected image of the cross hairs coincides first with the lower cross hair and then with the upper one (each reading is repeated five times and averaged, *h* and *i*). Read right- and left-hand scales as described above.

$$k = \text{micrometer reading, right-hand scale.}$$
$$l = \text{scale division, right-hand scale.}$$
$$m = \text{micrometer reading, left-hand scale.}$$
$$n = \text{scale division, left-hand scale.}$$

The positions of the normal are

$$\tfrac{1}{2}(h + i) + l - k = N_r \quad \text{(for the right-hand scale)}$$
$$\tfrac{1}{2}(h + i) + n - m = N_l \quad \text{(for the left-hand scale)}$$

The boundary angle *B* is

$$B_r = N_r - G_r \quad \text{(for right-hand scale)}$$
$$B_l - N_l - G_l$$
$$B = \tfrac{1}{2}(B_r + B_l)$$

The entire determination of *B* is repeated. The values of *B* are averaged in case the difference is less than 15′.

16-5g CALCULATIONS AND REPORT

With formulas 16-3 and 16-4, the refractive index n may be determined at any given spectral line and temperature. When many successive measurements need to be made, it is advisable to construct a table for the values of n against B. These need to be determined separately at each wavelength and temperature. Table 16-2 is an example of such a report.

Determining N. The refractive index N of the prism is needed and is determined against air ($n = 1$). Equation 16-3 gives

$$N^2 - 1 = \frac{(\sin B + \cos A)^2}{\sin A} \tag{16-5}$$

Example. The Refractive Index (n_D^{20}) of 2-Methylpentadecane. (See Table 16-2). The two Beckman thermometers showed a reading of 0.134 and 2.561, corresponding to 19.990 and 20.023°C. The refractive index has been determined at 20.006°C. (the deviation from 20° should be no more than 0.03°).

The averages of five micrometer positions are

$b = 4'21''$	$f = 6'36''$	$k = 14'25''$
$c = 5'58''$	$g = 243°15'$	$l = 63°30'$
$d = 6'10''$	$h = 1'1''$	$m = 14'50''$
$e = 54°15'$	$i = 3'3''$	$n = 243°30'$

The average value of B was found to be $9°3'27''$
A second determination gave $9°3'40''$
The final value was $9°3'40''$

With $A = 60°0'0''$ and $N = 1.752780$, $n_D^{20} = 1.433071$.
Record observations and calculations as in Form 16-1.

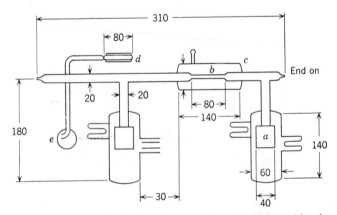

Fig. 16-8. Hydrogen lamp according to van Oort and van Heel [2]. *a.* Aluminum electrode. *b.* Capillary. *c.* Water jacket. *d.* Electric oven; tube filled with CuO. *e.* Sodium hydroxide solution.

16-6　The Hydrogen Lamp (Fig. 16-8)

A hydrogen lamp (made according to van Oort and van Heel [2]) is used for the measurement of the refractive index at the wavelength of the red, blue, and violet lines of the hydrogen spectrum. The light intensity of this lamp is considerably greater than that of the commonly used Geissler tubes.

Form 16-1　Refractive Index Reporting

	Borderline							Normal					
	R			L				R			L		
Below (b)		4	21						1	1			
Above (c)		5	58						3	3			
(b + c)		9	79						4	4			
$\frac{1}{2}(b + c)$		5	10		5	10			2	2		2	2
Scale line (c)	54	15		234	15			63	30		243	30	
$\frac{1}{2}(b - c) + (e)$	54	20	10	234	20	10		63	32	2	243	32	2
Position (d)		6	10		6	36			14	25		14	50
	54	14	0	234	13	34	N_R	63	17	37	234	17	12
							G_R	54	14	0	234	13	34
							N-G	9	3	37	9	3	38

Compound: 2-Methylpentadecane　　Name: Joe Doe
Spectral line: Sodium D line, 5893 Å　　Date:

Temperature: B_1 position 0.134 = 19.990°C; B_2 position 2.561 = 20.023°C　　Avg. = 20.006°C

A second set of measurements yielded

$$B = 9°3'43''$$
$$\text{Average } B = 9°3'4''$$
$$n_D^{20} = 1.433071$$

The lamp is made of Pyrex glass. The electrodes are of aluminum sheet 2 mm. thick and are mounted in such a way that the discharge has to turn once through 180° and once through 90° before reaching the capillary tube, in which metal particles are not wanted.

As the ends, containing the electrodes, are placed sideways, the radiation of the capillary tube in the longitudinal direction can be utilized ("end on"). In this way a small but very strong source of light is obtained. The diameter of the capillary tube is 3 mm., its length 80 mm.

The tube is filled with water vapor. During the discharge water is dissociated and hydrogen ions and atoms are obtained. Any H_2 molecules that might be formed are removed by a tube filled with 10 g. of CuO rods (diameter 0.5 mm., length 5 mm.), which is sealed to the discharge tube and is heated by a small electric oven (35 watts) to 270°C.

A very strong solution of NaOH in H_2O ensures the right vapor pressure of H_2O in the tube. At room temperature the pressure will be about 1 mm.

The tube is powered by a transformer. The power requirement is 400 watts at 1360 volts (current 300 ma).

16-7   References

1. N. Bauer, K. Fajans, and S. Z. Lewin in *Physical Methods of Organic Chemistry*, Vol. I in *Technique of Organic Chemistry*, Interscience Publishers, New York, 1959, Part 2, p. 1134.
2. W. P. van Oort and A. C. S. van Heel, *Rev. Sci. Instr.*, **20,** 319 (1949).

17

Polarimetry and
spectropolarimetry

A POLARIMETRY

17-1 Introduction

With a polarimeter the change in the direction of vibration of linearly [2] polarized light caused by its passage through an anisotropic substance can be measured. The change in direction is called *optical rotation* if it is caused by anisotropic refraction. *Dichroism* is the term applied when the change in direction is caused by anisotropic absorption or scattering.

17-2 Theory

The velocity of light changes, depending on the medium through which it travels. Its dependence on this medium is given by

$$\lambda_1 : \lambda_2 = v_1 : v_2 = n_2 : n_1 \qquad (17\text{-}1)$$

where λ_1, λ_2 are the wavelengths in the two media (usually air and a liquid), v_1 and v_2 the two velocities, and n_1 and n_2 the corresponding refractive indices.

Linearly polarized light passing through an inactive (isotropic) liquid gives rise to the situation shown in Fig. 17-1.

An optically active liquid has two refractive indices, n_d and n_l, for the *d*- and *l*-components of the linearly polarized light. Consequently $\lambda_d \neq \lambda_l$ and $v_d \neq v_l$, and the two components will get out of phase (see Fig. 17-2).

The optical rotation α, expressed in degrees, is given by

$$\alpha = \frac{1800l}{\lambda_0}(n_l - n_d) \qquad (17\text{-}2)$$

where l is the thickness of the liquid layer in centimeters, λ_0 is the vacuum wavelength, and n_l and n_d are the refractive indices. The rotation is positive when $n_l > n_d$ and negative when $n_l < n_d$. The circular birefringence (difference between n_d and n_l) could in principle be measured directly, i.e.,

$$(n_l - n_d) = \frac{\varphi' \lambda_0}{\pi l'} \qquad (17\text{-}3)$$

165

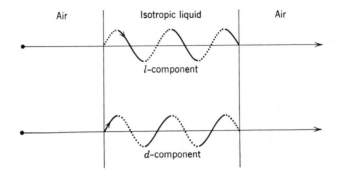

Fig. 17-1. Linearly polarized light passing through isotropic liquid. Heavy lines indicate vibration above the plane of the paper; broken lines, vibration beneath the plane. Superposition of the two drawings gives the resultant of the two coherent circular (*d* and *l*) components.

where φ' is the rotation. Solving for a rotation of $10°$ with $l' = 10$ cm. and $\lambda_0 = 5461$ Å (Hg green line), we obtain

$$(n_l - n_d) = \frac{10°(5461\,\text{Å})}{10\pi} = 3 \times 10^{-8}$$

too small a difference to be measured conveniently with common instruments. The specific optical rotation for a pure liquid is given by

$$[\alpha]_{\text{D}}^{25} = \frac{\alpha}{l\rho} \qquad (17\text{-}4)$$

and for a solution by

$$[\alpha]_{\text{D}}^{25} = \frac{100\alpha}{lc} \qquad (17\text{-}5)$$

where $[\alpha]_{\text{D}}^{25}$ is the specific optical rotation at $25°$ at the sodium D line (5890 and 5896 Å);

- α = observed rotation (degrees);
- l = length of the tube (dm.);
- ρ = density of the liquid (g./l.);
- c = concentration (g. of solute/100 ml. of solution).

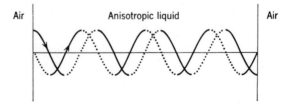

Fig. 17-2. Linearly polarized light resolved into two circular components.

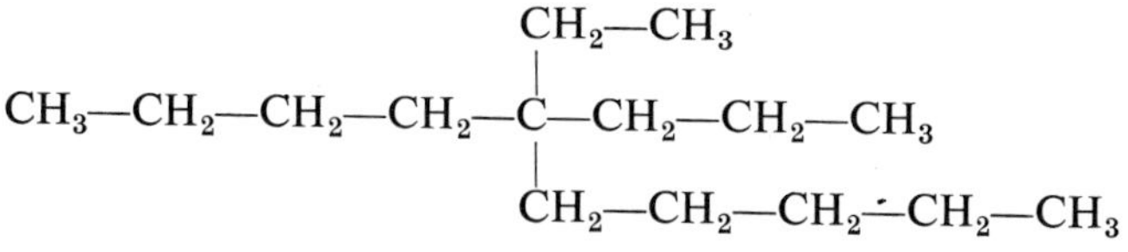

$$
\begin{array}{c}
CH_2-CH_3 \\
| \\
CH_3-CH_2-CH_2-CH_2-C-CH_2-CH_2-CH_3 \\
| \\
CH_2-CH_2-CH_2-CH_2-CH_3
\end{array}
$$

Fig. 17-3

17-3 Applications

A molecule has optical activity when it has neither a plane nor a center of symmetry (it may have an axis of symmetry).

Several general cases may be distinguished:

(a) A tetrahedral molecule in which the four substituents are different. A carbon atom containing four different substituents, R_1, R_2, R_3, and R_4, is called an asymmetric carbon atom.

(b) Spiranes, allenes, and diaryls in which ortho substituents prevent coplanarity of the rings.

(c) The helical structure of proteins.

The term molecular dissymmetry is applicable to cases (b) and (c).

Since the specific rotation [α] is also a function of the wavelength, i.e.,

$$[\alpha] = \sum \frac{L}{\lambda^2 - \lambda_n^{\ 2}} \tag{17-6}$$

we may predict an increase in [α] as the wavelength λ at which the measurement is carried out approaches λ_n, the wavelength of maximum absorption by the dissymmetric chromophore. When $\lambda = \lambda_n$, [α] = ∞ and the equation no longer holds.

It is evident that a dissymmetric hydrocarbon (see Fig. 17-3) which obeys all the classical requirements for optical activity, i.e.,

$$R_1 \neq R_2 \neq R_3 \neq R_4,$$

should have little or no optical activity when measured at 5461 Å, since (a) its light absorption will be in the vacuum ultraviolet region (below 1850 Å) and (b) the anisotropy is some distance from the asymmetric carbon [15].

Conversely, a molecule such as is shown in Fig. 17-4, should show very high rotatory power, since (a) its light absorption will be in the neighborhood of the wavelength used to measure the rotation, and (b) the chromophore itself is dissymmetric [9, 10, 16].

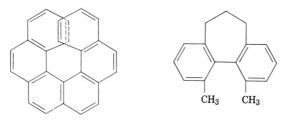

Fig. 17-4. Dissymmetric chromophores.

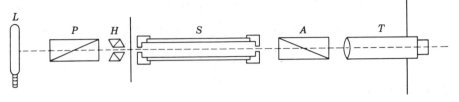

Fig. 17-5. Polarimeter.

17-4 The Rudolph Polarimeter

17-4a APPARATUS

A tube containing the solution to be analyzed is placed between two crossed Nicol prisms (see Fig. 17-5). The light from source L passes through prism P (polarizer), causing the light to become linearly polarized [1, p. 2203]. The light passes through the solution [S] and leaves it, having been rotated a number of degrees if the solution is optically active. Since the two Nicols P and A (analyzing prism) can be moved with respect to one another, a position of maximum brightness and total darkness as seen through the telescope T can be achieved. With no solution in the tube and the analyzer at $0°$, the system transmits no light (analyzer at right angles to polarizer) and a dark field is obtained. When an optically active solution is placed in the tube, the light emerging from the solution has been rotated and Nicol A again transmits (some) light. By rotating A until the field is dark again, the exact number of degrees the light has been rotated in solution is determined.

Since it is difficult to adjust to minimum light intensity, the half-shadow principle is applied. Two small Nicols H are placed between the polarizer P and the tube T. These prisms rotate the two halves of the light beam small amounts, ϵ, in opposite directions (Fig. 17-6). At $0°$ position of the analyzer A (with solution in the tube) the latter is at right angles to the polarizer P and consequently at right angles to the plane (or line) of polarization. This causes the left-hand part of the field to be dark (see Fig. 17-6a). Rotation through angle 2ϵ causes the view shown in Fig. 17-6c. After the solution is placed in the tube, the analyzer is rotated until the two halves are of equal intensity. The limiting factor is the sensitivity of the eye.

Under normal conditions (dark room, 10–20 min. in darkness) a difference in

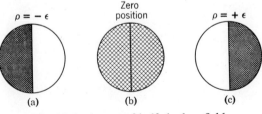

Fig. 17-6. Aspect of half-shadow field.

intensity of $\Delta B/B = 0.01$ or 0.02 can still be determined. The rotation corresponding to this is $\Delta \alpha = 0.005 \epsilon$. Since $\epsilon = 4°$ (8° on the scale division of the apparatus) α can be determined to $\pm 0.02°$.

17-4b PROCEDURE

(a) Fill one of the tubes with the solution to be analyzed. Avoid air bubbles and dirt. Do not tighten the screw caps too much, since they exhibit double refraction under pressure. Turn on the light source.

(b) Adjust the diaphragm D to the size of the tube used.

(c) Rotate the analyzer (without the tube in the apparatus) until the two halves appear to be equal in intensity, using first the notched knob. Tighten vertical screw and carry out fine adjustment with the micrometer. The analyzer position should be 0° at this point.

(d) Place the tube in the apparatus and adjust the analyzer to obtain matching halves. Read the scale. Levorotatory solutions give readings which should be subtracted from 360°. Repeat the operation three times.

(e) Loosen the vernier screw when the reading is finished. Empty the tube and clean it with distilled water.

17-4c CALCULATION AND REPORT

Using formula 17-5, calculate $[\alpha]_D^{25}$. The molecular rotation

$$[\alpha_M]_D^{25} = \frac{M}{100} [\alpha]_D^{25}$$

where M = molecular weight.

17-5 The Zeiss Precision Polarimeter (Fig. 17-7)

17-5a OPTICAL PATH (see Fig. 17-8)

Light from the mercury lamp Q is projected on the stops B via lens L_1. An image of 5 mm. is projected in the plane of L_3 by the objective L_2. The filter F

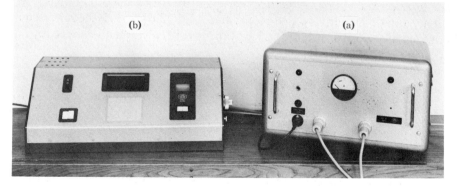

Fig. 17-7. Precision polarimeter (Zeiss). (a) Power supply. (b) Recorder.

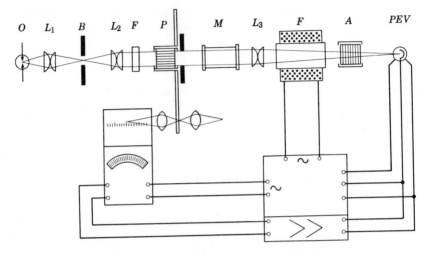

Fig. 17-8. Light path of Zeiss Precision Polarimeter.

selects the 365, 405, 436, 546, and 578 nm. lines from the spectrum. The polarizer P linearly polarizes the light of part of the light bundle. This light, narrowed to a 5-mm. bundle, passes through the solution M. Lens L_3 projects the emergent light on the analyzer A. A glass rod in the magnetic coil F (Faraday modulator) is also placed in the light bundle.

The analyzer A is fixed during the measurement and may be zeroed by rotation with an adjustment screw. The light rays then enter the photomultiplier tube PEV.

17-5b   PROCEDURE (see Figs. 17-9 and 17-10)

1. Starting the apparatus. Turn on *3-10* (Fig. 17-10) and wait 10 min. for the instrument to warm up.

2. Checking zero adjustment. Using coarse adjustment *2-5* (Fig. 17-9), rotate scale to zero reading on *2-2*. Correct deviations of the needle of *2-3* from a zero reading, using *2-4*. For very high precision it is useful to measure the zero reading by means of a polarimeter tube filled with solvent only and to correct for any deviations.

3. Measuring.
    (*a*) Adjust wavelength, using *2-1*.
    (*b*) Push right-hand button *2-7* to open window to polarimeter tube chamber. Insert polarimeter tube and close with *2-8*. The tube is brought into the light path automatically.
    (*c*) When an optically active compound has been placed in the tube, meter *2-3* will indicate a non-zero reading. When the needle has deflected to the right, it indicates that the substance is dextrorotatory; if to the left of the zero, levorotatory.

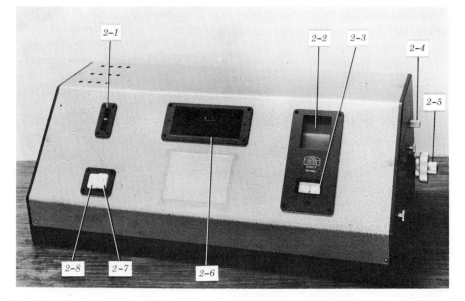

Fig. 17-9. Recorder part of Zeiss precision polarimeter. *2-1*. Filter knob. *2-2*. Opaque plate for part-rotation reading. *2-3*. Zero galvanometer. *2-4*. Zero knob. *2-5*. Coarse-fine adjustment. *2-6*. Tube container. *2-7, 2-8*. Pushbuttons.

Fig. 17-10. Front view of power and control console. *3-1*. Circuit control light. *3-2*. Galvanometer. *3-3*. Control light photomultiplier tube. *3-4, 3-5*. Mercury lamp control. *3-6, 3-7*. Screw connections for attaching the measuring instrument. *3-8*. Power inlet. *3-9*. Fuse. *3-10*. Off-on switch.

(*d*) Compensate the rotation, using *2-5*. If the meter *2-3* indicates a deflection to the right, turn *2-5* clockwise. When the rotation is large, the deflection of the needle in *2-3* first increases to a maximum right deflection before returning to a zero position. Compensate by turning fine adjustment on *2-3*. The angle of rotation is read off on the frosted glass *2-2*.

The vernier is divided into 0.1° scale divisions.

17-5c CALCULATIONS: EXTRAPOLATION TO OTHER WAVELENGTHS

To a first approximation, use can be made of the Drude equation, formula 17-7, to calculate the rotation at another wavelength than the one at which the rotation was measured. Consider conversion of the rotation from 546.1 nm. to that at 589.2 nm. (sodium D line).

$$\alpha = \frac{A}{\lambda^2 - \lambda_0^2}$$

where A and λ_0 are constants depending on the substance used.

Let α_1 be the rotation measured at $\lambda_1 = 546.8$ nm. and α_2 the rotation at $\lambda_2 = 577.0$ nm. Then $\alpha_3 =$ the desired rotation at $\lambda_3 = 589.2$ nm.

$$\frac{\alpha_3}{\alpha_1} = \frac{c}{c+1}$$

where

$$c = \frac{\lambda_2^2 - \lambda_1^2}{\lambda_3^2 - \lambda_1^2} \frac{\alpha_2}{\alpha_1 - \alpha_2}$$

The first term, $(\lambda_2^2 - \lambda_1^2)/(\lambda_3^2 - \lambda_1^2)$, equals 0.7205 and may be considered an apparatus constant.
Then

$$\alpha_{589} = \frac{\dfrac{\alpha_{578}}{\alpha_{546} - \alpha_{578}}}{\dfrac{\alpha_{578}}{\alpha_{546} - \alpha_{578}} + 1.3727} \alpha_{546}$$

17-6 Examples

A quartz plate shows a rotation of

$$\alpha_1 = 76.66° \text{ at } 546.1 \text{ nm.}$$
$$\alpha_2 = 67.99° \text{ at } 577.8 \text{ nm.}$$
$$\overline{\alpha_1 - \alpha_2 = \quad 8.67°}$$

Then
$$\frac{\alpha_2}{\alpha_1 - \alpha_2} = 7.842$$

Using the apparatus constant 0.7285,

$$c = 5.7129$$

Then
$$\frac{c}{c+1} = 0.85103$$

and
$$\alpha_3 = 0.85103 \times 76.66°$$
$$= 85.24°$$

The conversion factor 0.85103 compares favorably to the one of 0.85085 in the International Critical Tables.

17-6a ROTATION OF CAMPHOR [8]

Dissolve 600 mg. of camphor in 20 ml. of 95% ethanol and measure the rotation at 546 and 578 nm. Extrapolate, using equation 17-7 to the sodium D line. Calculate specific rotation and compare to the value given in [8].

17-6b ROTATION OF CINCHONINE

Dissolve 20 mg. cinchonine in 100 ml. of water and measure its rotation. Extrapolate to 589 nm.

B SPECTROPOLARIMETRY [3, 6, 17]

17-7 Introduction

The specific rotation of a compound is a function of the wavelength. This dispersion is determined by allowing light having different wavelengths to pass through the polarimeter.

Drude [1, 2] derived expression 17-6. In many cases the experimental results fit a one-term Drude equation (simple rotary dispersion)

$$[\alpha] = \frac{L}{\lambda^2 - \lambda_0{}^2} \qquad (17\text{-}7)$$

Here L (or A) and λ_0 are constants; λ_0 is that wavelength characteristic for the nearest absorption band of the molecule contributing to the optical activity. It is thus apparent that, when one nears an absorption band, λ approaches λ_0 and equation 17-2 tends to $-\infty$ or $+\infty$, depending on whether one approaches λ_0 from one side or the other. Then the equation is valid only to an inflection point on the curve $[\alpha]$ vs. λ near λ_0 but not at λ_0.

When more than one term of the Drude equation is needed, one is dealing with complex rotary dispersion.

Since equation 17-2 expresses $[\alpha]$ in degrees and decimal fractions thereof, and λ in centimeters (or millimeters), the following conversions are needed on transforming to the c.g.s. values:

$$\lambda_{c.g.s.} = (\lambda_1{}^2)^{1/2} \times 10^{-4} \text{ cm.}$$

and

$$L_{c.g.s.} = 1.7453 \times 10^{-3} (L)^{1/2} \times 10^{-4} \text{ cm.}^4/\text{g.}$$

where $1.7453 \times 10^{-3} = \pi/1800$.

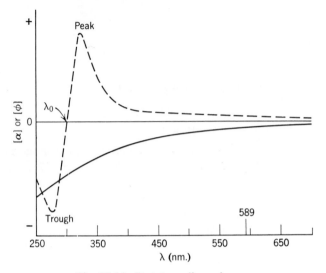

Fig. 17-11. Rotatory-dispersion curves.

The sign of the optical rotation changes in the neighborhood of an absorption band (abnormal rotary dispersion curve, see Fig. 17-11). For most organic compounds abnormal rotary dispersion occurs in the ultraviolet portion of the spectrum. Close relationships have been established between the shape of the rotary dispersion curve and the stereochemistry of optically active compounds. Consequently measurements of rotary dispersion have become important in the determination of the configuration of steroids, terpenes, and other natural products [2, 3, 4, 7, 9].

17-8 Principle

Using relatively simple means, a normal quartz spectrophotometer may be adapted for rotary dispersion measurements in the visible and ultraviolet region of the spectrum [5, 14].

Use is made of a Zeiss quartz spectrophotometer (see Chapter 19). The determination of a normal absorption curve is carried out by placing a cell containing the solvent in the light beam, adjusting slit width and intensity to the 100 reading on the instrument, placing the cell containing the unknown solution in the light beam, and recording directly the ratio of both light intensities from the meter reading. In order to carry out rotary dispersion measurements the normal cell holder is replaced by one containing, in addition to the cells, four Glann polarizing prisms (Fig. 17-12).

The directions of polarization of both prisms P_1 and P_2 are parallel (Fig. 17-13).

Both cells contain the solution to be measured. Consequently the plane of polarization is rotated through an angle α in both cases. The analyzers make angles θ_1 and θ_2 with the polarizers.

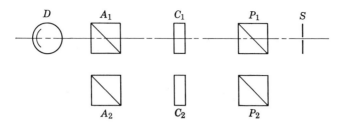

Fig. 17-12. *A.* Analyzer prisms. *P.* Polarizer prisms. *C.* Cells with solution. *S.* Slit for light emerging from monochromator. *D.* Detector (photomultiplier tube).

Let the intensity of the incident light be I_0; then the following equation holds for the transmitted light:

$$T_1 = \frac{I_1}{I_0} = K_1 \exp(-\epsilon cd) \cos^2(\theta + \alpha) \qquad (17\text{-}8)$$

K_1 expresses the loss in intensity due to the polarizing action of the prisms, the light absorption of the prisms, cells, and solvents, and losses due to reflection. The absorption of light of the substance dissolved is determined by the absorbance ϵ of the substance, its concentration c, and the path length d.

When the second set of prisms is placed in the light beam, we have

$$T_2 = \frac{I_2}{I_0} = K_2 e^{-\epsilon cd} \cos^2(\theta - \alpha) \qquad (17\text{-}9)$$

These deviations indicate that a direct reading can be made with the spectrophotometer according to

$$R_\alpha = \frac{T_1}{T_2} = K \frac{\cos^2(\theta_1 + \alpha)}{\cos^2(\theta_2 - \alpha)} \qquad (17\text{-}10)$$

In the ideal case the light paths are equal and $K = 1$. When they differ, K is unequal to 1 and, moreover, dependent upon the wavelength.

When $\theta_1 = \theta_2$ the sensitivity is equal to

$$S = \frac{dR_\alpha}{d\alpha} = -2 \sin 2\theta \frac{\cos(\theta + \alpha)}{\cos^3(\theta - \alpha)} \qquad (17\text{-}11)$$

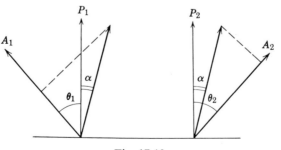

Fig. 17-13

For small values of α, $\tan \alpha = \alpha$ and

$$S = -4 \tan \theta \, \frac{1 - \alpha \tan \theta}{(1 + .\alpha \tan \theta)^3} \tag{17-12}$$

Maximum sensitivity is reached when

$$\frac{dS}{d\theta} = 0 \rightarrow \tan \theta = \frac{1}{\alpha} [2 \pm (3)^{\frac{1}{2}}] \tag{17-13}$$

17-9   Apparatus

The cell holder is shown in Fig. 17-14. The four Glann prisms [1, p. 2191] (dimensions $16 \times 16 \times 16$ mm., angle $\sim 9°$) are calcite prisms. The two parts of

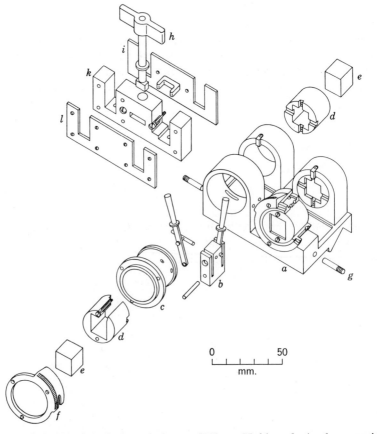

Fig. 17-14. Cell holder for spectropolarimetry [10]. *a*. Holder. *b*. Analyzer positioner. *c*. Adjustable prism holder ring. *d*. Prism holder. *e*. Glann prism. *f*. Analyzer adjustment ring. *g*. Pin. *h*. Knob to tighten cells. *i*. Plates holding cells. *k*. Cell holder. *l*. Cover plate.

each prism are separated by a narrow slit of air and are usable above 220 nm.; at shorter wavelengths appreciable light absorption takes place.

The prisms are mounted in holders d. The analyzers can be rotated using a ring (c, f). A stop b fixes the ring in position where $\theta = 45, 70, 80$, and $85°$.

The cells ($l = 1$ cm.) are placed in the holder at k and fastened, using h and the plate i. The cell holder is placed between the prisms, and the entire apparatus inserted in the spectrophotometer.

Calibration. An optically inactive substance ($\alpha = 0$) is put in the cells and

$$\frac{T_1}{T_2} = R_0 = K \qquad (17\text{-}14)$$

is determined. Then K is determined as a function of the wavelength between 220 and 600 nm. (every 10 nm.). The result is plotted on graph paper.

17-10   Determination of a Normal Rotary Dispersion Curve

The weighed optically active solution is placed in the cells. Follow the directions of Chapter 19. Determine R_α between 220 and 600 nm. every 10 nm. and calculate

Form 17-1

Name: Date:		Substance: Concentration:				$A =$ $B =$ $\lambda_0 =$ $\pm$ $L =$	
λ	Slit Width	θ	R_α	α	$[\alpha]$	$\dfrac{1}{[\alpha]}$	λ^2

α, using formula 17-10. Calculate the specific rotation [α]. Drude's equation may be transformed to

$$\frac{1}{[\alpha]} = \frac{\lambda^2}{L} - \frac{\lambda_0^2}{L} = A\lambda^2 + B \tag{17-15}$$

$1/[\alpha]$ is plotted against λ^2; the constants A and B are found by using the method of the least squares equation.

Knowing A and B,

$$\lambda_0 = \left(-\frac{B}{A}\right)^{\frac{1}{2}} \tag{17-16}$$

Calculate the standard deviation of λ_0. Record as shown in Form 17-1.

17-11   References

1. W. Klyne in *Determination of Organic Structures by Physical Methods*, E. A. Braude and F. C. Nachod, eds., Academic Press, New York, 1955, p. 73.
2. W. Heller and D. D. Fitts in *Technique of Organic Chemistry*, A. Weissberger, ed., Interscience Publishers, New York, 1960, Vol. I, Part III, p. 2147.
3. C. Djerassi, *Optical Rotatory Dispersion: Applications to Organic Chemistry*, McGraw-Hill Book Co., New York, 1960.
4. W. Klyne and A. C. Parker in *Technique of Organic Chemistry*, A. Weissberger, ed., Interscience Publishers, New York, 1960, Vol. I, Part III, p. 2335.
5. I. P. Dirkx, P. J. van der Haak, and F. L. J. Sixma, *Chem. Weekblad*, **56**, 151 (1960); I. P. Dirkx and F. L. J. Sixma, *Anal. Chem.*, in press (1964).
6. W. Klyne in *Advances in Organic Chemistry; Methods and Results*, R. A. Raphael, E. C. Taylor, and H. Wynberg, eds., Interscience Publishers, New York, Vol. I, 1960, p. 239.
7. J. F. King in *Elucidation of Structures by Physical and Chemical Methods*, Vol. XI in *Technique of Organic Chemistry*, A. Weissberger, ed., Interscience Publishers, New York, 1963, Part I, p. 370.
8. *Handbook of Chemistry and Physics*, Chemical Rubber Publishing Co., Cleveland, 1960, p. 3019.
9. E. L. Eliel, *Stereochemistry of Carbon Compounds*, McGraw-Hill Book Co., New York, 1962.
10. K. Mislow, C. Djerassi, and A. Moscowitz, *Ann. N.Y. Acad. Sci.*, **93**, 457 (1962).
11. K. Mislow, *Abstracts 10th National Organic Symposium*, American Chemical Society, Columbus, Ohio, June 16–20, 1963, p. 80.
12. G. G. Lyle and R. E. Lyle, "Optical Rotatory Dispersion," in *Determination of Organic Structures by Physical Methods*, F. C. Nachod and W. D. Phillips, eds., Academic Press, London, 1962, Vol. 2, pp. 1–87.
13. S. F. Mason, "Optical Rotatory Power," *Quart. Revs.* (London), **17**, 20–66 (1963).
14. I. P. Dirkx and F. L. J. Sixma, *Rec. trav. chim.*, **83**, 522 (1964).
15. J. H. Brewster *J. Am. Chem. Soc.*, **81**, 5475 (1959). For an attempt to confirm this prediction see, for instance, H. Wynberg, G. L. Hekkert, H. W. Bosch, J. P. M. Houbiers, and H. A. P. de Jongh, Abstracts 148th National Meeting, American Chemical Society, Chicago, Ill., Aug. 30, 1964.
16. K. Mislow, H. A. W. Glass, H. B. Hopps, E. Simon, G. H. Wahl, Jr., *J. Am. Chem. Soc.*, **86**, 1710 (1964).
17. J. G. Foss, *J. Chem. Educ.*, **40**, 592 (1963).

18

Colorimetry

18-1 Introduction

With a colorimeter the concentration of a solute may be determined from the intensity of the color of a solution.

When light is incident on a substance, it may be transmitted, reflected, scattered, or absorbed. Usually all four phenomena occur; in using a colorimeter reflected light and scattered light are neglected (note that this certainly leads to inaccuracies when the solution is not clear).

For the light absorbed, the law of Lambert-Beer holds:

$$I = I_0 \cdot 10^{-\epsilon cd} \quad \text{or} \quad \log \frac{I_0}{I} = \epsilon cd$$

where I_0 = intensity of incident light;

I = intensity of emergent light;

d = length of liquid through which light passes (cell width);

c = concentration;

$E = I_0/I$ (called absorbance, see Chapter 19 for new nomenclature);

ϵ = molar absorbance, i.e., absorbance when the concentration of 1 mole/l. is measured for $d = 1$ cm.

18-2 Principle

The concentration c can be determined by measuring I_0/I when ϵ has previously been determined from solutions of known concentration. Several procedures are possible:

1. *The incident light* may be (1a) white or (1b) monochromatic. Simple derivation shows that method 1a will lead to correct results only for cases where cd = constant.

2. *The detection* may be (2a) visually subjective or (2b) objective (with the aid of a photocell).

3. *The determination of I_0/I* may be done (3a) directly (when using method 2a), or (3b) by compensating the incident light I_0 to I. Method 3b is more accurate; method 3a is faster.

Method 2*a*, known as the "balancing method," depends on the fact (assuming Beer's law to hold) that, if two beams of light of equal intensity are passed through two columns of an absorbing solution containing different concentrations of solute, the intensities of the transmitted beams will appear the same when the column lengths are inversely proportional to the concentrations, or

$$c_a d_a = c_x d_x$$

where c_a = concentration a (known);
$\quad\quad d_a$ = length of column a (known);
$\quad\quad d_x$ = measured length of column x at balance;
$\quad\quad c_x$ = concentration unknown.
Note that since concentration × column length = constant the color of a solution *which obeys Beer's law* should not change when adding solvent.

18-3   Apparatus

Two simple colorimeters are shown in Figs. 18-1 and 18-2. The Coleman Junior Spectrophotometer (Fig. 18-1) requires no description. An Engel colorimeter is shown in Fig. 18-2. Light from source L enters cell C_2 *via* a filter F and ends at a photocell P. The intensity of L may be adjusted (coarse or fine) with the resistances R_1 and R_2. Knob K enables different filters to be inserted. The number on this knob indicates the wavelength of maximum transmission (e.g., filter 53 allows maximum transmission at 530 nm.). Knob H activates the photocell when pushed in.

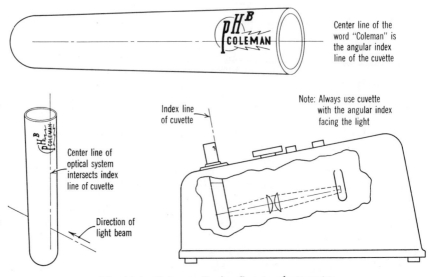

Fig. 18-1. Coleman Junior Spectrophotometer.

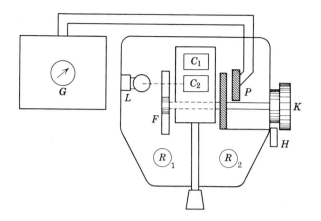

Fig. 18-2. Engel colorimeter.

18-4 Procedure

18-4a CALIBRATION

The calibration for a particular substance (the determination of the absorbance) is accomplished by measuring E at several known concentrations. Choose the latter on either side of the concentration expected in the unknown, and prepare a graph plotting E vs. c.

18-4b CHOICE OF FILTER

When no guide is available for the filter to be used, measure the concentration with all filters and choose the one for which E as measured is largest.

18-4c MONOCHROMATER

In practice the spectral region $\Delta\lambda$ transmitted should be small with respect to the width of the absorption band. Only a spectrometer using prisms or gratings will fulfill this condition. The filters in common colorimeters have fairly large bandwidths.

18-4d ACCURACY

By differentiating the formula for the Lambert-Beer law it is evident that maximum accuracy is obtained when E is between 0.1 and 1.1.

18-5 Examples

18-5a DETERMINATION OF AMINO ACIDS [2, 3]

Amino acids give a blue color with ninhydrine. The reaction is carried out in buffered solutions.

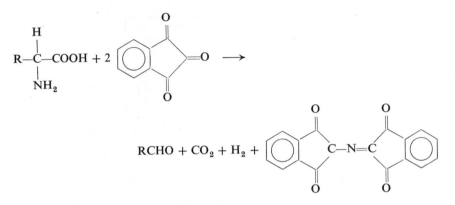

Ninhydrine Solution.   The ninhydrine solution should be prepared and kept in nitrogen atmosphere.

Tin(II) chloride ($SnCl_2·2H_2O$; 800 mg.) is dissolved in 500 ml. of a buffer solution (pH = 5.0). Add a solution containing 20 g. of ninhydrine in 500 ml. of methyl cellosolve. Transfer the mixture to a reagent bottle and keep under N_2.

Buffer Solution, pH = 5.0 (±0.1).   Citric acid ($C_6H_8O_7·H_2O$; 126.05 g.) is dissolved in 300 ml. of 4.0N NaOH and the solution made up to 3 l. Check the pH after dilution with an equal volume of water and correct if necessary.

Buffer Solution, pH = 5.28 (±0.02).   Citric acid ($C_6H_8O_7·H_2O$; 122.25 g.) is dissolved in 1 l. of water, and a solution containing 72 g. of NaOH in 1 l. of water is added. Add 34 ml. of hydrochloric acid ($d = 1.19$) and make up to 5 l. Finally add 5 g. of phenol. Check the pH of this solution and adjust by addition of HCl or NaOH. In order to change the pH by 0.01 units, 0.5 ml. of HCl ($d = 1.19$) or 0.25 ml. of NaOH (50%) is needed.

Methyl Cellosolve.   2-Methoxyethanol should be peroxide free (negative test with a 10% KI solution) and should give a clear solution upon dilution with water.

Ethanol-Water Mixture.   One volume of ethanol (6%) to one volume of water.

Procedure.   The solutions to be analyzed should not contain more than 0.3 μmole/ml.

Pipette 1.00 ml. of the solution to be analyzed into a clean, dry test tube (150 × 13). Each determination should be accompanied by a blank (1.00 ml. of distilled water).

Add 1.00 ml. of the buffer solution (pH 5.28), followed by 1.00 ml. of the ninhydrine solution. Stopper the test tube, using a rubber stopper covered with aluminum or polyethylene foil. Shake for 10 sec. without allowing the liquid to wet the stopper. Heat the test tube for 20 min. in a beaker of boiling water, cool, add 5.00 ml. of the ethanol-water mixture (1:1 vol./vol.). Shake for 1.0

min. and determine the absorbance at 570 nm. within 60 min. after removal from the water bath. Use a 1-cm. cell, with the blank as reference cell.

Calibration Curve. Since the reaction does not go to completion, it becomes necessary to determine a separate calibration curve for each amino acid. Use aqueous solutions of amino acids containing, respectively, 0.00, 0.05, 0.10, 0.18, 0.25, and 0.30 μmole/ml. Pipette 1 ml. of each of these solutions and proceed as described above.

Plot E vs. the number of micromoles of amino acid and use this as the calibration curve.

Assignment. Leucine, alanine, glycine, serine, phenyl alanine, aspartic acid.

18-5b DETERMINATION OF CARBOHYDRATES (Orcinol Method [4])

This determination is based upon the colored reaction products formed when carbohydrates are allowed to react with 3,5-dihydroxytoluene in the presence of sulfuric acid.

Reagent A. Sulfuric acid/water (3:2). (450 ml. of conc. sulfuric acid and 300 ml. of water).

Reagent B. Dissolve 2.0 g. of orcinol in 50 ml. of water. Add a cooled solution of 20 ml. of conc. sulfuric acid and 30 ml. of water. Keep this solution in the dark.

Procedure. To 15 ml. of reagent A add successively 0.5 ml. of reagent B and 1 ml. of the carbohydrate solution (0.01–0.04%). Shake well and heat for 10 min. in a beaker of boiling water. Cool, add 50 ml. of reagent A from a pipette (use rubber pipette balloon), and determine the absorbance at 530 nm. Use a blank (starting with 1 ml. of water) as a reference solution.

Assignment. Glucose, fructose, galactose, lactose, and saccharose.

18-5c DETERMINATION OF CARBOHYDRATES (Phenol Method [5])

This determination is based upon the colored reaction products formed when carbohydrates are allowed to react with phenol in the presence of sulfuric acid.

Procedure. Pipette 2 ml. of a carbohydrate solution (10–120 g. of carbohydrate) into a test tube. Add 1 ml. of a 5% phenol solution. Add *rapidly* (10–15 sec.) 5 ml. of conc. sulfuric acid. Allow to stand 10 min., shake well, and warm (25–30°) in a water bath for 15 min.

Prepare a calibration curve by dissolving 60 mg. of the carbohydrate in 1 l. of water and diluting 2.5 ml., 5 ml., 10 ml., 15 ml., and 20 ml. to 25 ml.

Calculation and Report. See § 18-4a.

18-5d EQUIPMENT

Colorimeter
Cell holder
Test-tube rack
6 Semimicro test tubes
2 Test tubes
Cells
Filters

18-6 References

1. W. West, "Colorimetry and Photometric Analysis," in *Technique of Organic Chemistry*, A. Weissberger, ed., Interscience Publishers, New York, 1960, Vol. I., Part III, p. 2021.
2. W. Troll and R. K. Cannon, *J. Biol. Chem.*, **200,** 803 (1953).
3. S. Moore and W. H. Stein, *J. Biol. Chem.*, **206,** 825–834 (1954).
4. M. Sørensen and G. Haugaard, *Biochem. Z.*, **260,** 247 (1933).
5. M. Dubois, K. A. Gilles, J. K. Hamilton, P. A. Rebers, and F. Smith, *Anal. Chem.*, **28,** 350 (1956).
6. Gustav Kortuem, *Kolorimetrie, Photometrie, und Spektrometrie*, Springer Verlag, Berlin, 1962.
7. B. Kakac and Z. J. Vejdelek, *Handbuch der Kolorimetrie*, Band I, *Kolorimetrie in der Pharmazie*, G. Fischer, Jena, 1961.

19

Ultraviolet

spectrophotometry

19-1 Introduction

With a quartz spectrophotometer the absorption spectrum between 210 and 1000 nm. may be determined. This is the region in which many unsaturated aromatic and heterocyclic organic compounds have electronic absorption bands.

19-2 Units and Definitions

Considerable confusion exists in the field of spectroscopy about the units employed. The following definitions and units have been adopted from the suggestions published in the *Journal of Analytical Chemistry* [1].

Absorbance, A, is the logarithm to the base 10 of the reciprocal of the transmission $= \log_{10}(1/T) = \log_{10}(I_0/I).$*

Absorptivity, a, is the absorbance divided by the product of the concentration of the substance (g./l.) and the sample path length (cm.) $= A/bc$.

Molar absorptivity, ϵ, is the product of the absorptivity and the molecular weight of a substance $= aM$.

The terms optical density, absorbancy, extinction $(= A)$; absorbancy index, specific extinction, extinction coefficient $(= a)$, and molar absorbancy index,

Table 19-1

Unit	Symbol	Definition
Micron	μ	10^{-4} cm.
Nanometer	nm.	10^{-7} cm.
Millimicron	mμ	10^{-7} cm.
Angstrom	Å	10^{-8} cm.
Wave number	ν	$1/\lambda$ (cm.$^{-1}$)
Frequency	ν	Number of cycles/unit (sec.$^{-1}$)

* A is measured directly. On the Beckman DU spectrophotometer, for example, A is read on the scale marked D (density); see § 19–10.

185

molar extinction coefficient, and molar absorption coefficient ($= \epsilon$) will not be used.

Table 19-1 lists the common units used and their symbols.

19-3 Theory

A combination of the laws of Bouguer, Lambert, and Beer states that the proportion of light absorbed by a transparent medium is independent of the intensity of the incident light and proportional to the number of absorbing molecules through which the light passes.

Thus:

$$I = I_0 \cdot 10^{-abc} \quad \text{or} \quad \log \frac{I_0}{I} = abc \qquad (19\text{-}1)$$

where $I_0 =$ the intensity of the incident light;
$\quad I =$ the intensity of light transmitted;
$\quad a =$ the absorptivity;
$\quad b =$ the cell length (cm.);
$\quad c =$ the concentration.

Since A, the absorbance, is the quantity actually measured, we rewrite equation 19-1:

$$\log_{10} \frac{I_0}{I} = A = abc \qquad (19\text{-}2)$$

When $c =$ moles/liter, the *molar absorptivity* (molar a) is denoted by ϵ, and

$$A = \epsilon bc, \quad \text{or} \quad \epsilon = \frac{A}{bc} \qquad (19\text{-}3)$$

(The units of ϵ are area/mole but are usually omitted.)

19-4 The Nature of the Light Absorption Process

In the region between 200 and 1000 nm. the important excitations are those of the π-electrons. Excitation of σ-electrons requires more energy and consequently takes places at shorter ($<$200 nm., vacuum ultraviolet) wavelengths. Bonding as well as non-bonding (lone-pair) π-electrons may undergo transitions from the ground state to an electronically excited state. The wavelength λ corresponding to the energy needed for such a transition is called the wavelength of maximum absorption ($\lambda_{\max}$) or absorption maximum. In many cases more than one such electronic transition is possible and many maxima are observed. Using the nomenclature of Mason [2], we may distinguish the following transitions (see Fig. 19-1).

$n \to \pi^*$: non-bonding π-electrons $\to$ antibonding π-level;
$\pi \to \pi^*$: bonding π-electrons $\to$ antibonding π-level;
$\sigma \to \sigma^*$: bonding σ-electrons $\to$ antibonding σ-levels.

In general, non-bonding lone-pair electrons are the least strongly bound in a molecule, and σ-electrons the most strongly bound.

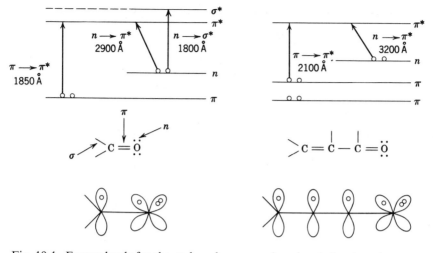

Fig. 19-1. Energy levels for the carbonyl group and conjugated carbonyl group.

19-5 Applications

19-5a STRUCTURAL PROBLEMS

The following generalizations serve to indicate the usefulness of ultraviolet spectroscopy in the solution of structural problems. (See Tables 19-2 and 19-3 and also [12], p. 94.)

Table 19-2 Wavelength of Maximum Absorption ($\lambda_{\max}$) and Molar Absorptivity ($\epsilon_{\max}$) of Classes of Organic Compounds

Type of Compound	$\lambda_{\max}$ (nm.)	$\epsilon_{\max}$	Comments
1. Saturated aliphatic compounds	150		
Amines	200–240	1000–4000	Usually two maxima
Halides	180–300	1500–3000	
Sulfides	210–230	1000	
2. Olefins	160–200	10,000	$\pi \to \pi^*$
3. Dienes	210–250	5–20,000	Alkyl substitution
4. Acetylenes	220–245	150–1000	produces red shift
5. Carbonyl compounds			of ~5 nm.
Saturated systems	150	30,000	$\pi \to \pi^*$
	170–180	10,000	$n \to \sigma^*$
	290–300	10–50	$n \to \pi^*$
α,β-unsaturated systems	215–240	5–15,000	$\pi \to \pi^*$
	320	10–100	$n \to \pi^*$
6. Aromatic systems	200–250	10–20,000	K-band Much fine
	260–280	1000–2000	B-band structure
7. Five-membered heteroaromatics	200–220	10–15,000	
	240–260	100–5000	
8. Six-membered heteroaromatics	250–300	1000–5000	
	300–350	200–1000	

Table 19-3   Table of Chromophores with Some Ultraviolet Absorption Data

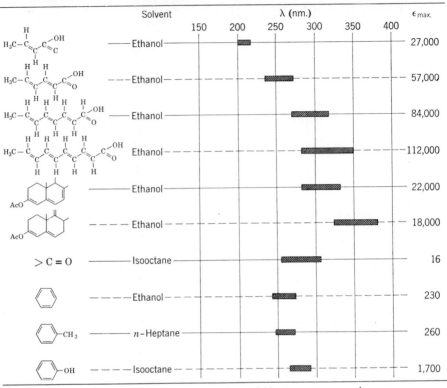

A compound showing *no* absorption above 210 mμ may contain

1. Aliphatic or alicyclic hydrocarbon groups.
2. Carboxyl, ether, or alcohol groups.
3. Fluorine or chlorine.
4. Primary or secondary amino groups.
5. Mercapto or nitrile groups.
6. Non-conjugated double bonds.

Such a compound *cannot* contain

7. A conjugated chromophore (dienes, α,β-unsaturated ketones).
8. Aromatic rings.
9. Aldehyde or keto groups.
10. Bromine or iodine.

Empirical rules relating structure to absorption maximum have been applied successfully to conjugated olefins and unsaturated carbonyl compounds. For details consult Brand and Scott [4, pp. 75, 80].

19-5b   ANALYTICAL APPLICATIONS

In order to analyze a mixture of two components (A and B), the absorbance is measured at two wavelengths [5, pp. 1910–1913]. Then

$$A' \text{ (observed)} = b(a_1'c_1 + a_2'c_2) \tag{19-4}$$

where A' = observed absorbance at λ';

    b = cell length (cm.);

    a_1' = absorptivity at λ' of species 1.

and

$$A'' = b(a_1''c_1 + a_2''c_2) \tag{19-5}$$

From a knowledge of the four absorptivities and the absorbance measurements at two wavelengths, the concentrations of each of the two components can be determined. It is desirable to select λ' and λ'' in such a manner that one component absorbs strongly and the other weakly at these wavelengths.

19-5c OTHER APPLICATIONS

See Chapter 28 (Molecular Weight Determination) and Chapter 24 (Dissociation Constants of Acids and Basis).

1. The pK of a substance may be determined spectrophotometrically if the spectrum of the acid and its anion (or the base and its cation) can be measured (see Chapter 24).

2. Since the absorption of non-conjugated chromophores is additive, a non-conjugated change in structure of a known chromophoric system may be used to determine its *molecular weight* (see Chapter 28).

3. The rate of a reaction may be followed spectrophotometrically by recording the decrease in the absorption of the starting material and the increase in the absorption of the product (see Chapter 30).

4. Conformational and stereochemical details of structure may be obtained [4, pp. 76–80] from shifts in absorption maxima.

19-6 Reporting the Data

An absorption spectrum is usually recorded graphically. The absorption is plotted as ordinate against the frequency or wavelength as abscissa. This means that many different units will be found in the literature. Thus T (transmission), A, $\log \epsilon$, and $E_{1\,cm}^{1\%}$ may be found plotted against λ or ν. Care must be exercised in consulting spectra containing different symbols. The following units are to be used in recording the data.

(*a*) When the molecular weight of the absorbing species is known, plot ϵ or $\log \epsilon$ against λ (scale 1 mm. = 1 nm.).

(*b*) When the molecular weight is unknown, when the material is not pure, and when mixtures are used; plot $\log E_{1\,cm}^{1\%}$ against λ, where $E_{1\,cm}^{1\%} = |A/cb|$ (c = conc. in grams per 100 ml., and b = path length in centimeters).

See Fig. 19-2 for a typical spectrogram and influence of solvents and pH on spectra.

19-7 General Directions

19-7a CLEANING THE CELLS

Glass cells may be used above 350 nm; quartz cells are suitable for the entire range from 200–1000 nm. The cells should be removed from the cellholder during cleaning and filling. They should never come into contact with alkaline reagents. Benzene-free alcohol is used to rinse the cells. Before each determination both cells are filled with solvent to check whether the transmission is equal. In case the alcohol rinsing proves insufficient, the cells should be soaked overnight in a bichromate-sulfuric acid solution (see Lange's *Handbook of Chemistry*, 9th Edition, p. 1776), and rinsed with distilled water followed by alcohol. Do not attempt to clean the outside of the cells by wiping in any other way than carefully with tissue paper. Remember that dirt, which may absorb ultraviolet light and may be invisible to the unaided eye, usually collects on the outside of the cell wall. Never touch the cell window with the fingers.

19-7b STANDARDIZING THE CELLS

The cells should be marked in such a manner as to allow ready identification. If matched cells are not being used, cell corrections should be determined. Fill both cells with distilled water (or the appropriate solvent). Choose as reference

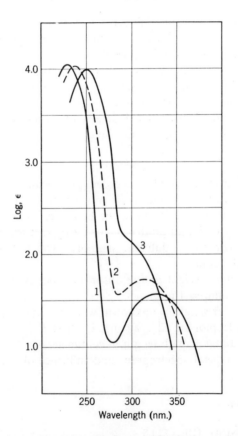

Fig. 19-2. A typical spectrogram and influence of solvents and pH on spectra. Mesityl oxides in (1) hexane, (2) methyl alcohol, and (3) 9N calcium chloride solution. (G. Scheibe, *Ber.*, **58**, 586 (1925).

cell the one showing the highest transmission over the largest part of the spectrum. Compare the transmission of the other cells to that of the reference cell as a function of the wavelength.

Table 19-4   Solvents for UV Spectroscopy
(Eastman Organic Chemicals Department, Eastman Kodak Co., Rochester 3, N.Y.)

Eastman Cat. No.	Solvent	UV Cut-off* (nm.)
S 297	Acetone	330
S 488	Acetonitrile	220
S 777	Benzene	280
S 444	Carbontetrachloride	265
S 337	Chloroform	245
S 702	Cyclohexane	210
S 997	Diethylether	220
S 467	Methanol	210
S 1227	Methylformate	260
S 212	Isopropanol	210
S 214	Pyridine	305
S 2396	2,2,4-Trimethylpentane	215

* The UV cut-off given is the wavelength at which the absorbance (optical density) of a 1-cm. layer is about 1.
Below 220 nm. cut-off values should be determined.

19-7c SOLVENTS FOR SPECTROSCOPY

Use Table 19-4 and Fig. 19-3 to determine a suitable solvent. Figure 19-3 gives a graphic representation of the cut-off wavelength of most common solvents. Solvent corrections are shown in Table 19-5.

Table 19-5   Solvent Corrections for $n \to \pi^*$ Transition of α,β-Unsaturated Ketones to Give Location in Ethanol [4]

Solvent	Correction to Ethanol (nm.)
Methanol	−1
Chloroform	0
Ether	+6
n-Hexane	+7

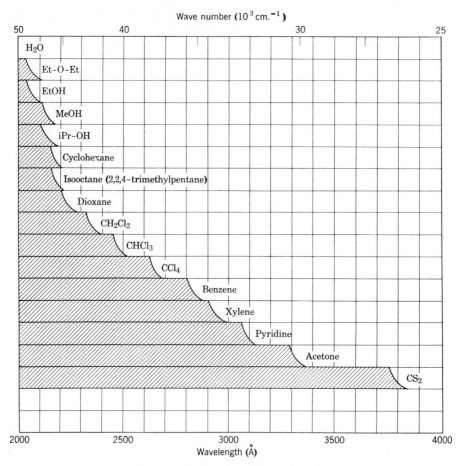

Fig. 19-3. Useful range of solvents in the ultraviolet region, for 1 cm. path length. Cut-off points are approximate, depending on purity of the solvent. (Used with permission from R. P. Bauman, *Absorption Spectroscopy*, John Wiley and Sons, New York, 1962)

19-8 Beckman DB Spectrophotometer (see Fig. 19-4)

19-8a APPARATUS

The Beckman DB spectrophotometer is a double-beam instrument. It may be operated manually as well as automatically.

White light (from a tungsten or hydrogen lamp) enters the monochromator *via* a mirror. A narrow bundle of light emerges. The intensity as well as the spectral width of this bundle is determined by the slit width.

A cell containing the solution and a reference cell (usually containing the solvent) are placed in the light beam. A system of vibrating mirrors causes the light to enter the two cells alternately (at a rate of 35 cycles/sec.). The light is received by a photomultiplier tube which translates the alternating "sample-reference" light

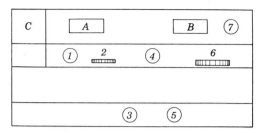

Fig. 19-4. Beckman DB spectrophotometer. *1.* Power control switch (positions: "off," "idle," "on," "scan"). *2.* Zero adjust. *3.* Manual micrometer slit adjust. *4.* 100% adjust ("Ref"). *5.* Slit program selector. *6.* Wavelength control. *7.* Pilot light. *A.* Galvanometer. *B.* Wavelength scale. *C.* Cover of sample compartment.

pulses into current pulses. These signals are magnified electronically and translated into a difference in voltage, allowing percentage transmission to be read on the instrument directly.

Light Source. The apparatus is equipped with a tungsten lamp for measurements in the 320–800 nm. region. A hydrogen lamp is used for the 200–350 nm. region. When the light-source selector knob is turned, a mirror inside the lamp compartment changes position, enabling either lamp to be used.

Monochromator. To the right, disk *6* is used to adjust the position of the prism in the monochromator, thus selecting the wavelength desired. The wavelength is read at *B.*

For manual operation the slit program selector *5* is switched onto "MAN." The slit width is adjusted with the manual micrometer slit adjustment *3.* The slit opens when the knob is turned counterclockwise. One complete turn is equal to 0.25 mm.; when eight turns have been made the maximum slit width of 2 cm. is obtained. The micrometer adjustment is calibrated to indicate 0.01 mm. of slit width and is used for fine work.

The apparatus is also equipped with an automatic slit adjustment. Before it is used the micrometer thimble *3* must always be returned to zero. Then the slit program selector *5* is turned to either the NAR or the MED position. The NAR position designates the narrow slit function and is intended for use with reference materials of high transmittance; the MED position, the medium slit function to be used with reference materials of lower transmittance.

19-8b   PROCEDURE (see Fig. 19-4) (Manual Operation, Double Beam)

Switching on the Apparatus. Turn switch *1* to "on": the electrical circuits are switched on. Allow the apparatus a minimum warm-up period of 10 min. (maximum stability is reached after 1 hr.).

For measurements in the visible region (320–800 nm.) move the light-source selector to the "visible" position. Turn the tungsten-lamp power switch to the "on" position.

For measurements in the ultraviolet region (200–350 nm.) verify that the hydrogen lamp is installed and the lamp power supply connected and operative. Fire the hydrogen lamp in accordance with its power supply instructions. Move the light-source selector to the UV position.

Measuring.   The "zero adjust" *2* allows the meter to be set at zero when no signal is present at the detector. The adjustment is made with knob *1* in position "on" and an opaque block in the sample beam.

The "100% adjust" (*4*), identified as REF on the front panel, adjusts the amplifier output current to the level required to cause a reading of 100% on the meter *A*, when sample and reference are equal.

To select the slit program to be used proceed in the following manner. Place a cell filled with the solvent to be used into the sample beam compartment (marked *S*) and compare its transmission against an empty air path in the reference compartment (marked *R*).

If solvent transmission (read on *A*) is 50% or above, set *5* at the NAR position. This position provides the narrowest programmed slit operation and therefore the best programmed resolution.

If solvent transmission is less than 50%, set *5* at the MED position.

If the manual slit control is to be used, set *5* in the MAN position. To check the manual slit zero, adjust *3* on the zero stop position and note the backgound level on the meter *A*. Then turn *3* counterclockwise until the meter reading just begins to increase. This point is the manual slit zero position.

Summary of Operations

	Knob Used
1. Choose light source.	Light-source selector
2. Choose slit program.	*5*
3. Position NAR and MED manual slit control on zero stop; position MAN slit adjustment.	*3*
4. Choose wavelength.	*6*
5. Fill both cells with solvent and place them in cell compartment (sample cell at *S*, reference cell at *R*).	Cell compartment
6. Adjust *A* to 100% transmission.	*4*
7. Empty sample cell, fill with sample solution, and replace at *S* (same position as in 5).	Cell compartment
8. Close cell compartment.	*C*
9. Read off transmission or absorbance.	*A*

19-9   Unicam Spectrophotometer Type SP-500 (Fig. 19-5)

19-9a   APPARATUS

White light from the light source *L* is focused by a system of mirrors (Fig. 19-6) on the entrance slit of the monochromator *M*. The emergent light passes the cell

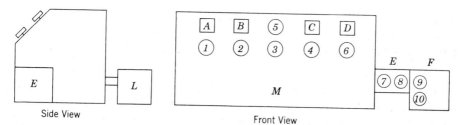

Side View   Front View

Fig. 19-5. Unicam Spectrophotometer Type SP-500. *1*. Wavelength knob. *2*. Transmission/density knob. *3*. "Off, check" knob. *4*. Dark current knob. *5*. Sensitivity control. *6*. Slit control. *7*. Filter slide. *8*. Cell slide. *9*. Dark current slide. *10*. Photocell slide (red out, blue in). *11*. Mirror knob. *12*. Lamp on/off. *A*. Wavelength scale. *B*. Transmission/density scale. *C*. Galvanometer. *D*. Slit width scale. *E*. Cell compartment. *F*. Photocell compartment. *L*. Lamp compartment. *M*. Monochromator.

compartment *E* and enters the photocell *F*. The apparatus contains two photocells, one (red) for the 1000–625 nm. region and one (blue) for the 625–185 nm. region.

The amplified photocell output current is balanced with a slide wire potentiometer *2* calibrated in both percentage transmission and optical density.

By means of a slide (*8*) the solvent cell is placed in the light beam and the galvanometer adjusted to zero. The solution cell is then placed in the light beam and the galvanometer brought to zero by using the transmission control knob (*2*). The transmission (or optical density) is read on scale *B*.

Light Sources. Like the Beckman DB, the instrument has a tungsten and a hydrogen lamp. The hydrogen lamp uses a stabilized 300-ma current; the tungsten lamp uses a large-capacity 6-volt battery.

Monochromator (Fig. 19-5). On the right-hand side of the monochromator, knob *6* is used to adjust the slit width. The scale expands progressively toward the

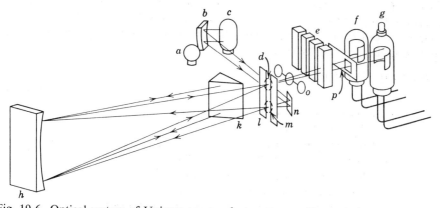

Fig. 19-6. Optical system of Unicam spectrophotometer. *a*. Tungsten lamp. *b*. Hollow mirror. *c*. Hydrogen lamp. *d*. Quartz lens. *e*. Quartz cells. *f,g*. Detectors. *h*. Collimation mirror. *k*. Quartz prism. *l*. Slits. *m*. Quartz plate. *n*. Flat mirror. *o*. Filters. *p*. Dark current slide.

narrower slit openings. Narrow slit openings can be read easily to 0.001 mm. The slits should never be closed tightly since they are damaged easily. To the left is knob *1* to adjust the wavelength, which is read on scale *A*.

Cell Compartment. The removable slide *8* in the cell compartment can hold four cells. This slide must be moved carefully at all times; the photocells are shock sensitive. During measurements the cell compartment should be closed. A slide consisting of three filters *7* against stray light is in front of the cell carriage. The desired detector is placed in the light beam with knob *10*; this also ensures the appropriate electrical connection. The dark current slide *9* in front of the detectors can be used to interrupt the light beam.

19-9b   PROCEDURE

Starting the Instrument. Check whether the slit is closed. Warm up the instrument by switching knob *3* on check. The hydrogen lamp is switched on by turning the switch on the power supply (left) down; 2 min. later the knob on the right side of the power supply is pushed on. The ammeter should read about 300 ma. When this is not the case the lamp should be switched off (left switch up).

Measuring. The deflection of the galvanometer needle at any given wavelength and cell content is determined, on the one hand, by the slit width (knob *6*), and gain (knob *5*), on the other hand, by the voltage (knob *2*). The sensitivity control allows a ten-fold variation in the electrical sensitivity; use can be made of this fact to operate at constant slit width. Switch *3* allows an increase in scale sensitivity by a factor of 10; when transmission is less than 10 % this switch is used to improve recording accuracy.

The slit should not be closed below 0.02 mm.; otherwise, refraction phenomena may occur.

Turning Off the Instrument. Push in the dark current slide *9*, switch off the hydrogen lamp (left switch on power supply), turn off electrical circuit *3*. Remove slide from cell compartment, clean cells, place cells in appropriate box, return slide, and close cell compartment.

Summary of Operations

	Knob Used
1. Switch *3* on "check."	*3*
2. Select wavelength desired.	*1*
3. Choose appropriate photocell.	*10*
4. Choose appropriate filter (see Fig. 19-6).	*7*
5. Check that dark current shutter is closed.	*9*
6. Check that cell compartment is closed.	*E*
7. Adjust dark current to zero reading on galvanometer. Check dark current after each transmission measurement.	*4* and *C*
8. Adjust sensitivity control, if necessary, by turning knob *5* three turns counterclockwise.	*5*

9. Place solvent cell in light beam.   *8*

10. Open the dark current shutter.   *9*

11. Adjust galvanometer to zero.   *6* and *C*

12. Repeat.   *5* and *C*

13. Place solution cell in light beam.   *8*

14. Turn switch to *10*.   *3*

15. Adjust galvanometer to zero.   *2* and *C*

16. Close dark current shutter.   *9*

17. Read off transmission (or optical density). With knob *3* on "1" the transmission scale reads 0–100%, the density scale, ∞–0.   *3*

18. If the transmission >10%, switch to "0.1." In this position the transmission scale runs from 0 to 10% and the density from ∞ to 1.   *3*

19. Repeat, starting with 1.

Comments.

(*a*) If more than one sample cell is being measured, all operations starting with 13 must be repeated.

(*b*) The choice of light source, filter, and detector is given in Table 19-6.

Table 19-6 Choice of Detector and Light Source with Unicam Spectrophotometer

λ (nm.)	Photocell	Lamp	Filter
185–320	Blue	Hydrogen	
320–400	Blue	tungsten	Filter slide in position 3
400–625	Blue	tungsten	
625–1000	Red	tungsten	

19-10 Beckman Quartz Spectrophotometer Model DU (see Figs. 19-7, 19-8, 19-9)

19-10a APPARATUS

Light from source *a* (Fig. 19-7) is focused *via* mirrors *b* and *c* on slit *d*. The light rays fall on *e*, are reflected by prism *f* (knob *4*, Fig. 19-9) rotates the prism, thus varying the wavelength) and mirror *c* again focuses the bundle in the plane of *d* through the cell *g* and into the phototube *h*.

As before, a tungsten lamp connected to a 6-volt d-c source is used for the 320–1000 nm. region, and a hydrogen lamp connceted to its own power supply for the 220–350 nm. region. Lamps cannot be switched automatically; the entire light-source compartment must be changed. However, recent power supplies and light sources permit changing without removal of compartment.

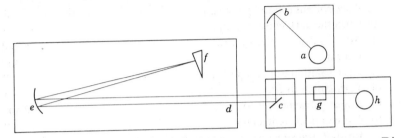

Fig. 19-7. Path of light bundle. *a.* Light source. *b.* Condensing mirror. *c.* Diagonal mirror. *d.* Entrance slit. *e.* Collimating mirror. *f.* Quartz prism. *g.* Absorption cell. *h.* Photo tube.

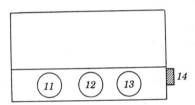

Fig. 19-8. Power supply for the hydrogen lamp. *11.* Power switch. *12.* Pushbutton. *13.* Filament control.

Two phototubes are available and are selected with knob *10* (Fig. 19-9). When this knob is pulled out, the ultraviolet- and blue-sensitive tube for the 200–625 nm. region is in use. When knob *10* is pushed in, the red-sensitive tube for the 600-1000 nm. region is in use. Make sure knob *10* is pulled out *all the way* in the ultraviolet region.

The cell compartment *E* has a removable slide adjusted with knob *8.* Four cells can be accommodated.

19-10b PROCEDURE (see Fig. 19-9)

Starting the Instrument

(*a*) When the tungsten lamp is used, connect lamp and spectrophotometer to a 6-volt d-c supply. Knob *9* should be in "off" position. The lamp is turned on by turning on the switch at the back of the lamphousing. Knob *2* is switched on "check." Knob *3* is rotated so that its position is five whole turns from either end position. Allow sufficient time (30–60 min.) for warming up and stabilization.

(*b*) When the hydrogen lamp is used, connect spectrophotometer to 6-volt d-c supply. Turn knob *9* to "off"; knob *2* to "check"; knob *3* to middle position. Connect power supply. Turn knob *11* (Fig. 19-8) to "on"; knob *13* to the furthest clockwise position. After 2 min. push knob *12* in to start the hydrogen arc. Knob *13* is turned counterclockwise to lower the filament temperature. Since the hydrogen lamp has a limited operating period, the stabilization time should be kept to a minimum. Usually 30 min. suffices.

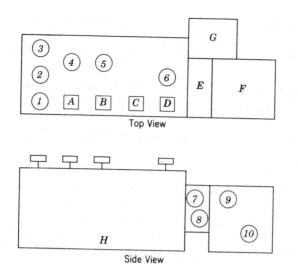

Fig. 19-9. Beckman quartz spectrophotometer model DU. *1*. Dark current knob. *2*. Selectivity switch. *3*. Sensitivity knob. *4*. Wavelength knob. *5*. Transmission/density knob. *6*. Slit control. *7*. Filter slide. *8*. Sample position knob. *9*. Shutter switch. *10*. Phototube knob. *A*. Wavelength scale. *B*. Transmission/density scale. *C*. Galvanometer *D*. Slit width scale. *E*. Cell compartment. *F*. Photocell compartment. *G*. Lamp compartment. *H*. Monochromator.

Summary of Operations during Measurement

		Knob Used
1.	Have selectivity switch on "check."	*2*
2.	Select wavelength.	*4*
3.	Choose phototube and filter (see Table 19-7).	*7* and *10*
4.	Close shutter switch ("off").	*9*
5.	Have galvanometer needle at zero.	*1*
6.	Place solvent and solution cell in cell compartment and close with cover	*E*
7.	Place solvent in light beam.	*8*
8.	Open shutter switch ("on").	*9*
9.	Have galvanometer needle at zero.	*6*
10.	Adjust needle exactly to zero position.	*3*
11.	Close shutter switch.	*9*
12.	Place solution in light beam.	*8*
13.	Move selectivity switch to "1.0." If transmission is less than 10% switch can be moved to "0.1."	*2*
14.	Have shutter switch "on".	*9*
15.	Adjust galvanometer to zero with transmission knob.	*5*
16.	Move shutter switch to "off".	*9*
17.	Record transmission or optical density.	*B*

Turning off the Apparatus. Close the shutter switch (*9*, Fig. 19-9) and turn off the selectivity switch *2*. Turn off lamp:

(*a*) The hydrogen lamp is turned off with switch *11* (Fig. 19-8). The power supply is disconnected.

(*b*) The tungsten lamp is turned off with the switch at the back of the lamp housing. The d-c supply is disconnected.

Table 19-7   Choice of Detector Light Source and Filter

Wavelength (nm.)	Photocell	Knob *10*	Lamp	Filter
220–350	Blue	Out	Hydrogen	None
320–400	Blue	Out	Tungsten	Yes
400–625	Blue	Out	Tungsten	None
600–1000	Red	In	Tungsten	None

19-11 Examples

19-11a   MEASUREMENT OF THE ULTRAVIOLET SPECTRUM OF BENZIL

Approximately 50 mg. of benzil is weighed accurately into a 20-ml. volumetric flask. Ten milliliters of 95% alcohol is added, and the benzil is dissolved by swirling. The flask is carefully filled to the mark with 95% alcohol. A 1-ml. aliquot is pipetted into a second 20-ml. flask and made up to the mark. This is repeated once more. Two cells are filled with solution and solvent, respectively, after having been rinsed at least twice with solution or solvent.

Measure transmission from 220 to 320 nm. every 5 nm. Near a maximum or minimum make a measurement every 2 nm. When the measurement is complete, remove the cells, rinse them with alcohol, dry them on tissue paper, and return them to the cell box. Do not touch cells on transparent surface. The cells are expensive; exercise due care.

Calculations and Report.   Record as shown in Form 19-1.

Calculate the molar absorptivity ϵ, using $\epsilon = A/bc$ (c = conc. in moles per liter; b = cell length), and plot ϵ vs. wavelengths (scale, 1 mm. = 1 nm.). Using semilog paper, also plot log ϵ vs. λ.

19-11b   ENOLIZATION

Dissolve 1.00 g of acetylacetone, $CH_3COCH_2COCH_3$, in 1000 ml. of water. Dilute 1 ml. of this solution to 200 ml. in a volumetric flask. This solution is divided into two equal parts by pouring one half into a 100-ml. graduated cylinder.

To one portion add 1 ml. of 0.1N sodium hydroxide. Shake well after addition.

The adsorption spectrum of the neutral and basic solutions are determined between 220 and 320 nm. Use 1-cm. cells with water in the reference cell, taking

Form 19-1

Name:	Compound:			
Date:	Solvent:			
Weight compound:	Instrument:			
Cell type:	Conc. flask 1:			
	flask 2:			
	flask 3:			

D scale reading = A = absorbance	Wavelength, λ (nm)	Flask No.	Position of Selectivity Switch	$\epsilon = \frac{A}{bc}$

5-nm. increments. Plot absorptivity against wavelength. Calculate the molar absorptivity of acetonylacetone at the wavelength of maximum absorption. Explain the difference in the spectra.

Note. Measure the basic solution as rapidly as is compatible with reasonable accuracy, and clean the cells *at once*.

19-12 Equipment

2 Volumetric flasks (20 ml.)
1 Volumetric flask (200 ml.)
2 Pipettes (1 ml.)
95% Ethyl alcohol (benzene-free)
Benzil
Acetylacetone

19-13 References

1. *Anal. Chem.*, **34**, 1852 (1962).
2. S. F. Mason, *Quart. Revs.*, **15**, 287 (1961).
3. Gillam, A. E., and E. S. Stern, *An Introduction to Electronic Absorption Spectroscopy in Organic Chemistry*, Edward Arnold, London, 1957.

4. J. C. D. Brand and A. I. Scott in *Technique of Organic Chemistry*, A. Weissberger, ed., Interscience Publishers, a division of John Wiley and Sons, New York, 1963, Vol. XI, Part I.

5. W. West in *Technique of Organic Chemistry*, A. Weissberger, ed., Interscience Publishers, New York, 1960, Vol. I, Part III.

6. C. N. R. Rao, *Ultraviolet and Visible Spectroscopy*, Butterworths Scientific Publications, London, 1962.

7. *Steric Effects in Conjugated Systems*, Proceedings of a Symposium held at the University, Butterworths Scientific Publications, London, 1958.

8. R. P. Bauman, *Absorption Spectroscopy*, John Wiley and Sons, New York, 1962.

9. H. H. Jaffé and M. Orchin, *Theory and Applications of Ultraviolet Spectroscopy*, John Wiley and Sons, New York, 1962.

10. Braude, E. A., "Ultraviolet and Visible Light Absorption," in *Determination of Organic Structures by Physical Methods*, E. A. Braude and F. C. Nachod, eds., Academic Press, New York, 1955, Ch. 4, pp. 131–194.

11. F. A. Matsen in *Chemical Applications of Spectroscopy*, Vol. IX in *Technique of Organic Chemistry*, A. Weissberger, ed., Interscience Publishers, New York, 1956.

12. R. M. Silverstein and G. C. Bassler, *Spectrometric Identification of Organic Compounds*, John Wiley and Sons, New York, 1963, Ch. 5.

20

Infrared spectrophotometry

20-1 Introduction

The infrared portion of the electromagnetic spectrum includes radiation with wavelengths between 0.8 and 100 μ.

Several parts are easily accessible experimentally (see Fig. 20-1).

(*a*) The near infrared (0.8–2 μ) requires quartz optics (see Chapter 19). It consists principally of overtones of the vibration-rotation spectrum.

(*b*) The 2–15 μ section is studied with the aid of sodium chloride prisms. Most of the fundamental frequencies of the vibration-rotation spectrum of organic compounds are found in this region.

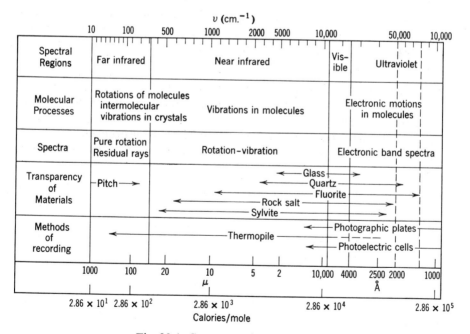

Fig. 20-1. Summary of spectroscopy.

(*c*) A potassium chloride prism is required for the region from 15–25 μ.

There are three ways in which the radiation may be recorded:

Wavelength (λ), expressed in μ or in cm.

Wave number (σ), expressed in cm.$^{-1}$ or K. (Kaiser, 1 K. = 1 cm.$^{-1}$)

Frequency (ν), expressed in sec.$^{-1}$

The relation between the quantities is given by

$$\sigma \text{ (cm.}^{-1}\text{)} = \frac{1}{\lambda \text{ (cm.)}} = \frac{10^4}{\lambda \ (\mu)} = \frac{\nu \ (\text{sec.}^{-1})}{c}$$

where c = the velocity of light in centimeters per second. The wave number is preferred as unit, since it is directly proportional to the energy.

20-2 Theory

The Bohr frequency relation:

$$\nu = \frac{10^4}{\lambda} = \frac{E' - E''}{hc}$$

states that absorption of radiation of frequency ν occurs when a molecule is raised from one molecular energy state (E'') to a higher one (E'). Infrared absorption deals with the vibrational energies of the atoms in a molecule.

A molecule having n atoms has $3n$ degrees of freedom: 3 translational degrees of freedom, 3 rotational degrees of freedom, and $3n - 6$ vibrational degrees of freedom.

The vibrations which are associated with a change in dipole moment are infrared active (selection rules) and correspond to strong or weak absorption bands in the infrared spectrum. In general, however, the number of bands observed does not entirely agree with a calculation based on these selection rules because:

(*a*) Some absorption bands are too weak to be observed.

(*b*) Two or more bands may coincide (degeneracy) or may be unresolved by the spectrophotometer.

(*c*) Some bands fall outside the region covered by the instrument

(*d*) In addition to the fundamental frequencies there may be overtones and combination tones.

Although in principle fundamental frequencies are frequencies of the entire molecule, experimentally one can correlate some of the observed frequencies with the vibrations of certain atoms or groups in the molecule. Use is made of these empirical correlations to establish the presence of certain functional groups. In the vibration-rotation spectrum the rotational fine structure of the vibration bands can be observed for gases only. In liquids and solids, interaction between the molecules obscures any fine structure. Since we will deal primarily with liquids and solids, the remainder of this discussion will treat the vibration spectrum only. Since molecular interactions differ in going from the liquid to the solid phase, the spectra of compounds will differ, depending on the phase.

Force Constants.   To a first approximation, a covalent bond may be looked upon as a spring with the atoms at either end. Using the spring model and Hooke's law, which expresses the stiffness of the spring in terms of the mass (of the atoms, in this case) and the frequency of vibration, we have

$$\tilde{\nu}_s = \frac{1}{2\pi c}\left(\frac{k}{\mu}\right)^{1/2} \tag{20-1}$$

where $\tilde{\nu}_s$ = frequency (cm.$^{-1}$);
  k = force constant (dynes/cm.);
  μ = reduced mass = $m_1 m_2/(m_1 + m_2)$.
  c = velocity of light

Table 20-1   Force Constants for a Few Similar Chemical Bonds in Different Molecules [2]

Molecule	Force Constants (10^5 dynes/cm)				
	C—H	C—C	C=C	C≡C	C≡N
Paraffins	4.8				
Olefins	5.1				
Acetylenes	5.9				
Aromatic compounds	5.0				
Ethane	4.79	4.60			
Propane		3.78			
Hexachloroethane		4.00			
Ethylene			10.8		
Propadiene			9.45		
Acetylene				14.9	
Propyne		5.30		14.7	
HCN	5.4				17.9
ClCN					16.6
BrCN					16.8
ICN					16.7
Cyanamide					17.0
Acetonitrile					17.3

Tables 20-1 and 20-2 list force constants for some common atom pairs. In order to use equation 20-1 conveniently for the calculation of force constants it may be rewritten as

$$\nu_{cm.^{-1}} = 1302.9\lambda^{1/2} \tag{20-2}$$

where $\lambda = k/\mu$.

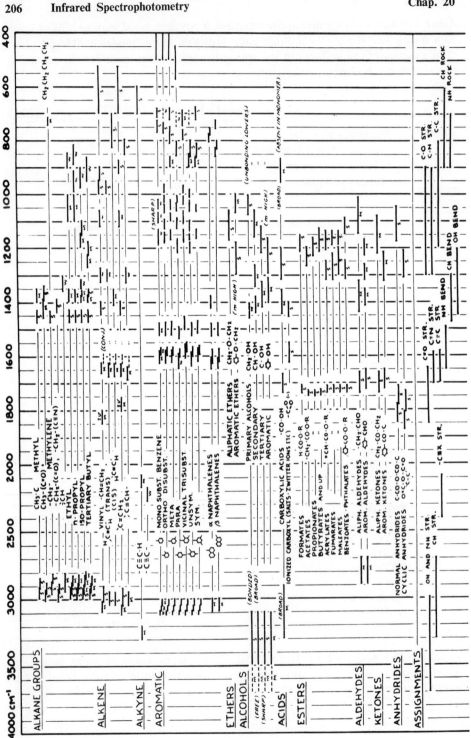

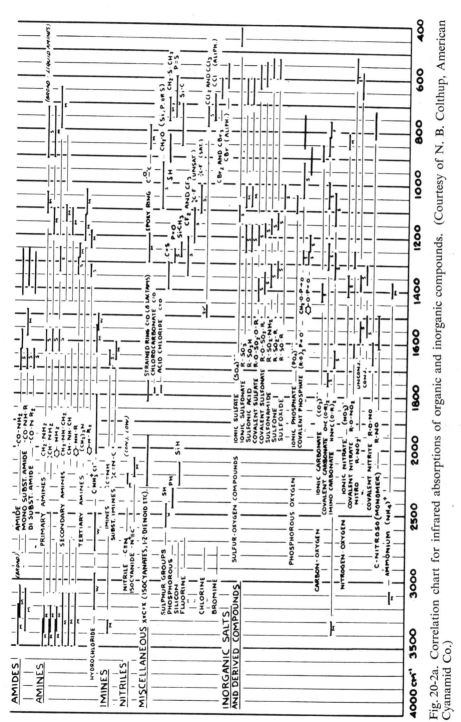

Fig. 20-2a. Correlation chart for infrared absorptions of organic and inorganic compounds. (Courtesy of N. B. Colthup, American Cyanamid Co.)

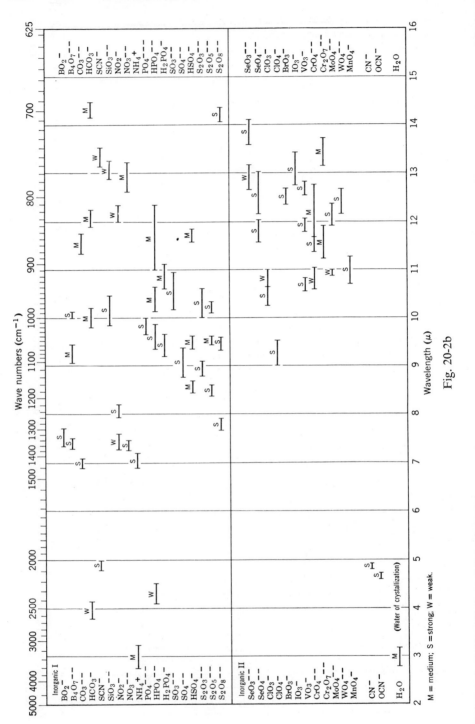

Fig. 20-2b

Table 20-2 Reduced Mass for Atom Pairs
and Force Constants

Force Constant	Atom Pair	$\mu^* = \dfrac{m_1 m_2}{m_1 + m_2}$
4.50	C—C	6
5.77	C—O	6.85
	C—N	6.46
9.77	C=C	6
17.2	C≡C	6
5.07	C—H	0.923
	O—H	0.941
12.06	C=O	6.85

* μ is expressed in units of m_H, where m_H =
mass of a hydrogen atom = 1.67339×10^{-24} g.

20-3 Applications

20-3a IDENTIFICATION

The infrared spectrum of a substance is a very characteristic property. The identity of two spectra is a strong indication of the identity of the two compounds. The spectra of structural isomers, *cis-trans* isomers, *syn-anti* isomers, and diasterio isomers usually show distinct differences. However, the differences between long-chain hydrocarbons, $CH_3(CH_2)_n$—CH_3, diminish as n increases. When $n = 76$ the spectrum can no longer be distinguished from that with $n = 77$. The spectra of optical antipodes are also identical, of course. Here again phase differences may cause difficulties, especially when an optically active compound is compared with its (synthetic) *d,l*-form.

20-3b GROUP ANALYSIS

In the region between 700 and 4000 cm.$^{-1}$ (15-2.5 μ) the characteristic vibration frequencies are found which indicate the presence of specific functional groups. Figure 20-2 and Table 20-3 give a survey of these frequencies, while Figs. 20-3 and 20-4 are examples of spectra.

Since the vibrations are those of the whole molecule, the position of a characteristic band may differ slightly from molecule to molecule. Therefore charts like the ones shown in Fig. 20-2 and Table 20-3 are useful for a first orientation only, and monographs [1] should be consulted for detailed information.

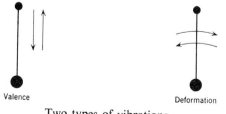

Valence   Deformation

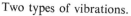

Two types of vibrations.

Table 20-3 List of Functional Groups and Principal IR Absorption Bands [2]

Group	Type of Vibration*	Wave Number (cm.$^{-1}$ appr.)	Wavelength (μ appr.)
OH	st	2500–3700	2.7–4.0
NH, NH$_2$	st	3200–3500	2.8–3.2
≡CH	st	3300	3.0
CH$_{arom}$	st	3030	3.3
CH$_{olef}$	st	3010–3100	3.2–3.3
CH$_{aliph}$	st	2840–2970	3.4–3.5
SH	st	2550–2600	3.8–3.9
PH	st	2350–2440	4.1–4.4
SiH	st	2100–2300	4.3–4.8
N=C=O	st	2270	4.4
C≡N	st	2040–2270	4.4–4.9
C≡C	st	2100–2270	4.4–4.8
—N=$\overset{+}{N}$=$\overset{-}{N}$	st–a	2130–2170	4.6–4.7
C≡O	st	2000–2100	4.8–5.0
C=C=C	st–a	1960	5.1
C=O	st	1540–1870	5.3–6.5
C=C$_{olef}$	st	1590–1690	5.9–6.3
C=C$_{arom}$	st	1500–1610	6.2–6.7
N=N	st	1570–1640	6.1–6.4
C=N	st	1470–1690	5.9–6.8
NH	d	1510–1640	6.1–6.6
COO$^-$	st–a	1540–1620	6.2–6.5
O—NO	st	1610–1670	6.0–6.2
NO$_2$	st–a	1500–1650	6.1–6.7
CH	d	1340–1490	6.7–7.5
P—C	st	1430–1450	6.9–7.0
CH$_{olef}$	r	1280–1430	7.0–7.8
CH$_3$	d	1360–1390	7.2–7.4
OH	d	1210–1450	6.9–8.3
COO$^-$	st–s	1300–1420	7.1–7.7
C—N	st	1020–1420	7.1–9.8
C—O	st	1050–1430	7.0–9.5
—N=$\overset{+}{N}$=$\overset{-}{N}$	st–s	1180–1340	7.5–8.5
C—NO	st	1310–1410	7.1–7.6
N—NO	st	1310–1410	7.1–7.6
C—F	st	1000–1400	7.2–10.0
SO$_2$	st–a	1300–1350	7.4–7.7
NO$_2$	st–s	1250–1350	7.4–8.0
P=O	st	1200–1300	7.7–8.3
C—O—C	st	1050–1200	8.3–9.5
=C—O—C	st	1230–1270	7.9–8.2
C=C=C	st–s	1060	9.4
C—O—C$_{cycl}$	st	1050–1150	8.7–9.5
P—O—C	st	1000–1230	8.1–10.0
Si—O	st	1000–1100	9.1–10.0
SO$_2$	st–s	1140–1160	8.6–8.8
S=O	st	1040–1060	9.4–9.6
C—O—O—C	st	820–890	11.2–12.2
OH	w	850–900	11.1–11.8
CH$_{arom}$	w	690–900	11.1–14.5
CH$_{olef}$	w	690–1000	10.0–14.5
P—O—P	st	930–970	10.3–10.7
P—F	st	800–900	11.1—12.5
P—N	st	720	13.9
C—S	st	600–700	14.3–16.7
P=S	st	600–650	15.4–16.7
C—Cl	st	600–800	12.5–16.7
P—Cl	st	500–600	16.7–20.0
C—Br	st	490–600	16.7–20.4
S—S	st	400–500	20.0–25.0

*st = stretching; d = deformation; r = rocking;
a = asymmetric; w = wagging; s = symmetric.

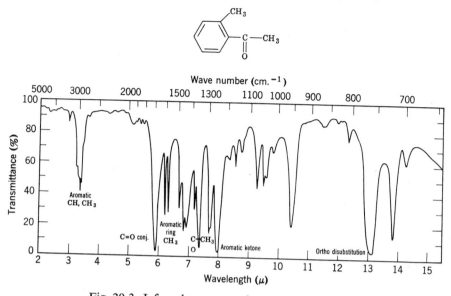

Fig. 20-3. Infrared spectrum of *o*-methylacetophenone.

The characteristic frequencies may be divided roughly into two groups: those belonging to valence and those belonging to deformation vibrations. Since the force constant needed to displace an atom in a direction perpendicular to the direction of the chemical bond (deformation vibration) is smaller that that needed for stretching and compression of the bond, we find the deformation vibration at lower frequencies (less energy required) than the valence vibrations.

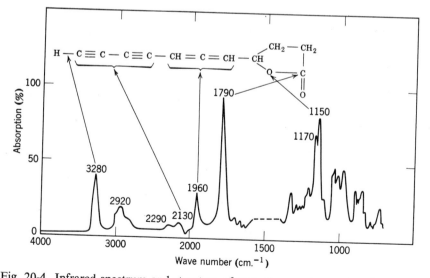

Fig. 20-4. Infrared spectrum and structure of nemotin, a polyacetylene from fungi [11].

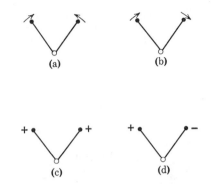

Fig. 20-5. Bending vibrations (see text for explanation).

Several different types of bending vibrations are recognized. Figure 20-5 shows a CH_2 group (C = ○ and H = ●) where a = scissor vibration; b = rocking vibration; c = wagging vibration and d = twisting vibration.

20-3c QUANTITATIVE ANALYSIS

When no interaction between components of a mixture occurs, the spectrum of the mixture will be the summation of the spectra of the components. The absorption due to one component increases with its concentration. A mixture of isomers may thus be subject to quantitative infrared analysis.

20-4 Instrumentation

Let I_0 be the intensity of the incident light and I that of the emerging light; then the determination of the absorption spectrum consists in the measurement of I/I_0 as a function of the wave number (σ). In principle a spectrophotometer consists of the following parts (see Fig. 20-9): light source (L), monochromator (M), detector (D), amplifier (A), and recorder (R).

The light source emits a continuous spectrum, and the monochromator transmits a narrow frequency portion of this spectrum. The detector translates the energy of this monochromatic radiation into an electric signal which can be observed after amplification. $I_0(\sigma)$ is measured first, after which $I(\sigma)$ is determined by placing the sample in the light path. When two conditions are fulfilled, $I/I_0(\sigma)$ may be determined. These conditions are (a) needle deflections must be a linear function of the light intensity, and (b) all conditions must remain identical during the time between the determination of I_0 and that of I. Usually a mechanical shutter is placed between the light source and the monochromator. In that case the detector transmits an alternating potential which can readily be amplified.

Transmission can be measured directly by using a double-beam instrument. The light beam from source L is split into two beams, of which one passes through sample S. By means of a rotating mirror (or set of mirrors) the two light beams alternately enter the slit of the monochromator; thus they are separated in time instead of in space. The electrical signals emitted by the detector have a phase

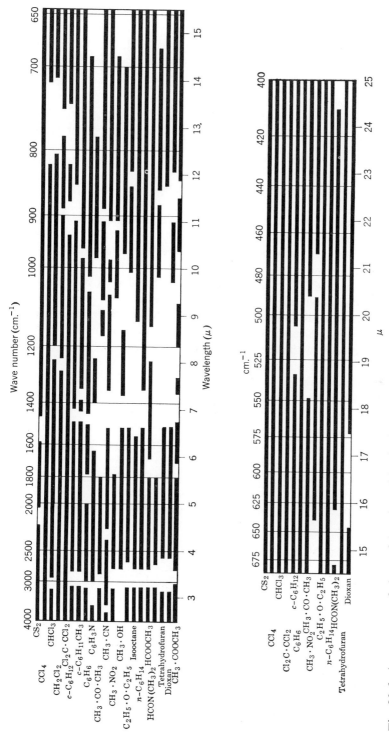

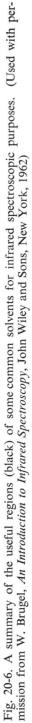

Fig. 20-6. A summary of the useful regions (black) of some common solvents for infrared spectroscopic purposes. (Used with permission from W. Brugel, *An Introduction to Infrared Spectroscopy*, John Wiley and Sons, New York, 1962)

difference. The circuit is arranged in such a manner that the amplifier emits a signal only when light beams of unequal intensity enter. This signal activates a motor which in turn controls a diaphragm placed in the reference beam. This diaphragm opens or closes until the intensities are equal. The diaphragm position furnishes I/I_0 and is recorded continuously. The advantages are as follows:

(a) Detection and amplification need not be linear.

(b) When the solvent is placed in one of the light beams and the solution containing the sample in the other, the absorption spectrum of the solute can be recorded.

Notes on the Instrumentation

1. The light source is usually a semiconducting rod brought to incandescence by an electric current.

2. The monochromater is usually a prism. The materials shown in Fig. 20-1 are most frequently used to make these prisms. Bear in mind that dispersion is at its maximum in the neighborhood of an absorption band. This is the reason that a potassium bromide prism is never used to cover the entire region but only the section from 15–25 μ. Ideally a prism should be used only in the region of its maximum dispersion. However, changing a prism frequently presents certain experimental difficulties, and most instruments limit themselves to one (NaCl) or two (NaCl and KBr) prisms. The prism and the mirror placed behind it are usually rotated with an electronically driven mechanism in such a manner that the spectrum is recorded as a linear function either of the wave number ($\bar{\nu}$) or of the wavelength (λ).

The energy distribution over the spectrum of the light source obeys a Boltzmann distribution. Consequently, different slit widths are required at different frequencies in order to insure that the detector receives a sufficient amount of energy. The adjustment of the slit width is also automated. Mirror optics are used throughout in order to avoid chromatic aberrations.

3. Several kinds of detectors may be used in the infrared region [2]. A thermoelement is the most frequent choice (a lead sulfide photoconduction cell is used in the near-infrared region). All the detectors react rapidly to changing light intensity (i.e., $f = 12.5$ sec.$^{-1}$).

20-5   Experimental Methods

The infrared spectrum may be determined for gases, liquids (solutions), and solids. Pure liquids are held between parallel sodium chloride plates in thin layers (0.01–0.1 mm.) (see Fig. 20-7). The choice of solvent becomes critical for solutions, since no solvent (containing C—C, C—H, C—O, O—H, C—S, S—H, C-halogen, C-N bonds) is transparent over the entire range (2–50 μ). The simpler the molecules of the solvent, the fewer will be the number of absorption bands. Consequently CS_2 and CCl_4 are among the best solvents available. Water and alcohol are virtually useless for this purpose. In addition, water renders NaCl cells opaque, and all materials (solvents, liquids, solids) should be dried thoroughly before use. Figure 20-6 gives a summary of solvent absorption.

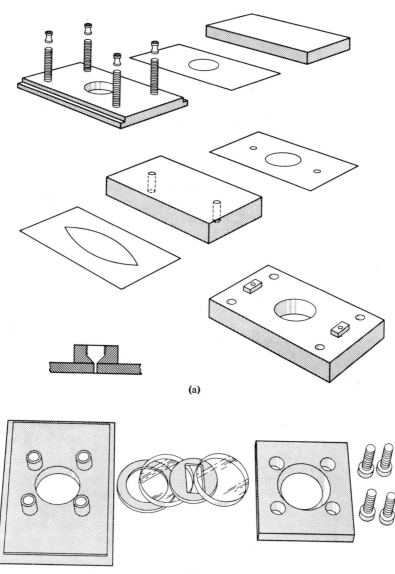

(a)

(b)

Fig. 20-7. Infrared cells. (a) Fixed liquid cell. (b) Demountable cell. (Courtesy of Perkin-Elmer Corp.)

When a double-beam instrument is used, an adjustable cell is frequently placed in the path of the second light beam. This cell, filled with pure solvent, will serve to compensate the absorption for solvent. In regions where absorption of solvent is very strong, compensation is not feasible and a different solvent must be used. See Fig. 20-7 for an example of two types of cells.

Solids are powdered and mixed with KBr by pressing them into virtually transparent pellets. Solids may also be suspended in paraffin oil (Nujol).

20-5a   PREPARATION OF A POTASSIUM BROMIDE PELLET*

To Prepare Powder. One part of sample and 200 parts of KBr are loaded into a metal tube with two $\frac{1}{8}$-in. steel balls and vibrated for 5 min. [6].

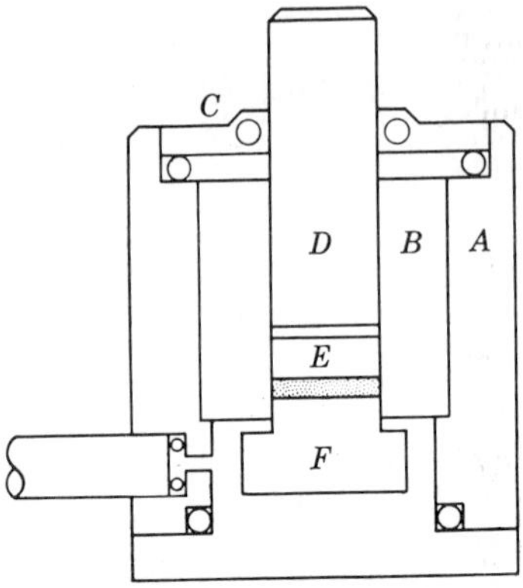

Fig. 20-8. Potassium bromide pellet die and assembly.

To Prepare the Die to Receive the Powder

1. Thoroughly clean parts *B*, *D*, *E*, and *F* (a test-tube brush is suitable for *B*) in Fig. 20-8.
2. Hold *B* upright and place *F* in the upper end.
3. Hold *A* inverted and slide it over *B* and *F* until *B* touches the lip in *A*.
4. Turn the assembly upright.

To Load with Powder

1. Drop a measured quantity of powder into the bore of *B*.
2. Distribute the powder by lightly shaking until the surface of *F* appears evenly covered.
3. To complete distribution, slowly insert the plunger *D* and rotate it a few times, holding it against the powder with a light finger pressure.
4. Very slowly withdraw the plunger (if withdrawn quickly, it may take some of the powder with it). The surface of the powder should now be perfectly smooth and show no cracks or pits.
5. Drop the top pellet *E* into *B* (polished surface down) and press down lightly with the plunger *D*. Complete the assembly with the 0-ring and top cap *C*.

To Evacuate and Press

1. Connect a vacuum line to the pipe in *A* and pump down to less than 2 cm. Hg. A good filter pump is adequate, but a backing pump is better.
2. Maintain the vacuum for 1–5 min.
3. Apply to *D* for 1 min. a pressure of approximately 8 tons for 13-mm. disks, 12 tons for 15-mm. disk, 15 tons for 16-mm. disk.
4. Release pressure and vacuum after 1–2 min.

To Remove Disk

1. Remove *C* and *D*. Invert *A*; *B* will slide out with *E* and *F* in it.
2. Remove *F* from *B* (this may require light leverage with a small screwdriver).
3. Replace *B* in *A*. Slide *D* into *B*.
4. Slowly apply pressure to *D* until it moves down far enough to free the disk from *B*.
5. Remove *D*, invert the assembly on a flat surface, and lift off *A*. The disk should by lying free on *B*.

* Using evacuable KBr Die Mk III, Research and Industrial Instruments Co., 116 Lordship Lane, London.

Additional Notes

1. The measured quantity can be judged by volume for most purposes. Weighed amounts may be used when required, normally in the range 0.1–1.0%. The disk should weigh at least 99% of the weight of the powder.

2. One to 5 minutes of pumping is a general-purpose figure. With very dry powders, 15 sec. may be sufficient. More prolonged pumping will help to dry damp powders.

Recognition of Faults in the Disks. The commonly occurring faults can be classified into those due to bad powder and those due to faulty use of the die, although any combination of faults can occur in a single disk. Seven faults, with their causes and remedies, are listed below.

1. FAULT. Disk scatters small percentage of incident light. Good visibility of distant objects through disk.
   Cause. General grain size of powder too coarse.
   Remedy. Continue grinding powder.
2. FAULT. Disk shows number of white spots, otherwise clear.
   Cause. Few coarse grains among otherwise fine powder.
   Remedy. Grind powder more evenly.
3. FAULT. Marked scattering of light throughout disk. Poor visibility of distant objects.
   Cause. Impurities. Even mixtures containing as little as 5% of a second halide show this effect.
   Remedy. Use pure halides.
4. FAULT. Irregular "blotchy" appearance rather similar to effect of coarse powder (combination of 1 and 2).
   Cause. Usually associated with dampness or coagulation of powder.
   Remedy. Dry and break up powder.
5. FAULT. Disk flaking.
   Cause. Excessive grinding of powder.
   Remedy. Grind fresh material for shorter period.
6. FAULT. Disk opaque over part of area.
   Cause. Insufficient pressure possibly coupled with bad distribution.
   Remedy. Re-pass same disk. Take more care in distributing powder next time.
7. FAULT. Disk perfectly clear when removed from die, but developing internal cloudiness after interval of from 1 min. to several hours.
   Cause. Lack of vacuum.
   Remedy. Check vacuum. More prolonged pumping.

This list of faults refers to disks of pure halide not containing samples. With the normal mixtures of 0.1–1.0% sample, disks will often be only translucent, depending on the nature of the sample.

Hints. It is helpful if all the KBr die components can be kept warm, e.g., in an oven or on a hot plate. This enables the disk to be warm when removed from the die; it will consequently be safe from fogging for a few minutes even if the room humidity is high. If the disk is below room temperature, it will fog immediately. The heat is also helpful in removing residual moisture from the powder during pumping. Finally, there is no risk of corrosion of the die. All parts of the die, ESPECIALLY THE TWO PELLETS E AND F, WHICH ARE NOT CHRO-MIUM PLATED, should be kept thoroughly clean and, when not in use, stored in an oven or, if an oven is not available, in a desiccator. An oven can also be used for drying and storing the halide powder and the disk.

Apart from the effect of insufficient pressure, which can be easily recognized, any initial imperfection in the disk will be DUE TO THE POWER. The necessity for using pure halides, finely powdered, cannot be overstressed.

20-5b   PREPARATION OF A SUSPENSION IN PARAFFIN OIL (Nujol Mull)

About 2–6 mg. of solid is powdered in an agate mortar. Then 1 or 2 drops of Nujol (a high-boiling paraffin mixture) is thoroughly mixed with the powder. The mull is transferred to one of the salt plates. The second salt plate is placed on top, and the mull is spread evenly over the surface by carefully pressing the salt plates together. Examine the translucency of the plates and mull by holding them up to the light. With some practice and care an evenly distributed, virtually homogeneous-appearing mull can be prepared.

Notes

1. *Do not* use the salt plates to crush or grind the solid. This might scratch the plates.

2. Other possible fluids are Fluorolube (a perfluoro hydrocarbon) and hexa-chlorobutadiene. A disadvantage of the former is the fact that the salt plates become difficult to clean.

3. The salt plates can be cleaned with dry chloroform or carbon tetrachloride.

20-6   Perkin-Elmer Model 137 (Infracord) (Fig. 20-10)

20-6a   APPARATUS

The Perkin-Elmer Infracord Model 137 is a double-beam instrument. The light source (see Fig. 20-9) is an electrically heated blackened rhodium rod. The mono-chromator contains sodium chloride prisms kept at 70°. A slit control is set to a fixed program and corresponds to a resolution of about 0.4 μ. The range from 2.5 to 15 μ can be scanned in 12 min. Modifications with KBr optics (model 1370) and a grating (1376) are now available. The latter allows an increase in range to 0.83 μ.

20-6b   PROCEDURE

1. Move the penholder slightly to the right so that it is free of the drum.

2. Switch knob S_1 (Fig. 20-10) to "on" and wait about 10 min.

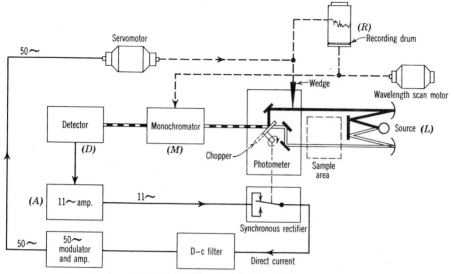

Fig. 20-9. Infracord block diagram.

3. Remove the drum D from the instrument by carefully pulling upward.

4. Attach graph paper on drum. Take care that the line on the paper coincides with the line on the drum, and fit the paper carefully to the top edge.

5. Replace the drum in its holder. Make certain that it fits into the appropriate slots.

6. Place cell (see Fig. 20-7) containing the liquid, solution, or Nujol suspension in the first light beam.

7. Switch knob S_3 on "reset" and hold in this position. Now turn the drum counterclockwise (to the 2.5 μ region) as far as possible. Turn S_3 to position "stop."

8. Turn switch S_2 clockwise until transmission is about 90%.

9. Again turn S_3 to "reset" and slowly rotate the drum clockwise by hand from 2.5 μ to 15 μ to see that absorption is neither too little (barely any deflection

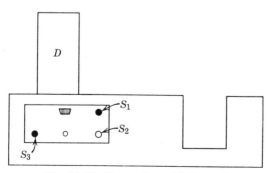

Fig. 20-10. Front view of Infracord.

Fig. 20-11. Perkin-Elmer Infracord spectrophotometer.

of penholder) nor too great. If necessary, change concentration of solution or thickness of liquid layer. Return drum to 2.5 μ position.

10. Attach pen to penholder and place pen against the paper. Check whether a vertical line is drawn when the light beam is interrupted briefly with the hand. Turn switch S_3 to position "scan."

11. When spectrum has been taken (appr. 12 min.) turn S_3 to "stop."

12. Turn S_2 counterclockwise.

20-7   Examples

20-7a   EFFECT OF ISOTOPE SUBSTITUTION ON THE POSITION OF ABSORPTION BANDS

Determine the gas spectrum of chloroform. Place 1 drop of chloroform in the gas cell. The chloroform evaporates in a few moments. Use recording paper which has scale divisions linear with respect to the wavelength. Remove one sodium chloride window, allowing the chloroform to escape. Replace window and determine the spectrum of deuterochloroform. The C—H and C—D out-of-plane bending vibration is shown at 8 and 11 μ respectively. Using equation 20.1, calculate the frequency of the C—D vibration from the frequency of the C—H vibration. Assume that k does not change. Explain the difference between the calculated and the observed value.

20-7b HYDROGEN BONDS

Take the infrared spectrum of two solutions of cyclohexanol having concentrations of 1 and 0.1 molar in carbon tetrachloride. Use cells of 0.1 and 1-mm. path length, respectively. Use a cell filled with pure carbon tetrachloride to compensate for solvent absorption. Place the latter in the light path farthest away from you. Use recording paper calibrated in cm.$^{-1}$ The absorption band at 3600 cm.$^{-1}$ is due to those O—H vibrations not associated with hydrogen bonding. The broad band at 3350–3400 cm.$^{-1}$ is probably due to hydrogen bonding. Why is this band at a lower frequency than the O—H stretching vibration at 3600 cm.$^{-1}$? What phenomenon is interpreted in terms of *inter-molecular* hydrogen bonds?

Take the spectrum of 1 and 0.1 molar salicylaldehyde. These spectra show one strong band in the region of 3000–4000 cm.$^{-1}$. Explain.

20-7c POTASSIUM BROMIDE PELLET

Mix 3 mg. of benzil well with 600 mg. of potassium bromide. Use a mortar and pestle, followed by a steel ball vibrator. Press the pellet as described in § 20-5. Take the spectrum, using paper linear in wavelength. Compare the spectrum to the one in the Sadtler collection.

20-8   References

1. L. J. Bellamy, *The Infrared Spectra of Complex Molecules*, Methuen and Co., London, 1958.
2. W. Brügel, *Introduction to Infrared Spectroscopy*, John Wiley and Sons, New York, 1962.
3. R. P. Bauman, *Absorption Spectroscopy*, John Wiley and Sons, New York, 1962.
4. D. H. Anderson, N. B. Woodall, and W. West in *Techniques of Organic Chemistry*, A. Weissberger, ed., Interscience Publishers, New York, 1960, Vol. I, Part III, p. 1959.
5. A. R. H. Cole in *Technique of Organic Chemistry*, A. Weissberger, ed., Interscience Publishers, New York, 1963, Vol. XI, Part I, p. 133.
6. J. J. Kirkland, *Anal. Chem.*, **27**, 1537 (1955).
7. H. H. Nielsen and R. A. Oetjen in *Physical Methods in Chemical Analysis*, W. G. Berl, ed., Academic Press, New York, 1950, Vol. I, p. 356.
8. G. Herzberg, *Molecular Spectra and Molecular Structure*, Van Nostrand Co., Princeton, N.J., 1954.
9. H. Hoyer in *Methoden der organischen Chemie*, Houben Weyl, ed., G. Thieme Verlag, Stuttgart, 1955, part 2, p. 795.
10. C. Flett, *Physical Aids to the Organic Chemist*, Elsevier Publishing Co., Amsterdam, 1962.
11. J. D. Bu'Lock, *Quart. Revs. (London)*, **10**, 371 (1956).
12. M. Bent Wilson, in *Determination of Organic Structures by Physical Methods*, F. C. Nachod and W. D. Phillips, eds., Academic Press, New York, 1962, Vol. 2.
13. H. A. Szymanski, *Infrared Handbook*, Plenum Press, New York, 1962.
14. A. D. Cross, *An Introduction to Practical Infra-Red Spectroscopy*, Butterworths Scientific Publications, London, 1960.

21

Nuclear magnetic
resonance spectroscopy

21-1 Introduction

Absorption of radio-frequency energy occurs during the transition of a nucleus from a lower to a higher energy state. The frequency at which this absorption occurs is called the *resonance frequency* and for a given nucleus is a characteristic which depends only on the field strength *at that nucleus*. Since the applied field induces a magnetic moment in the electrons about the nucleus, the applied field needed to induce this transition differs from nucleus to nucleus, depending on the electron distribution. This effect by the electrons is called *magnetic shielding*, and the different shielding factors are called *chemical shifts*. At 60 megacycles per second (Mc./sec.) most common protons absorb over a range of 600 cycles per second. This amounts to $600/60,000,000 = 10$ parts per million (p.p.m.). To obtain adequate resolution it becomes necessary to measure chemical shifts accurately to about 0.01 p.p.m.

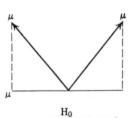

Fig. 21-1. Hydrogen atom in magnetic field. Nuclear moment μ.

21-2 Theory

Some atomic nuclei possess a nuclear spin and a corresponding magnetic moment. The most important nuclei are H^1, H^2, C^{13}, N^{14}, O^{17}, F^{19}. Many other nuclei, for instance C^{12} and O^{16}, do not possess a magnetic moment.

In an external magnetic field H_0, the nuclear angular momentum I is quantized. The allowed components of I are defined by the quantum number m, which may have the values $2I + 1$. For H^1, $I = \frac{1}{2}$. Thus only $2(\frac{1}{2}) + 1$ values or two values are possible (see Fig. 21-1), namely $m_1 = -\frac{1}{2}$ and $m_2 = +\frac{1}{2}$.

The components of the nuclear "magnetic moment" can therefore have the values

$$\mu_{\mathrm{H}} = -\tfrac{1}{2}g\frac{h}{2\pi} \quad \text{and} \quad \mu_{\mathrm{H}} = +\tfrac{1}{2}g\frac{h}{2\pi}$$

where g = magnetogyric ratio (= 5.58554 for H^1) = ratio of the magnetic moment to the mechanical moment h = Planck's constant.

$$+\tfrac{1}{2}g\,\frac{h}{2\pi}\,H_0 \quad \text{and} \quad -\tfrac{1}{2}g\,\frac{h}{2\pi}\,H_0$$

The nuclear spins divide equally between these two energy levels. Transition from one energy level to the other will be accompanied by absorption or emission of energy according to the equation

$$h\nu = E = g\,\frac{h}{2\pi}\,H_0$$

Thus

$$\nu = g\,\frac{H_0}{2\pi}$$

A hydrogen nucleus in a magnetic field of 10,000 gauss has a resonance frequency at 42.6 Mc. (see Table 21-1).

Table 21-1

Nucleus	Natural Abundance	Nuclear Spin	Nuclear Magnetic Moment	g	ν (Mc.) at $H_0 = 10^4$ gauss
H^1	99.98	$\tfrac{1}{2}$	2.79277	5.58554	42.57
H^2	0.0156	1	0.85741	0.85741	6.54
C^{12}	98.9	0	0	0	...
C^{13}	1.1	$\tfrac{1}{2}$	0.7023	1.4046	10.71
N^{14}	99.62	1	0.4037	0.4037	3.08
O^{16}	99.76	0	0	0	...
O^{17}	0.039	$\tfrac{5}{2}$	−1.893	−0.757	5.77
F^{19}	100	$\tfrac{1}{2}$	2.628	5.256	40.07

Nuclear magnetic resonance (NMR) spectrometry is usually carried out at a constant frequency by variation of the external magnetic field. Thus the latter determines the value of H_0 at which resonance takes place.

The resonance condition

$$\nu = \frac{g}{2\pi}\,H$$

is valid only for $H = H_k$ = the magnetic field at the nucleus.

The value of H_k is usually not identical to the value of the external field H_0, since a small but noticeable effect is exerted by the immediate surroundings of the nucleus.

Thus hydrogen atoms in the molecule will exhibit resonance at different values of H_0, depending upon their positions in the molecule. The most important application of NMR to organic chemistry depends upon this phenomenon.

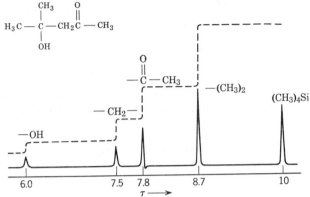

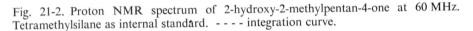

Fig. 21-2. Proton NMR spectrum of 2-hydroxy-2-methylpentan-4-one at 60 MHz. Tetramethylsilane as internal standard. - - - - integration curve.

21-2a CHEMICAL SHIFT

Electron densities vary from place to place in a molecule. The external magnetic field induces an opposing field in the electron cloud (diamagnetic shielding). This causes H_k to be smaller than H_0. To satisfy the resonance condition a different external field will have to be applied for every hydrogen atom which finds itself in different electrical surroundings. This shift in the field strength is called chemical shift. Since this difference amounts to a few parts per million, very high demands are made on the stability with which the external field can be applied. The chemical shift is proportional to H_0. In practice the value of H at which resonance occurs for the sample is compared with that of a reference substance:

$$\delta = \text{chemical shift} = \frac{H_{\text{sample}} - H_{\text{ref}}}{H_{\text{ref}}} \times 10^6$$

Water, benzene, chloroform, or tetramethylsilane (TMS), giving just one resonance line (peak), are common reference substances. They may be used as external or internal standards.

The area under each peak is approximately proportional to the number of identical hydrogen atoms (Fig. 21-2).

21-2b SPIN-SPIN COUPLING (see Fig. 21-3)

Interaction between groups of magnetic nuclei (coupling) can give rise to the splitting of resonance lines. This phenomenon can be observed only with high-resolution spectrometers and can give valuable additional information about structure.

As we have seen, the values of the nuclear spin of the atom in the magnetic field can be $(2I + 1)$. Therefore the internal field of a nearby atom can be influenced in $(2I + 1)$ different ways. For hydrogen, where $I = \frac{1}{2}$, the possibilities are as follows.

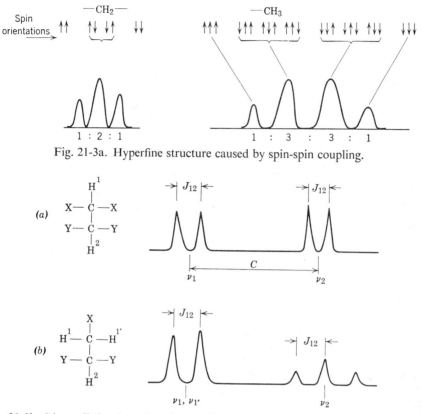

Fig. 21-3a. Hyperfine structure caused by spin-spin coupling.

Fig. 21-3b. Line splitting by spin-spin coupling. J_{12}. Coupling constant. C. Chemical shift. (a) Two protons. (b) Three protons (cf. [9]).

A proton adjacent to a —CH— group shows a resonance line split into two lines (doublet) of equal intensity.

A proton adjacent to a —CH$_2$— group shows a resonance line split into $(2I + 1)^2 =$ four lines of which two coincide. Thus a triplet of intensity ratio 1:2:1 is observed.

An adjacent —CH$_3$ group causes splitting into $(2I + 1)^3 =$ eight lines, of which two sets of three coincide, resulting in a quartet with ratios of intensities of 1:3:3:1.

21-2c IDENTIFICATION OF A STRUCTURE [17]

A combination of a knowledge of the chemical shift and the rules governing the spin-spin coupling provides us with a powerful tool for the identification of the structure of organic compounds. Figure 21-4 shows the NMR spectrum of diethyl fumarate. Note the following features:

(a) A peak at 0 p.p.m. ($\tau = 10$) due to tetramethylsilane (TMS) added as internal standard.

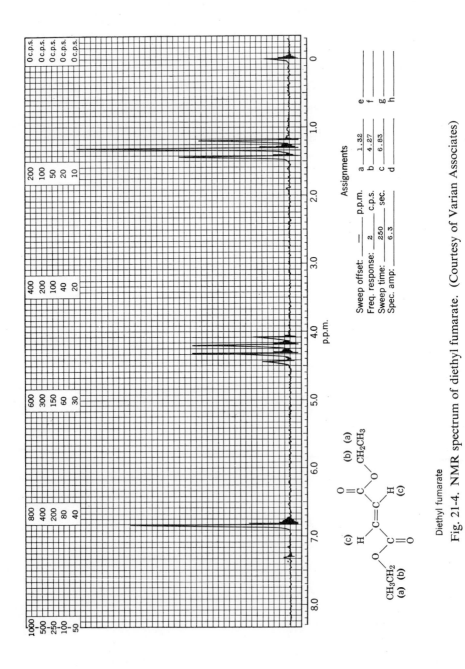

Diethyl fumarate

Fig. 21-4. NMR spectrum of diethyl fumarate. (Courtesy of Varian Associates)

(b) A triplet centered around 1.32 p.p.m. ($\tau = 8.7$) due to the protons of the —CH_3 portion of the ethyl group. The triplet is caused by spin-spin coupling of the three (identical) protons with the two protons of the methylene portion of the ethyl group.

(c) The quadruplet centered around 4.27 p.p.m. ($\tau = 5.73$) due to the methylene protons (split in turn by the methyl protons).

(d) A singlet at 6.83 p.p.m. ($\tau = 3.17$) caused by the two (*trans*) vinyl protons.

21-2d SUMMARY OF NMR

1. Nuclear spin $I \rightarrow$ magnetic moment $\mu = \gamma \dfrac{h}{2\pi} I$, where γ = gyromagnetic ratio.

In magnetic field H_0: energy $E = -\mu H_0$ parallel or antiparallel. Proton has two possible orientations:

$$E_1 = +\mu H_0$$
$$E_2 = -\mu H_0$$

$$\Delta E = 2\mu H_0 h\nu = \Delta E \rightarrow \nu = \frac{\gamma}{2\pi} \cdot H_0;$$

frequency proportional to field

Proton: $I = \frac{1}{2}$, $\mu = 1.41 \times 10^{-23}$ erg/gauss,
$\quad\quad \nu = 42.6$ Mc./sec. for $H_0 = 10$ kgauss.

2. Broad lines in solids are due to local dipole fields. In liquids lines are sharp, since local fields are averaged because of molecular motions.

3. Chemical shift (in liquids) is caused by shielding or deshielding of protons by electrons (diamagnetism). It is proportional to H_0 and therefore expressed as parts per million (magnitude 1–10 p.p.m.). An increase in shielding means (Fig. *A*)

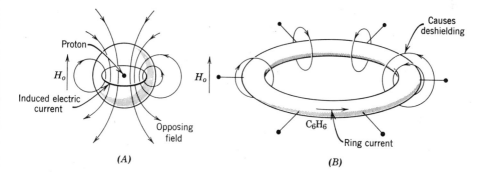

(A)   (B)

an increase in the internal opposing field and therefore resonance at higher H_0. When protons are outside a system, the opposite effect (Fig. *B*) is observed.

4. Spin-spin coupling causes line splitting. Coupling is transmitted by electrons. It is expressed in cycles per second, since it is an energy concept. Equivalent protons give rise to $n + 1$ lines whose intensity follows Pascal's triangle (1:1, 1:2:1, 1:3:3:1, 1:4:6:4:1, . . .). The extent of splitting is the coupling constant J (cycles per second).

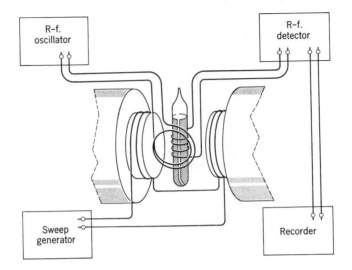

Fig. 21-5. Schematic diagram of a double-coil spectrometer.

21-3   Instrumentation

The sample (Fig. 21-5) is contained in a tube between the poles of an electro-magnet. The tube is surrounded by an oscillator coil; the axis of the latter is perpendicular to the magnetic field. The axis of the receiver coil is perpendicular to both the axis of the oscillator coil and the magnetic field. A signal is transmitted to the receiver when the magnetic field and the oscillator frequency are tuned so that NMR is exhibited by the sample.

The current through the main coils of the electromagnet is kept constant. Small additional coils are placed on the magnetic poles. This enables a slight variation on the constant magnetic field to be superimposed. Thus we can "sweep" the region of magnetic field strength within which resonance may be expected. For a block diagram see Fig. 21-6.

21-4   Applications

Proton NMR can furnish a great deal of qualitative as well as quantitative information about molecular structure and chemical reactions. Some uses are as follows:

(*a*) Identification of individual components in a mixture.
(*b*) Determination of number of protons in an empirical formula.
(*c*) Determination of potential barriers.
(*d*) Study of hydrogen bonding.
(*e*) Measurement of reaction rates (e.g., enolization).
(*f*) Determination of structure (including stereochemical structure).
(*g*) Determination of aromatic character.

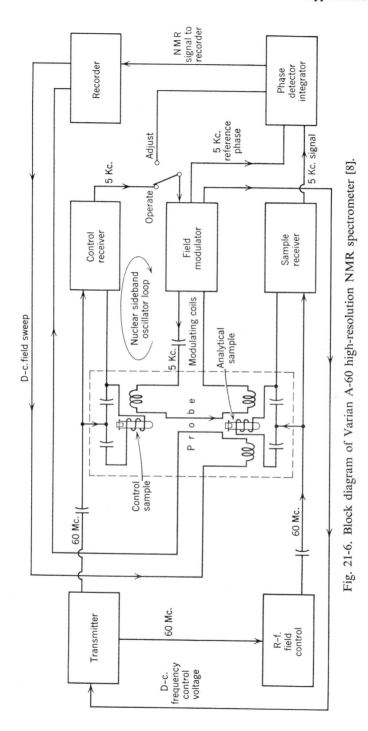

Fig. 21-6. Block diagram of Varian A-60 high-resolution NMR spectrometer [8].

21-5   Units and Definitions

δ = chemical shift parameter (p.p.m.)

$$= \frac{\Delta \cdot 10^6}{\text{oscillator frequency (c.p.s.)}}$$

where Δ = line separation between sample and reference.

$$\tau = 10 - \frac{\Delta(Me_4Si) \cdot 10^6}{\text{oscillator frequency (c.p.s.)}} \text{ (p.p.m.)}$$

$= 10 - \sigma(Me_4Si)$

J = coupling constant (c.p.s.)

= line separation of multiplets due to spin-spin interaction

= field independent.

21-6   Solvents

Any solvent whose own proton NMR does not interfere with that of the sample may be used. In practice solvents are chosen which (*a*) have no protons and (*b*) give one well-defined singlet. Typical solvent are carbon tetrachloride, chloroform, deuterochloroform, benzene, acetone, toluene, deuterium oxide (D_2O), and acetone-d_6.

21-7   Sample Preparation

If the sample is a liquid, 2–3 ml. is placed in the 5-ml. NMR sample tube and a drop of tetramethylsilane (TMS) is added as internal standard. If the sample is not a liquid, it should first be dissolved in the solvent (§ 21-6). Solvents containing a known amount of TMS may be stored for immediate use. Concentrations of solute may range from 1 to 20%.

21-8   Varian NMR Spectrometer A-60

21-8a   APPARATUS

The A-60 analytical NMR spectrometer manufactured by Varian Associates includes the following (see also Fig. 21-6):

(*a*) A magnet system, consisting of a 6-in., 14,092-gauss water-cooled magnet provided with a solid-state power supply.

(*b*) A spectrometer control console, including a radio-frequency transmitter and receiver used to excite the sample and to receive the NMR signal. A large flat-bed recorder allows recording of the spectrum.

(*c*) (Optional) Temperature control probe, allowing thermostatic control of the sample tube.

21-8b   OPERATING CONTROLS (Fig. 21-7)

Console Front Panel

1. On button.

2. Off switch. *Do not* turn off at end of experiment.

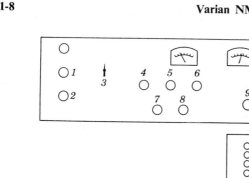

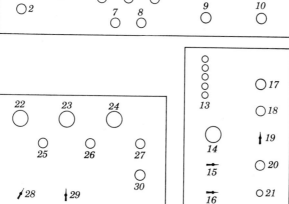

Fig. 21-7. Operating controls of the Varian A-60 NMR spectrometer.

3. *Operate—standby.* Switch to operate before experiment is started.
4. *Integral amplitude.* Should be *off* during recording of spectrum.
5. *Filter bandwidth.* Controls noise at recorder input.
6. *Spectrum amplitude.* Adjusts amplitude of signal.
7. *Detector zero.* Used during integration.
8. *Detector phase.* Controls dispersion mode.
9. *R-f. field.* Controls r-f. excitation.
10. *Y gradient.* Optimizes resolution.
11. *Cycle light.* Usually off during operation; on for a few minutes when "on" (*1*) is pushed.
12. *Field.* Adjust so that frequency meter reads in black region.

Recorder Operation Controls
13. *Sweep time.* Five buttons provide five speeds in seconds.
14. *Sweep offset.* Allows shift downfield.
15. *Normal sweep.* Controls direction carriage.
16. *Fast sweep.* Ten seconds full chart.
17. *Sweep width.* Controls amplitude of sweep current.
18. *Sweep zero.* Controls sweep adjustment.
19. *Pen.* Controls pen position.
20. *Recorder zero.* Controls base-line setting.
21. *Integral reset.* Returns integration pen (when on) to zero.

Front Panel Test Controls
22–27. Control magnitude and direction of magnet currents.
28. *Spinner.* Controls air volume regulating sample spinning rate.

29. Homogeneity. On "operate" when taking a spectrum.

30. Test. Switch used for system checking.

21-8c PROCEDURE: ADJUSTING TO TMS AT "0"

The initial optimization of the instrument is best done by the assistant. Assuming x-z, y-gradient, and curvature controls in test control section to have been set properly with the "homo-adjust" sample, insert TMS sample. (Consult Instruction Manual.)

Note. Take great care in inserting sample. It is very difficult to remove broken glass from the sample holder (a sample tube costs about $4).

1. Insert TMS sample tube in plastic spinner turbine and place in probe assembly.
2. Switch position:

(9) R-f. field	0.2	(14) Sweep offset 000	
(6) Spectrum amplitude	1.6 × 1	(5) Filter bandwidth 4.0	
(13) Sweep time	250	(4) Integral amplitude off	
(17) Sweep width	500		

3. Run spectrum for a few cycles on either side of the TMS peak. Adjust sweep zero to place the TMS peak on "0" of the chart. Note that slight differences in peak position occur when running pen from right to left or from left to right. Run sample spectrum in same direction as used to "0" TMS.

21-8d OBTAINING SPECTRUM OF SAMPLE

1. Remove TMS sample and insert unknown sample. Adjust air pressure (reducing valve) to synchronize light on spinnerette (25 r.p.s.).
2. Run spectrum with "pen" *19* in "up" position, using fast sweep *16*. Observe both pen deflection and signal level meter. Adjust spectrum amplitude *6* and filter bandwidth *5* until appropriate signal to noise levels are obtained.
3. Run spectrum with "pen" *19* in auto position, using normal sweep *15*.

21-8e INTEGRATION

1. Without changing *6*, *17*, *9*, or *18*, change sweep time *13* to "100." Turn integral amplitude *4* to "80."
2. Adjust detector zero *7* so that there is no drift of the pen after releasing the integral reset *21* button.
3. Adjust *4* setting to keep integration on chart.
4. Turn off *4* when integration has been completed.

21-9 Interpretation of Data [7, 4, 11]

21-9a CHEMICAL SHIFT

As explained in § 21-2a, the chemical shift parameter is dependent upon the electron density around the nucleus. Solvent and temperature effects exist (when association phenomena are all involved), and extrapolation to infinite dilution is

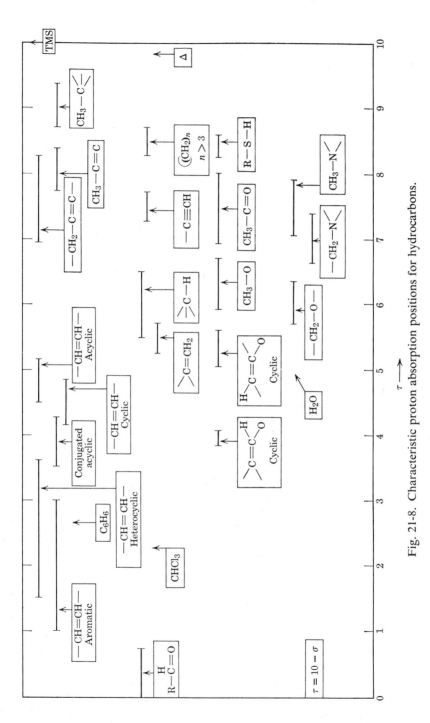

Fig. 21-8. Characteristic proton absorption positions for hydrocarbons.

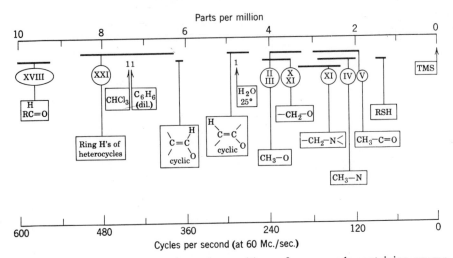

Fig. 21-9. Characteristic proton absorption positions of compounds containing oxygen, nitrogen, and sulfur. (Used with permission from Bentley in Vol. XI of A. Weissberger, *Technique of Organic Chemistry*, Part I, John Wiley and Sons, New York, 1963).

often needed to correlate data. Since NMR is essentially a directional effect (in contrast to ultraviolet absorption spectroscopy, for instance), it is not surprising that no completely general correlation exists between chemical shift and electron density. Thus the geometric relationship between the C-H bond and the direction of the surrounding bonding and non-bonding orbitals are important in determining the extent of the magnetic shielding and thus the chemical shift. Figures 21-8 and 21-9 and Table 21-2 give a survey of the range of chemical shifts for some typical classes of compounds.

21-9b   COUPLING CONSTANTS

Coupling constants between geminal and vicinal protons may vary between 0 and 20 c.p.s. Table 21-3 gives some of these constants. Note that *cis* protons have smaller J's than *trans* protons. Since spin-spin coupling and the corresponding line splitting observed are always due to the interaction of two (or more) protons having different chemical shifts, protons can be identified by their coupling constants.

21-9c   SPIN SYSTEM

The letters A, B, C, . . . , X, Y, Z and subscripts 1, 2, 3, . . . are used to identify the spin systems of spectra [2]. The letters refer to the chemical shifts; the numbers, to the number of nuclei with a particular chemical shift. For nuclei with *similar* chemical shifts letters close to one another in the alphabet are chosen. Thus an *ABX* pattern means that there are three nuclei in the spectrum, two with similar chemical shifts, one with a greatly different chemical shift. Since spin systems have certain symmetry elements, recognition of the spin system of a molecule aids in the

Table 21-2 Chemical Shifts

Protons	Chemical Shift in τ	Protons	Chemical Shift in τ
$(CH_3)_4Si$	10.0		
CH_3—C	9.1	CH_3—O	6.7
C—CH_2—C		Ar—NH_2	6.5*
	8.5–8.8		
C—CH—C		CH_3—O—CO	6.2
│			
C			
		CH_3—O—Ar	6.2
C—NH_2	8.4*	H_2C=C	5.3
CH_3—C=C	8.2	H—C=C	4.7
		│	
CH_3—C=O	8.0	C—OH	4.7*
CH_3—S	8.0	CO—NH_2	3.0*
CH_3—N	7.8	H—Ar	2–3
H—C≡C	7.7	Ar—OH	2.3
CH_3—Ar	7.6	CHO	0.2
CH_3—N—CO	7.2	COOH	−0.8
│			

* Positions very variable because of hydrogen bonding effects.

understanding of the spectrum. For theoretical treatment see [1], [2], [3], and [11]. See Fig. 21-10 for some examples.

Note that spin systems include only protons which cause mutual spin-spin coupling. Thus molecules may possess more than one spin system. Which spin system(s) do you assign to the spectrum of Fig. 21-4?

$A_2 B_2$ System

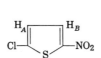

A B System

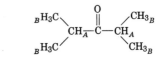

A B_3 System

Fig. 21-10.

Table 21-3 Typical Spin Coupling Constants for Protons (in cycles per second)

System	J_{11}^*	J_{12}^*	J_{13}^*	Other J's*
	12–15	2–9	0.0	0.0 (J_{14})
	0–3.5		0.5–2.0	4–10 (J_{23})
		1–3		
			2–3	
		6–14 (*cis*) 11–18 (*trans*)	0.5–2.0	
		10–13		
		7–10	2–3	0–1 (J_{14})
	~12	5–8 (aa)† 2–3.5 (ae)† 2–3.5 (ee)†		

* Subscripts refer to carbon atoms to which interacting hydrogens are bonded.
† a = axial; e = equatorial.

21-10   References

1. L. M. Jackman, *Applications of Nuclear Magnetic Resonance Spectroscopy in Organic Chemistry*, Pergamon Press, London, 1959.
2. J. A. Pople, W. G. Schneider, and H. J. Bernstein, *High Resolution Nuclear Magnetic Resonance*, McGraw-Hill Book Co., New York, 1959.
3. H. S. Gutowsky, "Nuclear Magnetic Resonance," in *Technique of Organic Chemistry*, A. Weissberger, ed., Interscience Publishers, New York, 1960, Vol. I, Part IV.
4. J. D. Roberts, *Nuclear Magnetic Resonance*, McGraw-Hill Book Co., New York, 1959.
5. H. Conroy, "Nuclear Magnetic Resonance in Organic Structural Elucidation", in *Advances in Organic Chemistry: Methods and Results*, R. A. Raphael, E. C. Taylor, and H. Wynberg, eds., Interscience Publishers, New York, 1960, Vol. II.
6. E. M. Purcell, *Science*, **107,** 433 (1948); F. Bloch, *ibid.*, **118,** 425 (1953).
7. J. B. Stothers, "Applications of Nuclear Magnetic Resonance Spectroscopy," in *Technique of Organic Chemistry*, A. Weissberger, ed., Interscience Publishers, a division of John Wiley and Sons, New York, 1963, Vol. XI.
8. *High Resolution NMR Spectra Catalogue*, Varian Associates, Palo Alto, Calif., 1962.
9. J. D. Roberts, *Angew. Chem.*, **75,** 20 (1963).
10. E. I. Snyder and J. D. Roberts, *J. Am. Chem. Soc.*, **84,** 1582 (1962).
11. K. Wiberg and B. J. Nist, *Interpretation of NMR Spectra*, W. A. Benjamin, New York, 1962.
12. J. D. Roberts, *An Introduction to the Analysis of Spin-spin Splitting in High-resolution Nuclear Magnetic Resonance Spectra*, W. A. Benjamin, New York, 1961.
13. R. E. Richards, in *Advances in Spectroscopy*, H. W. Thompson, ed., Interscience Publishers, New York, 1962, Vol. II.
14. H. Strehlow, *Magnetische Kernresonanz und chemische Struktur*, Band VII, *Fortschritte der physikalischen Chemie*, D. Steinkopf, Darmstadt, 1961.
15. J. D. Roberts, "Nuclear Magnetic Resonance," *J. Chem. Educ.*, **38,** 581–584 (1961).
16. R. M. Silverstein and G. C. Bassler, *Spectrometric Identification of Organic Compounds*, John Wiley and Sons, New York, 1963, p. 71.

IV

Electrochemical methods

22

Potentiometry

22-1 Introduction

The pH meter is essentially a sensitive voltmeter used to measure the e.m.f. of a cell (consisting of a glass electrode, the solution, and a calomel electrode). Either the pH or the e.m.f. (in millivolts) can be read directly on the instrument.

The pH meter fitted with appropriate electrodes can be used to carry out potentiometric titrations, such as acid-base titrations, determination of halogens, and redox titrations. The main advantages lie in the application to small quantities of substances, to very dilute solutions, and to weak acids and bases. Color in the solution does not affect the accuracy of the determination.

A ACID-BASE TITRATIONS

22-2 Apparatus

The acid-base titration curves furnish the following information:

(*a*) The number of acid and/or basic groups in the molecule.

(*b*) The equivalent weight of an unknown substance; this in turn allows calculation of possible values of the molecular weight.

(*c*) The dissociation constants (pK_a) of the acidic or basic group. Important information about the nature of this group can be obtained from the pK_a (phenols or carboxylic acids, for instance).

(*d*) The purity (of a known substance).

22-2a ELECTRODES

A cell consisting of a glass electrode, solution, and a calomel electrode is used in acid-base titrations.

Glass Electrode (Fig. 22-1a). The glass electrode should never become dried out. Rinse with water after use in aqueous solution (be careful; the electrode is fragile).

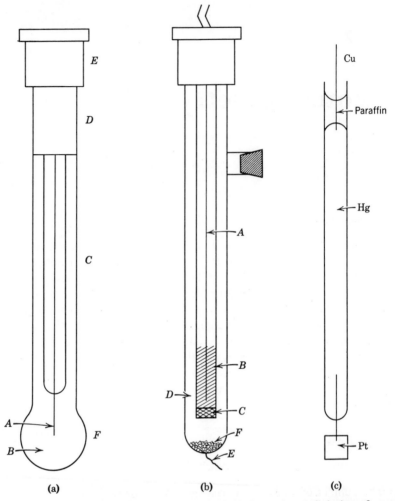

Fig. 22-1. Electrodes. (a) Glass electrode. *A.* Ag-AgCl electrode. *B.* Solution of constant pH and constant Cl^- ions. *C.* Insulating glass. *D.* Insulation. *E.* Electrode cover. *F.* pH-sensitive membrane glass—relatively good conductor. (b) Calomel electrode. *A.* Amalgamated Pt wire. *B.* Hg-$HgCl_2$ paste. *C.* Porous plug. *D.* Saturated DCl solution. *E.* Sealed asbestos string. *F.* KCl crystals. (c) Platinum electrode.

Use alcohol or ether for a first rinse when the electrode has been immersed in solutions containing oils or fats. Never try to clean the very end of the electrode with a towel. Instead, use a wet piece of cotton, dabbing carefully against this fragile part. When not in use the glass electrode is kept in a tube containing a buffer solution at pH 7. For prolonged periods wrap the electrode in cotton soaked with water and glycerine.

Calomel Electrode (Fig. 22-2b). The calomel electrode is filled with a saturated salt solution. The cap at the bottom and the stopper at the top should be removed during the experiment. The potassium chloride solution slowly flows from a capillary at the bottom into the liquid. The level of the potassium chloride should therefore be higher than that of the liquid.

When a measurement has been completed, rinse the outside of the electrode with distilled water. Stopper first at the bottom and then at the top. Crystallization of the KCl may cause plugging up of the electrode. This becomes evident when the asymmetry potential is abnormally high. Loosen carefully by tapping the glass, holding the electrode in a horizontal position. If necessary, warm in a beaker of water to 30–40°.

Determinations in Strongly Alkaline Media. Do not use the glass electrode for any appreciable time in a medium with pH > 10. When measurements have been carried out at pH > 10, soak the electrode in water for a considerable period of time to ensure reliable readings.

High Temperatures. Normal measurements can be carried out to 40°. For still higher temperatures check with the assistant.

22-3   Procedure

Carefully weigh about 10 mg. of the organic acid or base into a 50-ml. beaker (using the boat, Fig. 28-1a). Dissolve the material in a known volume (V_0) of distilled water and insert both electrodes, a thermometer, and a capillary into the solution. Use a stream of pure nitrogen, bubbling through the capillary, as a means of agitating the solution and dispelling dissolved carbon dioxide. Add 0.10 ml. of $0.05N$ sodium hydroxide (or hydrochloric acid) from a microburette, wait 1 min., and record the pH. Continue adding 0.1 (or smaller) portions of alkali or acid, waiting 1 min. each time before reading the pH. Plot the pH against the milliliters of added solution. Change the quantity of liquid being added during the experiment so that ΔpH remains nearly constant. Continue titrating until no further appreciable pH changes occur.

Close the nitrogen flow, and switch off the pH meter. Rinse electrodes with distilled water, and place glass electrodes in a beaker with water. Stopper the calomel electrode.

22-3a   DETERMINATION OF END POINT

(*a*) Plot pH for each titration against V (volume of liquid added) (Fig. 22-2).

(*b*) Select four or five measurements on either side of the end point and plot ΔpH/ΔV against V (see Fig. 22-3). Take a low value (0.05 ml.) for ΔV. The graph then permits direct reading of the end point (in milliliters of liquid).

Very weak acids or bases furnish a graph with a very flat maximum (see Fig. 22-3).

(*c*) Method of Fortuin [7]. Add the titrant in small constant volumes ($\Delta V \leq 1\%$

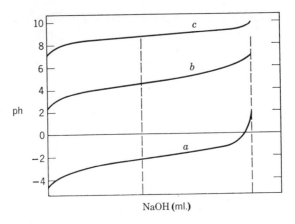

Fig. 22-2. Titration curves. *a*. Strong acid, pK = −2. *b*. Weak acid, pK = 5 (e.g., a carboxylic acid). *c*. Very weak acid, pK = 10 (e.g., a phenol).

total volume) in the neighborhood of the end point. Use a stirring rod to remove drops from the end of the burette.

Observe a constant waiting period (until the potential changes by less than 2 mv./min.). Record the total quantity of titrant added and the reading of the pH meter after each addition. The titration is finished when the potential change is smaller than the previous one.

Calculate the change in potential corresponding to each addition of titrant. Let the three largest changes be Δ_0, Δ_1, and Δ_2 ($\Delta_0 \geq \Delta_1 \geq \Delta_2$).

Calculate $R_1 = \Delta_1/\Delta_0$ and $R_2 = \Delta_2/\Delta_1$.

Find ρ corresponding to R_1 and R_2, using Nomograph 22-1.

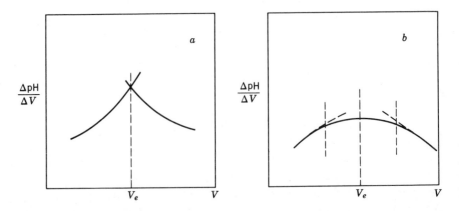

Fig. 22-3. Determination of equivalent point. Curve *a*. Strong acid + strong base. Curve *b*. Titration of a weak acid or base; the equivalent point is found by halving the flat maximum.

Nomograph 22-1   For Reading ρ- and x-Values (Effect of Dilution Neglected)   (From Fortuin [7])

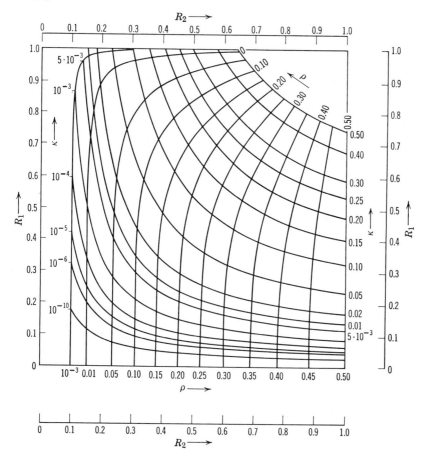

The total volume of titrant (V_e) at the end point is

$$V_e = V_i + \rho\,\Delta V \text{ (if } \Delta_1 \text{ precedes } \Delta_0)$$

or $$V_e = V_i - \rho\,\Delta V \text{ (if } \Delta_1 \text{ precedes } \Delta_1)$$

V_i = total volume of titrant (ml.) added at the potential between Δ_0 and Δ_1.

B   POTENTIOMETRIC HALOGEN DETERMINATION

Titrate the solution, using a silver nitrate titrant. A silver electrode serves as an indicator electrode; a calomel electrode, as reference. The latter is connected *via* an ammonium nitrate bridge to the titration flask. Connect the silver electrode to the pH meter at the contact marked "calomel electrode," and the calomel electrode to the other contact (marked "glass electrode"). Check whether the meter is grounded.

Add the silver nitrate solution slowly with stirring. The potential changes little at first, and then more rapidly near the end point. Record the burette reading and meter reading after every drop when nearing the end point. When the latter has been passed, the potential returns to a constant value. Plot the needle deflection and burette reading, and determine the end point from the graph.

C   REDOX ANALYSIS [2, 5, 6]

22-4   Principle

The *redox potential* is the potential assumed by an "indifferent" metal (bright platinum) electrode with respect to a solution containing an oxidizing or a reducing substance. The calomel electrode is used as reference electrode. When the oxidation or reduction is reversible (for instance, quinone-hydroquinone) the term *redox system* is used.

Most organic redox systems involve the transfer of two electrons. Since both redox potentials are often very similar, it is usually impossible to separate the two (one electron) steps.

22-5   Theory

In a univalent redox system

$$\text{Ox.} + ne^- \rightleftharpoons \text{red.}$$

The potential E (volts) is given by

$$E = C + \frac{RT}{nF} \log \frac{[\text{ox.}]}{[\text{red.}]} \tag{22-1}$$

C (or E^0) is the normal potential at the particular pH (the potential where [ox.] = [red.]). The normal potential is independent of the pH when ox. and red. differ only in the number of electrons. When there is a difference in the number of hydrogen atoms, C changes by 0.06 volt for every pH unit (when red. contains one hydrogen atom more than ox.), and by 0.03 volt when the difference is two hydrogen atoms. (This factor, 0.06 volt, is valid only at 29.5°C. At 30° it is 0.0601; at 25°, 0.0591; and at 20°, 0.0581.) Thus it becomes necessary to work in buffer solutions. In addition it is important to remove oxygen from the solution. The redox potential can be measured with a pH meter. This procedure is carried out analogously to the acid-base titration.

The number of millivolts is plotted against the number of milliliters of titrant (oxidant or reductant).

22-6   Reductive Titration

The cell consists of a bright platinum electrode (Fig. 22-1c), the solution, a KCl-agar bridge, a saturated KCl solution, and a calomel electrode. The platinum

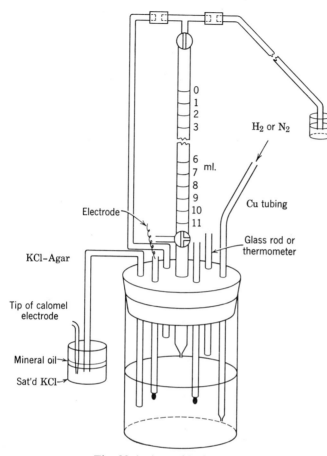

Fig. 22-4. Assembly for titrations [2].

electrode is cleaned with a 10% NaOH solution and carefully rinsed with distilled water.

The titration flask (4 cm. diameter, 12 cm. deep) contains 20–40 ml. of solution (see Fig. 22-4). Pure nitrogen is bubbled through the solution during the titration at the rate of 3 bubbles per second. The nitrogen is purified by passage through a pyrogallol solution (1 vol. of 15% pyrogallol solution + 3 vol. of 30% potassium hydroxide solution) and a chromous chloride solution (10 g. of chromium dissolved in 100 g. of conc. HCl); the hydrogen formed is displaced by nitrogen. To check the nitrogen, pass it through a 0.1% solution containing reduced indigo sulfate. Do not pass the nitrogen through rubber tubes after purification. Use a flexible 2-mm. copper tube instead. (Use Dekhotinsky cement for joints.)

22-7 Calculations and Results

Plot E against milliliters of titrant. The result is a curve shown in Fig. 22-5.
Knowing the titer of the titrant makes it possible to calculate the strength of the

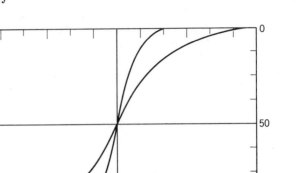

Fig. 22-5. Relationship between potential E and extent of reduction in a reversible redox system. A. Transfer of an electron. B. Transfer of two electrons.

solution from the end point. The curve (Fig. 22-5) should be symmetrical about its center. Even without knowing the titer, valuable information may be gained from the shape of the curve.

First determine E_i (index potential). This is the difference between E at 25% and 50% oxidation. Within 0.2 mv. this should be identical to the difference between 50 and 75% oxidation. When this is the case, the following rules hold (§ 22-1).

1. $E_i = 28.6$ mv. (at 30°C.), a univalent redox system.
2. $E_i = 14.3$ mv., a bivalent redox system.

For other cases ($E_i > 40$ mv., etc.) consult [2], p. 2998.

22-8 Oxidants and Reductants

Some useful oxidants are bromine, chlorine, potassium ferricyanide, and benzoquinone.

Reductants are sodium hydrosulfite (sodium dithionite ($Na_2S_2O_4$)), titanous chloride, chromous chloride, and leuco dyes. Note that most reductants are unstable and must either be prepared just before use or kept under special conditions [2].

22-9 References

1. R. G. Bates, *Electrometric pH Determinations*, John Wiley and Sons, New York, 1954.
2. C. Tanford and S. Wawzonek, "Potentiometry," in *Technique of Organic Chemistry*, A. Weissberger, ed., Interscience Publishers, New York, 1960, Vol. I, Part IV, p. 2915.
3. E. Abrahamczik in *Methoden der organischen Chemie*, Houben-Weyl, ed., G. Thieme Verlag, Stuttgart, 1955, Band III/2, p. 139.
4. K. Cruse in *Methoden der organischen Chemie*, Houben-Weyl, ed., G. Thieme Verlag, Stuttgart, 1955, Band III/2, p. 25.

5. U. Fritze in *Methoden der organischen Chemie*, Houben-Weyl, ed., G. Thieme Verlag, Stuttgart, 1955, Band III/2, p. 64.

6. M. von Stackelberg in *Methoden der organischen Chemie*, Houben-Weyl, ed., G. Thieme Verlag, Stuttgart, 1955, Band III/2, p. 259.

7. J. M. H. Fortuin, *Anal. Chim. Acta*, **24,** 175 (1961).

8. G. Gran, *Acta Chem. Scand.*, **4,** 559 (1950).

9. G. Gran, *Analyst*, **77,** 661 (1952).

10. E. Bishop and G. D. Short, *Analyst*, **87,** 467–477 (1962).

23

Conductometry

23-1 Principle

The resistance of a solution is given by

$$R = \frac{\rho l}{0}$$

where l = the length
and 0 = the cross section of the material.

The specific resistance ρ is the reciprocal of the specific conductance κ. Since l and 0 are usually unknown, we use

$$R = \frac{C}{\kappa}$$

where C = cell constant determined by measuring the resistance of a solution having a known specific conductance κ.

At a concentration c, the equivalent conductance

$$\Lambda = \frac{1000\kappa}{c} \text{ ohm}^{-1} \text{ cm}^2$$

As $c \to 0$, $\Lambda \to \Lambda_\alpha$.

23-2 Applications

Conductometry may be used to study the dissociation of weak electrolytes, to measure the concentration of ionic substances and to determine the extent of hydrolysis or the solubility of slightly soluble salts.

23-3 Apparatus

23-3a CONDUCTIVITY CELLS

The cells consist of Pyrex glass and sealed platinum electrodes. The resistance R_1 of the solution in the cell is measured. The conductance κ is

$$\kappa = \frac{\text{cell constant}}{R}$$

Potassium chloride is usually used to determine the cell constant. See Table 23-1 for the specific conductance at three temperatures.

Table 23-1* **Specific Conductance of Standard Potassium Chloride Solutions (ohms^{-1} cm.$^{-1}$)**

	Grams of KCl per 1000 g. of H$_2$O		
Temp. (°C.)	76.627	7.4789	0.74625
0	0.065176	0.0071379	0.00077364
18	0.097838	0.0111667	0.00122052
25	0.111342	0.0128560	0.00140877

* G. Jones and B. C. Bradshaw, *J. Am. Chem. Soc.*, **55**, 1780 (1933).

23-3b   TEMPERATURE CONTROL

The temperature coefficient of conductance is 2%/°C. for most ions. A thermostat containing oil instead of water is recommended [2].

23-3c   CONDUCTIVITY WATER

Redistill distilled water from a small quantity of permanganate. Collect in a thoroughly clean container protected from CO$_2$ and NH$_3$. Demineralized water using an ion-exchange resin (Chapter 9) may also serve for this purpose.

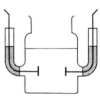

Fig. 23-1. Conductivity cell.

23-3d   CONDUCTOMETRIC TITRATIONS

The titrations are carried out in the conductivity cell shown in Fig. 23-1. The conductance is measured after each addition of reagent from a microburette (see Fig. 23-2).

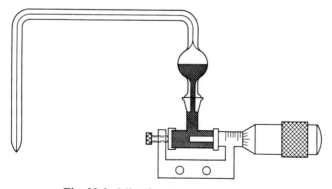

Fig. 23-2. Microburette, capacity 0.7 ml.

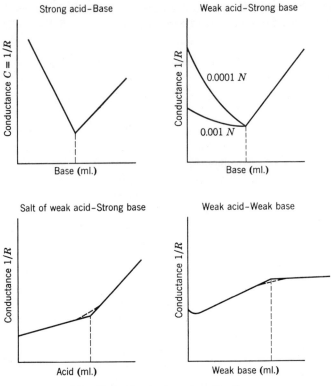

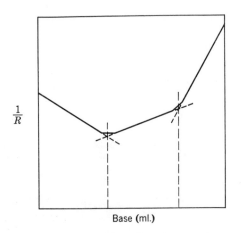

Fig. 23-3. Conductometric titration curves.

Fig. 23-4. Conductometric titration of a mixture of strong and weak acid.

Prepare a plot of κ or $1/R$ against volume added. The intersection of the two lines obtained locates the end point. See Figs. 23-3 and 23-4 for examples of titration curves obtained under the conditions specified.

23-4 Examples

23-4a DETERMINATION OF THE DISSOCIATION CONSTANT OF ACETIC ACID

Prepare a $0.1N$ solution of acetic acid in distilled water. Determine the exact concentration by conductometric titration with NaOH. Measure the specific conductance κ and calculate Λ. For weak electrolytes Ostwald's law for the classical dissociation constant holds:

$$\kappa_c = \frac{\Lambda^2 c}{(\Lambda_\infty - \Lambda)\Lambda_\infty}$$

Dilute the solution 2, 4, 8, 16, 32, and 64 times, and determine Λ each time. Plot Λ against c and find Λ_∞ by extrapolation. Calculate κ_c and the pK. For comparison determine the pK potentiometrically (see Chapter 22).

23-4b OTHER EXAMPLES

Formic acid	Benzoic acid	Glutaric acid
Acetic acid	Malonic acid	
Propionic acid	Succinic acid	

23-4c DETERMINATION OF EQUIVALENCE POINT

Titrate an acid with $0.1N$ NaOH and a base with $0.1N$ HCl. Stir well after each addition, wait a little while, and measure the conductance.

Determine the conductance for at least 5 points before and after the equivalence point. Determine the equivalent point by extrapolation of the graph.

23-4d EQUIPMENT

Conductivity cell	Thermostat
Conductivity water	Microburette
Potassium chloride solution	

23-5 References

1. E. Abrahamczik in *Methoden der organischen Chemie*, Houben-Weyl, ed., G. Thieme Verlag, Stuttgart, 1955, Band III/2, p. 190.
2. T. Shedlovsky in *Technique of Organic Chemistry*, A. Weissberger, ed., Interscience Publishers, New York, 1960, Vol. I, Part IV, p. 3011.
3. R. Livingston, *Physico-chemical Experiments*, The Macmillan Co., New York, 1947.
4. B. L. Murr, Jr., and V. J. Shiner, Jr., *J. Am. Chem. Soc.*, **84**, 4672 (1962).

24

Dissociation constants
of acids and bases

24-1 Introduction

The determination of the dissociation constant of an acid or a base is usually carried out potentiometrically, conductometrically, or spectrophotometrically. The constant provides a useful insight into the structure of the acid or base and may be employed for identification purposes.

24-2 Theory

The strength of a monobasic protonic acid can be expressed by means of the equilibrium constant K_a of the dissociation equilibrium or by $pK_a = -\log K_a$.

$$\text{RCOOH} \overset{K_a}{\rightleftharpoons} \text{RCOO}^- + \text{H}^+$$

The equilibrium constant K_a of an acid HZ is given by

$$K_a = \frac{a_{\text{H}^+} a_{\text{Z}^-}}{a_{\text{HZ}}} = K_a' \frac{f_{\text{H}^+} f_{\text{Z}^-}}{f_{\text{HZ}}}$$

Usually the value of pK_a' is sufficiently accurate. pK_a may be obtained by extrapolation to ionic strength zero.

The law of mass action shows that

$$pK_a' = pH + \log \frac{[\text{RCOOH}]}{[\text{RCOO}^-]} \qquad (24\text{-}1)$$

The strength of a base is usually expressed by means of the pK_a' value of its conjugate acid:

$$\text{BH}^+ \overset{K_a}{\longrightarrow} \text{B} + \text{H}^+$$

$$pK_a' = pH + \log \frac{[\text{BH}^+]}{[\text{B}]} \qquad (24\text{-}2)$$

24-2a   CORRECTION FOR HYDROLYSIS [1]

A correction for hydrolysis needs to be made for very weak acids or bases. This can be done by using the formula

$$pK_a' = pH + \log \frac{\frac{1}{2}C - [H^+]}{\frac{1}{2}C + [H^+]} \tag{24-3}$$

24-2b   CORRECTION FOR IONIC STRENGTH

To a first approximation the following formula holds:

$$(pK_a)_{corr.} = pK_a' + \tfrac{1}{2}(\mu)^{1/2}$$

where $\mu = \frac{1}{2} \sum_i m_i z_i^2$, with m_i = number of g. ions of kind i per liter and z_i = charge of ion i.

24-3   Applications

The pK_a' values are useful for the identification of the acidic or basic functional group in a compound or mixture. Figure 24-1 shows the pK values of some functional groups [2]. See [3] for further applications to the determination of structures.

In order to distinguish between various kinds of acidic and basic groups use may be made of their differences in heat of dissociation. The heat of dissociation can be determined by carrying out a potentiometric titration at various temperatures. Monocarboxylic acids usually have a ΔH_{diss} less than 2 kcal./mole, phenols about 6 kcal./mole, and basic groups more than 5 kcal./mole [4].

24-4   Method I. Potentiometric p*K* Determination

Dissolve a carefully weighed quantity of the acid or base in water (free of carbon dioxide) and titrate according to the procedure described in § 22-2b. Determine the equivalent point and calculate the purity of the compound.

Plot the results graphically (Fig. 24-2) and determine the pH at 1/4, 2/4, and 3/4 neutralization. Calculate the values of p*K* (using formula 24-1 or 24-2) and average.

The details of the titration curve show up better when a differential curve is drawn. Run a blank by adding to the same volume of water as was used in the titration the appropriate quantities of acid and base. The blank is subtracted, by volume, from the titration curve (Fig. 24-4). The differential curve furnishes the "H⁰ binding capacity" of the base as a function of the pH. The p*K* is calculated from the pH values at 1/4, 2/4, and 3/4 neutralization. Figure 24-3 shows the titration curve for a dibasic acid.

24-5   Method II. Conductometric Determination

In § 23-3a the method to determine the dissociation constants of weak acid by conductometry is described.

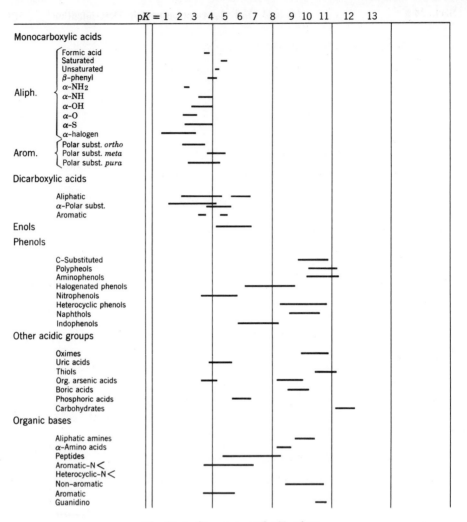

Fig. 24-1. Structure and pK values.

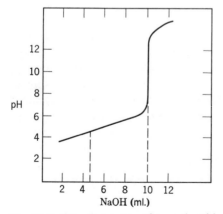

Fig. 24-2. Titration curve of a weak acid.

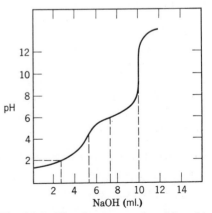

Fig. 24-3. Titration curve of maleic acid.

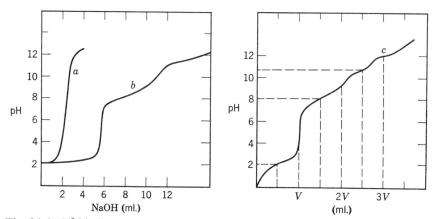

Fig. 24-4. H^0 binding capacity of a tribasic acid. *a*. Blank. *b*. Titration curve. *c*. Difference curve.

24-6   Method IIIA.   Spectrophotometric Determination

Dissolve a carefully weighed quantity of the substance in a buffer solution. The pH of this solution should be in the neighborhood of the pK of the substance (carry out a rough pK determination according to method I). The concentration of [RCOOH] and [RCOO⁻] or [BH⁺] and [B] may now be measured spectrophotometrically.

> *Examples. Phenol.* Use freshly distilled phenol and prepare a solution of 6×10^{-4} mole/l. (0.0564 g./l.). Using this solution, prepare the following five dilutions.
>
> (*a*) 5 ml. of standard + 5 ml. of 0.1N NaOH solution. Assume all molecules present as phenolate anions.
> (*b*) 5 ml. of standard + 5 ml. of 0.1N HCl solution. Assume only undissociated phenol molecules.
> (*c*) 5 ml. of standard + 5 ml. of buffer solution of pH 9.1 (prepared from 0.1N Borax and 0.1N NaOH).
> (*d*) Repeat, using buffer pH $\simeq 9.6$.
> (*e*) Repeat, using buffer pH $\simeq 10.0$.
> Check the pH of the buffer solutions with a pH meter.
>
> First measure the entire spectrum of solutions (*a*) and (*b*). Select three wavelengths at which the absorptivity of the undissociated molecule and that of its ion differ appreciably. For phenol these wavelengths occur in the neighborhood of the absorption maximum of the phenolate ion (280, 285, and 290 nm.). Calculate the molar absorptivity of the ion (ϵ_i) and of the undissociated molecule (ϵ_m) at each of these wavelengths, using the formula

$$\epsilon = \frac{1}{cl} \log \frac{I_0}{I} \qquad (24\text{-}4)$$

> where c = concentration (moles/l.);
> $\qquad l$ = path length (cm.).

Now measure the absorptivity of (c), (d), and (e) at the three wavelengths. Let the molar absorptivity at a particular wavelength be ϵ; then

$$\epsilon = x\epsilon_i + (1 - x)\epsilon_m$$

where $x =$ fraction of phenol molecules present as ion. Thus

$$x = \frac{\epsilon - \epsilon_m}{\epsilon_i - \epsilon_m} \quad \text{and} \quad pK = pH + \log \frac{1 - x}{x} \tag{24-5}$$

Three values of pK are thus found at each of the three wavelengths. Average the nine values.

Report.   Record as shown in Form 24-1.

Form 24-1

Name:		Substance:					
Date:		Standard solution:			mg./l.		
Solution	Standard (ml.)	Buffer (ml.)	I/I_0	λ	ϵ	x	pK
(a)				λ_1			
(b)				λ_2			

Add a graph showing the entire spectrum of (a) and (b).

Other Examples.
 1. *p*-Cresol.
 2. Pyridine.
 3. Quinoline.

24-7   Method IIIB. Spectrophotometric pK Determination [5]

When v_1 l. of hydrochloric acid solution (concentration a, moles/l.) is added to v_2 l. of a weak base (concentration b, moles/l.), the resulting solution obeys the following equation:

$$\begin{cases} c_a = [H^+] + [BH^+] = \dfrac{v_1 a}{v_1 + v_2} \\[2mm] c_b = [B] + [BH^+] = v_2 b(v_1 + v_2) \\[2mm] x = \dfrac{\epsilon - \epsilon_m}{\epsilon_i - \epsilon_m} = \dfrac{[BH^+]}{c_b} \end{cases}$$

Furthermore:

$$K = \frac{[B][H^+]}{[BH^+]} = \frac{[B]\{c_a - [BH^+]\}}{[BH^+]}$$

$$pK = \log \frac{[BH^+]}{[B]} - \log \{c_a - [BH^+]\}$$

$$pK = \log \frac{x}{1-x} - \log \{c_a - c_b x\} \tag{24-6}$$

When x is determined spectrophotometrically (see method IIIA), the pK can be calculated. First determine ϵ_m and ϵ_i. This allows an appropriate estimate of c_b. Roughly determine pK according to method I and calculate the concentration (c_a) when $x = 1$. Use these data to prepare three solutions for which ϵ at three wavelengths is to be determined. Since $\mu \ll 0.02$ with this method, no correction for the ionic strength is needed.

Report. Record as shown in Form 24-2.

Form 24-2

Name: Date:		Substance: Standard solution: Acid *(a)* moles/l. Base *(b)* mg./ml. = moles/l.						
Solution	v_1 l. Standard Solution Acid	v_2 l. Standard Solution Base	λ	I/I_0	ϵ	x	pK
1			λ_1 λ_2 λ_3				

24-8   References

1. J. S. Morley and J. C. E. Simpson, *J. Chem. Soc.*, 1014 (1949).
2. T. V. Parke and W. W. Davis, *Anal. Chem.*, **26**, 642 (1954).
3. H. C. Brown, D. H. McDaniel, and O. Häfliger in *Determination of Organic Structures by Physical Methods*, E. A. Braude and F. C. Nachod, eds., Academic Press, New York, 1955, p. 567.
4. E. J. Cohn and J. T. Edsall, *Proteins, Amino Acids, and Peptides, as Ions and Dipolar Ions*, Reinhold Publishing Co., New York, 1943, p. 82.
5. A. V. Willi, *Helv. Chim. Acta*, **40**, 2019 (1957).

6. J. F. King in *Technique of Organic Chemistry*, A. Weissberger, ed., Interscience Publishers New York, 1963, Vol. XI, Part I, p. 316.

7. A. Albert and E. P. Serjeant, *Ionization Constants of Acids and Bases*, John Wiley and Sons, New York, 1962.

8. I. M. Kolthoff, *Acid-Base Indicators*, The Macmillan Co., New York, 1937.

9. L. Meites, *Polarographic Techniques*, Interscience Publishers, New York, 1955.

25

Polarography

25-1 Introduction

Polarography is a method of analysis which depends upon electrolytic reduction (or oxidation) of a substance at a metal surface. Potentials are measured while known currents are flowing. By plotting current against potentials, a curve is obtained which gives information about the materials present. The method is very sensitive, being capable of giving results with solutions of 10^{-6} mole/1. concentrations. During the reaction a negligible amount of substance is reduced. Figure 25-1 is a schematic drawing of a polarograph.

25-2 Theory

A dropping mercury electrode (cathode) and a relatively large mercury anode are placed in the test solution A. The substance A is reduced to B at the cathode. Let the original concentrations of A and B be [A] and [B], and those at the cathode [A*] and [B*]. Since in general less than 1% of A is reduced, [A] remains constant. Thus during the experiment

$$[A] = \text{constant}, \quad [B] \cong 0, \quad [A^*] \leq [A]$$

Applying a potential V, we have

$$V = E_{cath} + E_{an} + IR$$

where E_{cath} = potential drop at cathode;
  E_{an} = potential drop at anode;
  IR = potential drop in the solution (I = current and R = resistance).
When a relatively large quantity of salt is added to the solution, the resistance of the cell remains the same. E_{an} is a constant also; when the salt is a chloride, the anode is a calomel electrode and E_{an} is known. Then

$$V = E_{cath} + \text{constant}$$

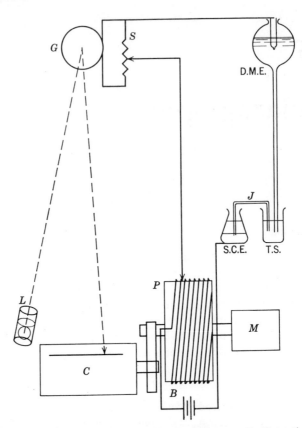

Fig. 25-1. Polarograph and electrolytic cell. *B*. Battery. *P*. Potentiometric wheel. *M*. Motor. *C*. Camera. *L*. Light. *G*. Mirror galvanometer. *S*. Shunt. D.M.E. Dropping mercury electrode. T.S. Test solution. S.C.E. Saturated calomel half-cell. *J*. Agar bridge junction. (Used with permission from A. Weissberger, *Technique of Organic Chemistry*, Vol. I, Part IV, p. 3159, Interscience Publishers, New York)

Assuming the reduction of A to be a reversible process, then, according to Nernst's law,

$$E_{\text{cath}} = E_{\frac{1}{2}} + \frac{RT}{NF} \ln \frac{[\text{A}^*]}{[\text{B}^*]}$$

$$= E_{\frac{1}{2}} + \frac{RT}{NF} \ln \frac{[\text{A}^*]}{[\text{A}] - [\text{A}^*]} \tag{25-1}$$

where $E_{\frac{1}{2}}$ is the half-wave potential for the redox system. Molecules of A accept electrons at the cathode and are transformed into B.

Fresh molecules of A diffuse to the cathode to be reduced. A diffusion current passes therefore through the cell. Ilkovic's equation states that

$$i_d = 0.607n([\text{A}] - [\text{A}^*])n(D_{\text{A}})^{\frac{1}{2}} \text{ ampere} \tag{25-2}$$

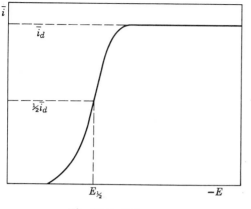

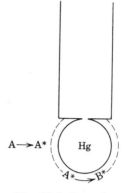

Fig. 25-2. Polarogram.   Fig. 25-3. Reactions at
                                          mercury drop.

where D_A = diffusion coefficient of A;
      N = capillary constant;
      $\bar{i}_d$ = diffusion current.

By elimination of [A*] from equations 25-1 and 25-2 we obtain a relation between i_d and E which is shown in Fig. 25-2.

The rate of reduction (A* → B*) is rapid compared to the supply of new molecules A by diffusion (A → A*). When the voltage is large enough, the current through the cell is determined by the diffusion of A to the dropping electrode. Thus i reaches a constant value, proportional to the concentration of A in the solution.

Even when no reducible substances are present, a certain current (rest current) passes through the cell. Every mercury drop, with its double layer, may be looked upon as a tiny condenser (see Fig. 25-3). Every time a new drop is formed this condenser must be charged. The rest current caused by this phenomenon must be subtracted from the $-E\bar{i}$ curve (see Fig. 25-4).

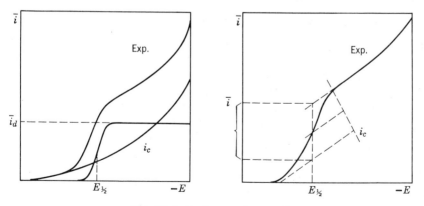

Fig. 25-4. Rest current correction.

25-3 Applications

25-3a QUALITATIVE ANALYSIS

The equations given in § 25-2 are applicable only for reversible systems. In many cases, especially with organic compounds, we are dealing with irreversible reactions. Even under these conditions the polarographic method may be used, since the half-wave potential $E_{1/2}$ becomes a characteristic quantity for a substance under strictly specified external conditions. Polarographic reduction in general succeeds with compounds which can be reduced by chemical (i.e., non-catalytic means.

Some of these types of compounds are:

(a) Many carbonyl groups, especially those conjugated with double bonds and aromatic systems.
(b) Some polyenes.
(c) Organic halides (except fluorides).
(d) Organic nitrogen compounds (except amines and hydrazines).
(e) Peroxides.
(f) Oxalic acid, phthalic acid.
(g) Disulfides.

Oxidizable compounds are, for example, ascorbic acid, hydroquinone, and mercaptans.

See [5] for a complete survey.

25-3b QUANTITATIVE ANALYSIS

In principle, [A] can be calculated from $\bar{i}_d$ by means of equation 25-2. In practice a calibration curve is used. The relation between $\bar{i}_d$ and the molarity of the solution retains its validity only when all conditions of the experiment are carefully defined. Thus the temperature $\bar{i}_d$ increases ($1\frac{1}{2}\%$/degree), the drop time and the sensitivity of the galvanometer must be specified. A reproducibility of 1% can be reached in favorable cases.

25-3c AMPEROMETRIC TITRATION

This technique, capable of greater accuracy, can be used when a polarographic determination of the substance titrated is possible. The potential is held constant during the titration, at a value higher than the half-wave potential.

The diffusion current is measured as a function of the amount of reagent added. Curves like those in Fig. 25-2 are obtained, with the equivalent point indicated by a change in slope. Some examples (see [2], p. 316) are as follows:

(a) Determination of phenol, m-aminophenol, p-aminosalicyclic acid, 8-hydroxyquinoline, and styrene with $KBr/KBrO_3$.
(b) Determination of picric acid by titration with methylene blue.
(c) Determination of mercaptans (including cystine) by titration with silver nitrate.

(*d*) Determination of oxalates by titration with lead nitrate.

(*e*) Determination of dimethyl glyoxime by titration with nickel ions.

(*f*) Determination of salicyl aldoxime by titration with copper ions.

25-4 Apparatus

The apparatus (Fig. 25-5) consists of a glass part (electrolysis vessel and electrodes) and an electrical part. In addition provisions should be made for bubbling purified (oxygen free; use pyrogallol solution) nitrogen, saturated with solvent vapor, through the solution.

25-4a GLASS PART (Fig. 25-5)

This consists of a mercury reservoir (*C*) connected with plastic tubing (*H*) to the capillary (*K*) in the electrolytic cell (*G*). Raising and lowering the reservoir adjusts drop time. The capillaries must be handled with care and kept meticulously clean. Use the test tube (*E*) filled with distilled water for the capillaries when not in use.

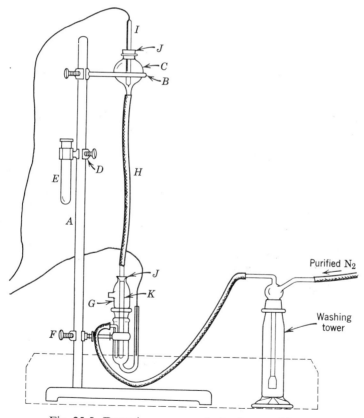

Fig. 25-5. Dropping mercury electrode assembly.

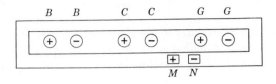

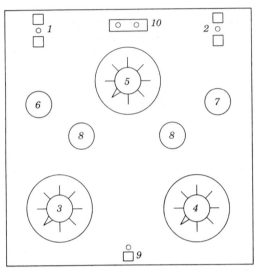

Fig. 25-6. Manual polarograph (electrical part).

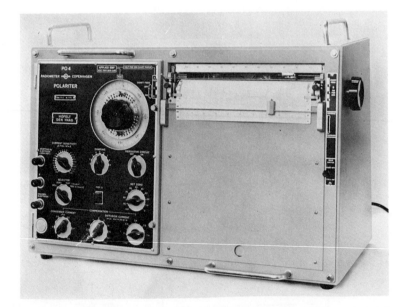

Fig. 25-7. Self-recording polarograph (electrical part). (Courtesy of Radiometer, Copenhagen)

25-4b ELECTRICAL PART (Fig. 25-6)

This consists of a 4-volt battery and a manual polarograph. (See Fig. 25-7 for a recording polarograph.)

25-4c POLAROGRAPH

1. Switch controlling battery voltage.
2. Standardizing switch:
   "0" = position when no measurements are made.
   "Polaro" = position during normal operation.
   "Std. cell" = position for standardization.
3. Potentiometer (0 to −2.3 volt in 0.1-volt increments).
4. Potentiometer (0 to 0.10 volt in 0.01-volt increments).
5. Sensitivity knob (1 to $\frac{1}{500}$).
6. Compensator knob.
7. Standardizing of potentiometers. Switch *1* to "normal" and *2* to "std. cell." Adjust *7* so that the galvanometer shows no deflection when *2* is switched to "0." Repeat occasionally during a measurement.
8. Not used. Turn counterclockwise.
9. Damping of galvanometer.
10. Connection to extend region to −4.3 volt.
11. BB = battery connection.
    CC = second battery (used with *8*).
    GG = galvanometer.

25-5 Properties of the Dropping Electrode

25-5a RADIUS OF THE CAPILLARY

The radius of the capillary may be determined by measuring the critical pressure, i.e., the pressure which just prevents mercury from flowing through the capillary. Place the capillary in a $0.1N$ KCl solution (surface tension = σ = 380 dynes/cm. at 25°). Slowly raise the mercury reservoir until the mercury meniscus remains level with the opening of the capillary. The pressure P_c is equal to the centimeters of mercury. The radius of the capillary ρ is:

$$\rho = \frac{2\sigma}{gdP_c}$$

where g = gravitational constant
and d = density of mercury.
   In $0.1N$ KCl at 25°

$$\rho = \frac{573}{P_c} \text{ (microns)} \tag{25-3}$$

25-5b CAPILLARY CONSTANT (N)

The capillary constant N (see § 25-2) is equal to the ratio of the pressure P to the amount of mercury m flowing through the capillary in a second. Poiseuille's law states

$$N = \frac{\pi Pr^4 t}{8Vl} \rightarrow \frac{V}{t} = \frac{\pi Pr^4}{8Nl}$$

V is the volume of liquid with viscosity N, which with pressure P flows through a capillary (length l, radius r) in t seconds.

$$m = \frac{Vd}{t} = \frac{\pi Pr^4 d}{8Nl} \; .$$

where d is the density of the liquid; therefore

$$N = \frac{P}{m} = \frac{8Nl}{\pi r^4 d}$$

At 25° this becomes (P in centimeters of mercury, l and r in centimeters)

$$N = 2.1567 \times 10^{-10} \, l/r^4 \text{ (cm. sec./mg.)} \tag{25-4}$$

25-5c ELECTROCAPILLARY CURVE

The surface tension of mercury varies with the applied potential and reaches a maximum at about -0.6 volt. This means that drop size varies with voltage. Since the total rate of flow remains constant, the drop time varies.

Determine drop time as a function of applied potential between -0.5 and -1.9 volt (in increments of 0.1 volt).

25-6 Solutions

The solution to be polarographed (usually 3–5 ml.) consists of the following:

1. A solvent (water, or mixtures of water and alcohol, dioxan); the solvent should be free from reducible impurities and obviously should not itself be reducible.

2. A salt (0.1–1N) such as KCl, NH$_4$Cl, NR$_4$Cl. The choice of the cation is determined by the voltage desired. In strongly acidic media the useful negative potential range is obtained by H$^+$ (-1.1 volt at pH $= 0$); in neutral media by the cations (-1.8 volt for Na$^+$, K$^+$, NH$_4^+$; -2.0 volt for Li$^+$; -2.6 volt for R$_4$N$^+$). The positive potential range is limited by the cation (-0.2 volt for OH$^-$ at pH 14; $+0.3$ volt for Cl$^-$). The concentration of the salt is usually 100 times that of the substance to be reduced.

3. A buffer solution (0.1–1M). Since protons play an important role in most cathodic reductions of organic molecules, the half-wave potential moves to more negative values with increasing pH (see § 22-4). The concentration of the buffer is about 100 times that of the substance. In most cases the buffer and salt are one and the same substance. Suitable buffers are Borax and sodium acetate-acetic acid.

4. A surface-active agent.

5. The substance to be reduced (10^{-2} to 10^{-5} mole/l.).

Note. Since dissolved oxygen will also be reduced at the cathode, it must be removed with nitrogen.

25-7 Procedure

1. Raise the mercury reservoir until mercury flows from the capillary.

2. Turn on battery and a-c current. Allow a 15-min. warm-up period.

3. Add mercury to the electrolysis vessel, followed by the test solution (3–5 ml.).

4. Pass a slow stream of purified nitrogen through the solution for about 10 min.

5. Insert capillary, making sure the mercury drop is formed under the surface of the solution. Adjust to a rate of 1 drop every 2–3 sec.

6. Standardize potentiometer. Switch *1* to "normal," read galvanometer, briefly switch *2* to "std. cell" and adjust *7* to return galvanometer to original position. Switch *2* to "polaro."

7. Switch *5* to "$\frac{1}{5}$" and check to see that the light spot does not go off the galvanometer scale at a potential of -1.8 volt (at pH 4–14; -1.0 volt at pH 0). The deflection should be about 6 cm.

8. Using *3* and *4*, adjust potentiometers to zero. Use "zero set" knob to adjust galvanometer to zero.

9. Turn off the nitrogen flow (remove and stopper outlet if desired).

10. Increase the potential, using *3* and *4* until $\bar{i}_d$ has been reached. Read the average current on the galvanometer for each new potential. In the region where *i* increases rapidly, *E* must be increased by 0.01-volt increments. Record height of reservoir, sensitivity setting, and temperature.

11. Check potentiometer (see 6).

12. Turn *2*, *3*, and *4* to zero. Raise the reservoir. Clean the capillary and leave in (*e*).

13. Clean apparatus.

14. Take a polarogram of the solution without the substance.

15. Switch *1* to "off" and the galvanometer switches to "shorted" and "off." Pour mercury into appropriate waste bottle.

Note. Do not allow solution to enter capillary.

25-8 Report

Plot *i* against *E* (1 cm. = 0.1 volt). Also plot $\Delta i/\Delta E$ against *E*; use the maximum in the graph to determine the half-wave potential. Prepare an $i - E$ graph on a blank (solution without substance) and subtract. Determine $\bar{i}_d$ from the graph thus obtained (see Fig. 25-4). Record name, date, substance, concentration, temperature, drop time, and sensitivity setting. When an automatic recorder is used, the *true* half-wave potential is obtained from the observed half-wave potential with the formula:

$$E_{\frac{1}{2}} = [(RL \times \text{voltage span}) - (LK \times 8.93 \times 10^{-6})] - (\text{initial voltage})$$

25-9   Examples

25-9a   NITRO AROMATICS

Dissolve 40 mg. of freshly distilled nitrobenzene in 100 ml. of ethyl alcohol. Pipette 0.2, 0.4, 0.6, 0.8, and 1.0 ml. in 10-ml. volumetric flasks. Add 0.8, 0.6, 0.4, 0.2, 0.0 ml. of alcohol. Add 1 ml. of a solution containing $1N$ NH_4Cl and 1% of gelatin and fill to the mark with the buffer solution in 50% alcohol.

Buffer Solution.
   A.   148.7 ml. of $0.01M$ Borax ($Na_2B_4O_7 \cdot 10H_2O$-sodium tetraborate) in 50% alcohol and 40.5 ml. of $0.05N$ NaOH in 50% alcohol ($0.1N$ NaOH diluted with alcohol).
   B.   8.0 ml. of $0.2M$ acetic acid in 50% alcohol and 192 ml. of $0.02M$ sodium acetate in 50% alcohol.
   C.   185.0 ml. of $0.2M$ acetic acid in 50% alcohol and 15.0 ml. of $0.2M$ sodium acetate in 50% alcohol.
   D. $0.05N$ HCl in 50% alcohol.
The pH's of these buffers as determined by the pH meter are, respectively, 10.9, 6.97, 4.57, and 2.2.

25-9b   OTHER NITRO COMPOUNDS

o-, *m*-, and *p*-Nitrobenzoic acid; 1- and 2-nitronaphthalene; *o*-, *m*-, and *p*-chloronitrobenzene.

25-9c   AZO COMPOUNDS

Azobenzene; *p*-methoxy-, *p*-hydroxy-, *p*-aminoazobenzene

25-9d   HYDROQUINONE

Prepare buffer solutions of pH 6.0, 7.0, and 8.0, using $0.2N$ potassium monohydrogen phosphate and dilute hydrocloric acid. Check pH with pH meter. Add 1 ml. of a solution of 0.1 g. of hydroquinone in 20 ml. of water to 30 ml. of the buffer solution. Pass pure nitrogen through the solution and take a polarogram between +0.2 and −0.5 volt. The cathodic part of the curve is caused by reduction of benzoquinone formed by air oxidation.
   Plot half-wave potential against pH, since

$$\frac{\Delta E_{\frac{1}{2}}}{\Delta \text{pH}} = -0.0591 \frac{a}{n}$$

where a is the number of hydrogen ions and n is the number of electrons involved in the reduction.

25-9e   OTHER EXAMPLES

Acetophenone, benzophonone; 2,4-dinitrophenylhydradrazones of aldehydes and ketones.

25-9f EQUIPMENT

Polarograph and accessories
Purified (distilled) mercury
Wash bottles (for nitrogen purification)
Volumetric flasks (100 ml., 50 ml., 10 ml.)
2 Pipettes (1 ml.)

25-10 References

1. O. H. Müller in *Technique of Organic Chemistry*, A. Weissberger, ed., Interscience Publishers, New York, 1960, Vol. I, Part IV, p. 3155.
2. M. von Stackelberg in *Methoden der organischen Chemie* (Houben-Weyl), Georg Thieme Verlag, Stuttgart, 1955, Band III/2, p. 295.
3. J. E. Page, *Quart. Revs.*, **6**, 262 (1952).
4. I. M. Kolthoff and J. J. Lingane, *Polarography*, Interscience Publishers, New York, 1952, Vols. I and II.
5. K. Schwabe, *Polarographie und Chemische Konstitution organischer Verbindungen*, Akcademie Verlag, Berlin, 1957.
6. R. P. Linstead, J. A. Elvidge, and M. Whalley, *A Course in Modern Techniques of Organic Chemistry*, Butterworths Scientific Publications, London, 1955.
7. C. L. Stong, *Sci. American*, **207**, 3, 247 (1962). This is a superb description of a useful homemade polarograph.
8. P. Zuman and I. M. Kolthoff, *Progress in Polarography*, Interscience Publishers, New York, 1962.

V

Miscellaneous

physical methods

26

Melting point curves

A DETERMINATION OF PURITY BY USE OF MELTING POINT CURVES

26-1 Introduction

The method is based on the determination of the temperature–time curve obtained when a constant quantity of heat per unit time is added to a substance. The apparatus described is suitable for substances melting (without decomposition) between 25 and 300°. The temperature–time curve allows calculation of the amount of impurity if the latter is small (less than 2%).

26-2 Principle

In order to keep the addition of heat a constant it is necessary to maintain a constant temperature differential between the sample and its surroundings. Since the temperature–time curve is usually determined over a range no larger than 15°, the amount of heat added is determined by this differential.

The temperature–time curve obtained is compared to one of a sample containing a known amount of additional impurity. In case of mixed-crystal formation the added impurity should be the same as the original one.

26-3 Theory

The temperature–composition (Tx) diagram is shown in Fig. 26-1. In the vicinity of A = 100% the curves meeting in A can be considered straight lines with slopes $\tan \alpha$ and $\tan \beta$ to a first approximation (Fig. 26-2). For a eutectic, $\tan \beta = \infty$.

The line $T_a N$ represents the final melting points of samples containing increasing amounts of impurity. Line $T_a M$ represents the corresponding initial melting point. The following derivation for the final melting point T_f of a sample with amount of impurity $p\%$ can be made:

$$T_a - T_f = p \tan \alpha = pc_f$$

For the initial melting point T_m:

$$T_a - T_m = p \tan \beta = pc_m$$

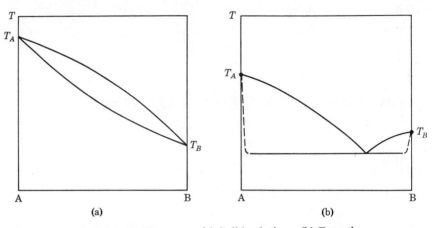

Fig. 26-1. Tx diagrams. (a) Solid solution. (b) Eutectic.

At F the sample P is entirely liquid, at M it is entirely solidified, and at V, in between, the fraction y present as liquid is

$$y = \frac{UV}{UW}$$

Now

$$T_a - T_y = p \tan \gamma = pc_y$$

$$c_y = \frac{c_f c_m}{c_f + y(c_m - c_f)}$$

and consequently

$$T_y = T_a - \frac{c_f c_m}{c_f + y(c_m - c_f)} p$$

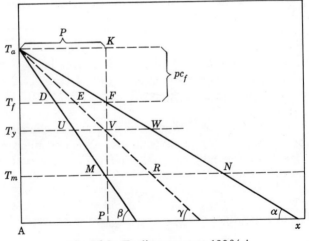

Fig. 26-2. Tx diagram near 100% A.

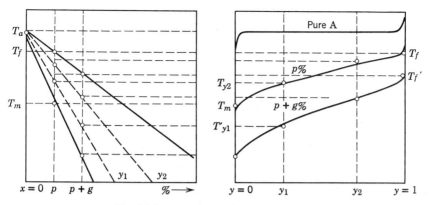

Fig. 26-3. Transformation to T_y curves.

This shows that a sample containing p mole % of impurity has an equilibrium temperature (T_y) at which the fraction y in the liquid phase is proportional to p.

In a eutectic system (no miscibility in the solid phase), where $\tan \beta = \infty$,

$$T_y = T_a - \frac{c_f p}{y}$$

The determination of the amount of impurity rests upon determining T_y for the sample containing $p\%$ impurity and a sample to which an (extra) known quantity $(q\%)$ of impurity is added, care being taken that y has the same value in both cases.

Compare the T_x and T_y diagrams (see Fig. 26-3). For the sample p

$$T_{y1} = T_a - pc_{y1}$$

For the sample $(p + q)$

$$T'_{y1} = T_a - (p + q)c_{y1}$$

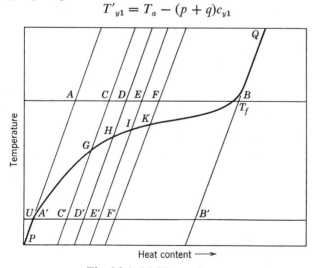

Fig. 26-4. Melting point curve.

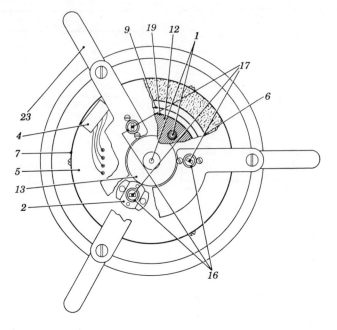

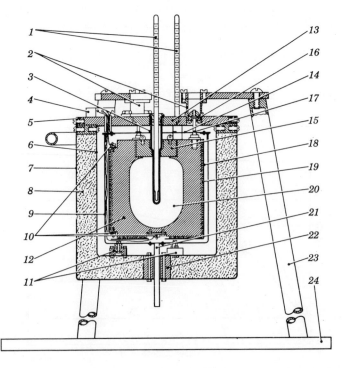

so that

$$T_{y1} - T'_{y1} = qc_{y1}$$

and

$$c_{y1} = \frac{T_{y1} - T'_{y1}}{q}$$

For a second value of y

$$T_{y2} = T_a - pc_{y2} \quad \text{and} \quad c_{y2} = \frac{T_{y2} - T'_{y2}}{q}$$

Then

$$p = \frac{T_{y2} - T_{y1}}{c_{y1} - c_{y2}} \tag{26-1}$$

with a eutectic mixture $c_y = c_f/y$ so that

$$T_{y2} - T_{y1} = pc_f \left(\frac{1}{y_1} - \frac{1}{y_2} \right)$$

When the points $y = \frac{1}{2}, \frac{1}{3}, \frac{1}{4}$, etc., are used, $T_{1/3} - T_{1/2} = T_{1/4} - T_{1/3} = \frac{1}{2}(T_{1/4} - T_{1/2})$, etc. Thus we can simply average over all the points.

In reality the temperature is determined as a function of the total amount of heat added (Fig. 26-4). Assume a constant specific heat over the narrow temperature range. Assume furthermore that the heat of fusion is constant between 0 and 2 mole % of B. Every line between PU and QB (or their extrapolation) corresponds to the heat of fusion. Lines which correspond to constant fractions y can be obtained by drawing any two horizontal lines AB and $A'B'$ and dividing these into equal parts. The lines connecting corresponding points on AB and $A'B'$ are lines having a constant value for y.

The highest precision is reached in that part of the curve where dT/dy is large, i.e., where y is small.

26-4 Apparatus

The apparatus (Fig. 26-5) consists of a hollow copper block *12* closed by a cover *13*. This block, insulated by a thin layer of air, is surrounded with a metallic jacket *9*. Finally the entire apparatus is surrounded by an insulating jacket *7*.

Fig. 26-5. Apparatus for determining temperature-time curves. *1*. Anschütz thermometer. *2*. Clamp holding top plate to block—brass. *3*. Sample holder—glass. *4*. Heating coil connection. *5*. Top plate—transite. *6*. Inner jacket of insulation vessel—argentan, high-polished. *7*. Outer jacket of insulation vessel—brass. *8*. Insulation—slagwool. *9*. Reflection shield—argentan, high-polished. *10*. Heating coil connection. *11*. Reflection shield attachment-eternit. *12*. Block—copper, nickel-plated. *13*. Insulation cover—eternit. *14*. Reflection shield cover—argentan, high-polished. *15*. Reflection shield lock—copper, nickel-plated. *16*. Insulated block suspension—eternit. *17*. Block suspension—stainless steel. *18*. Heating coil—Nichrome, glass-insulated. *19*. Heating coil protection—copper, nickel-plated. *20*. Heating compartment. *21*. Tube—brass. *22*. Connection between inner and outer jacket insulation vessel—eternit. *23*. Stand—steel tubing. *24*. Stand—wood.

An opening *3* in the block contains an iron tube containing about 0.5 ml. of mercury and the thermometer T_2. A glass vessel (inside diameter 0.60 cm., outside diameter 0.67 cm.) can be suspended in the opening. This vessel contains the substance to be examined and a thermometer T_1 of 0.50 cm. outside diameter. The sizes given have been chosen in order to obtain optimum results. Do not deviate from these sizes.

Heating takes place electrically with a variac. A metallic pipe *21* is placed underneath the apparatus. Air is passed through this pipe when the difference between T_1 and T_2 is too large.

Cleaning the Glass Vessel. Rinse carefully with alcohol and acetone; dry thoroughly.

26-5 Procedure

The substance to be examined is finely powdered, and 170–180 mg. is placed in the glass vessel. An Anschütz thermometer having a range at least 7° above the melting point of the substance is passed through a cork which fits the glass vessel and placed loosely in the substance. The glass vessel is placed in the center cavity of the block, and an ordinary thermometer is put into the second hole in the block. The block is warmed to 5–7° above its melting point; when all of the substance has melted the Anschütz is centered (from the bottom and sides of the glass vessel). The glass vessel is removed and the substance allowed to crystallize.

The glass vesssel is replaced in the apparatus and heated until thermometer T_2 reads 14° less than the melting point. This temperature is maintained until T_1 is 2–3° lower than T_2. This difference is maintained by careful adjustment of the variac. By noting the time and the variac settings in two or three trial runs a temperature difference $T_2 - T_1$ of 2–3° can be maintained within 0.1°. During melting the variac setting must be decreased slowly.

When T_1 shows a temperature about 14° below the melting point the temperature (of T_1) is recorded at 1-min. intervals until it reaches a point 5° above the melting point (estimate to 0.01°). When the rise in temperature is less that 0.1°/min. 2–4 min. readings should be made. Record the time every fifth observation. The Anschütz thermometer T_1 is removed from the glass vessel and allowed to cool slowly upon completion of the measurements; rapid cooling ruins the accuracy of the Anschütz. Set the variac at zero; then disconnect the current and cool the apparatus with air.

26-5a   CALCULATION OF *P*

T_1 is plotted against time (1 cm. = 1°, 2 mm. = 1 min.). Draw a line through the points and extrapolate the straight lines representing the heating up of solid and liquid (*PUA* and *QBB′* of Fig. 26-4). Draw the horizontal line (*AB*) just above the final melting point. Draw points *C*, *D*, *E*, and *F* so that

$$AC = \tfrac{1}{5}AB; \quad AD = \tfrac{1}{4}AB; \quad AE = \tfrac{1}{3}AB; \quad AF = \tfrac{1}{2}AB$$

Draw a second horizontal *A′B′* at the bottom of the melting point curve and place the corresponding points *C′*, *D′*, *E′*, *F′* on it. Draw the lines *CC′*, *DD′*, *EE′*,

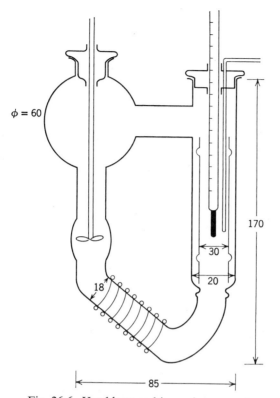

$\phi = 60$

170

30

20

18

85

Fig. 26-6. Hershberg melting-point apparatus.

and FF'. These intersect the curve at G, H, I, and K, corresponding to temperatures T_g, T_h, T_i, and T_k. Record name, date, sample data, and the number of the thermometer used.

26-5b FURTHER ADDITION OF IMPURITY

Weigh out (in a weighing bottle) 10 mg. of the "impurity" followed by 1 g. of sample. Melt the two substances over a microburner and pour into a mortar. Powder the mixture.

26-5c METHOD A (NO MIXED CRYSTALS)

When

$$\tfrac{1}{3}(T_g - T_k) = \tfrac{1}{2}(T_h - T_k) = T_i - T_k$$

falls within the experimental error, all six differences between the four temperatures are added. Let this summation be ΔT for the sample p and $\Delta T'$ for the sample $(p + q)$; then

$$\frac{p}{p+q} = \frac{\Delta T}{\Delta T'}$$

26-5d   METHOD B (MIXED CRYSTALS)

Determine the four slopes, C_{y1}–C_{y4}, and with this information calculate six values of p, using equation 26-1. Average these values, giving a threefold weight to $y = \frac{1}{5}$, $y = \frac{1}{2}$ and a twofold weight to the combinations $y = \frac{1}{5}$, $y = \frac{1}{3}$ and $y = \frac{1}{4}$, $y = \frac{1}{2}$.

26-5e   CALCULATION OF THE (FINAL) MELTING POINT (T_a) OF PURE A

Let T_f be the final melting point of the sample containing p mole % impurity, and T_f' that of the sample containing $(p + q)$% impurity. Then

$$T_a - T_f = p \tan \alpha$$

and

$$T_a - T_f' = (p + q) \tan \alpha \qquad \text{(see Fig. 26-3)}$$

Thus

$$T_a = T_f + \frac{p}{q}(T_f - T_f')$$

26-5f   ACCURACY

In systems without mixed crystal formation the minimum amount of impurity that can be determined is 0.01%. When mixed crystals form, the accuracy depends on the system but is usually better than 0.1%.

26-5g   EQUIPMENT

1 Anschütz thermometer	1 Glass vessel
1 0–360° Thermometer	Benzoic acid
Mortar and pestle	Cinnamic acid

B   DETERMINATION OF CONFIGURATION BY USE OF MELTING POINT DIAGRAMS OF OPTICALLY ACTIVE SUBSTANCE   (The Method of Quasi Racemates [2])

26-6   Introduction

The T_x diagram of optical antipodes (Fig. 26-7) usually belongs to one of the following types:

A: A racemic compound (mandelic acid).
B: A series of mixed crystals having a maximum for the racemic mixture (carvoxime).
C: A compound having a constant melting point (camphor oxime).

A T_x diagram can also be prepared by using one of the antipodes of compound A and one of a (related) substance B. When the configuration of A closely resembles that of B, then the D-form of A (A_D) will exhibit a different T_x diagram

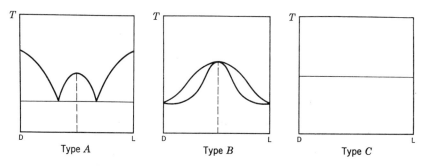

Fig. 26-7. T_x diagram of two optical antipodes.

with the D-form of B (B_D) from the one with the L-form of B (B_L). The following cases have been observed:

1. One curve is of type P (mixed crystals) (Fig. 26-8); the other of type Q (eutectic). Mixed crystal forming shows a closer configurational relation than eutectic forming. Thus:

$$A_D + B_D, \text{ mixed crystals (curve } P)$$
$$A_D + B_L, \text{ eutectic} \qquad \text{(curve } Q)$$

2. One curve is of type R (compound), the other of Q. In this case R shows a closer relation:

$$A_D + B_D, \text{ compound (curve } R)$$
$$A_D + B_L, \text{ eutectic} \quad \text{(curve } Q)$$

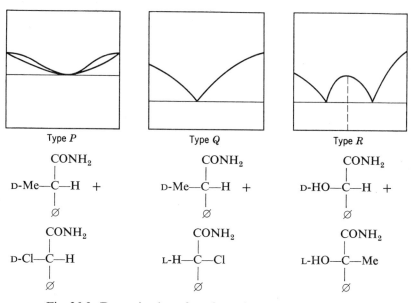

Fig. 26-8. Determination of configuration, using Tx diagrams.

3. One curve is of type *P*, the other of type *R*. Mixed crystal forming shows a closer relationship:

$$A_D + B_D, \text{ mixed crystals (curve } P)$$
$$A_D + B_L, \text{ compound} \quad \text{(curve } R)$$

This method can be used to correlate stereochemical configurations of related compounds. It yields a positive result only in cases where the $A + B_D$ diagram is totally different from the $A + B_L$ diagram.

26-7 Procedure

Since usually only a little material is available, a micromelting point is taken. Accurately weigh out at least nine different mixtures of (A and B_D) and (A and B_L). Powder and mix thoroughly. Fill a melting point capillary and determine the melting points (softening point and final melting point), using an Anschütz thermometer (Fig. 26-6). Heat the melting point bath at a constant rate of 1°/min. Reproducibility should be within 0.5°. Check this.

If sufficient material is available, determine the macromelting points, using the apparatus described under § 26-4. Determine the temperature–time curve at constant heating rate. To save time choose $T_2 - T_1$ so that the temperature rise is 1°/min.

26-8 References

1. W. M. Smit, *Rec. trav. chim.*, **75**, 1309 (1956).
2. E. L. Eliel, *Stereochemistry of Carbon Compounds*, McGraw-Hill Book Co., New York, 1962, p. 106.
3. A. Fredga, *Tetrahedron*, **8**, 126 (1960).
4. J. Timmermans, *Rec. trav. chim.*, **48**, 890 (1929).
5. J. E. Ricci, *Tetrahedron*, **18**, 605 (1962).
6. E. L. Skau, J. C. Arthur, Jr., and H. Wakeham in *Technique of Organic Chemistry*, A. Weissberger, ed., Interscience Publishers, New York, 1959, Vol. I, Part I, p. 287.
7. J. Timmermans, *J. chim. phys.*, **49**, 162 (1952).
8. H. Lettré, *Ergeb. Enzymforsch.*, **9**, 1 (1943).
9. R. M. Secor, *Chem. Revs.*, **63**, 297 (1963).

27

Semimicro boiling point determination

27-1 Introduction

The boiling point of a substance is the temperature at which the vapor pressure of the substance is equal to the external (atmospheric) pressure.

A rapid and reliable method for the determination of boiling points has been described by the C.I.P.C. (Central Institute for Physico-chemical Constants, Utrecht, Netherlands). The method may be used for pressures between 20 and 760 mm. Hg and temperatures between 25 and 250°C.

27-2 Principle

The liquid under investigation runs down along a spiral from the actual container and enters a strongly heated zone. The vapor thus formed escapes through the core of the spiral, passing and heating the liquid from the container. This type of indirect heating is conducive to the establishment of an equilibrium between liquid and vapor.

The temperature of the boiling liquid is determined with an Anschütz thermometer. The boiling point of water at the same pressure is determined immediately afterwards. Finally, a second determination is made at a pressure several millimeters of mercury different from the first one. This enables us to calculate the boiling point of the substance at a certain standard pressure.

27-3 Apparatus

27-3a GLASS PART

The apparatus (Fig. 27-1) consists of two nearly identical parts (I and III) connected *via* the absorption vessel (II). The substance under investigation is placed in part I, and water in part III. Both parts consist of the following:

A capillary C surrounding:

A spiral B made of glass or platina;

A long, wide tube, the lower part of which serves as boiling space;

An inner tube M, the lower constricted portion of which is surrounded by the

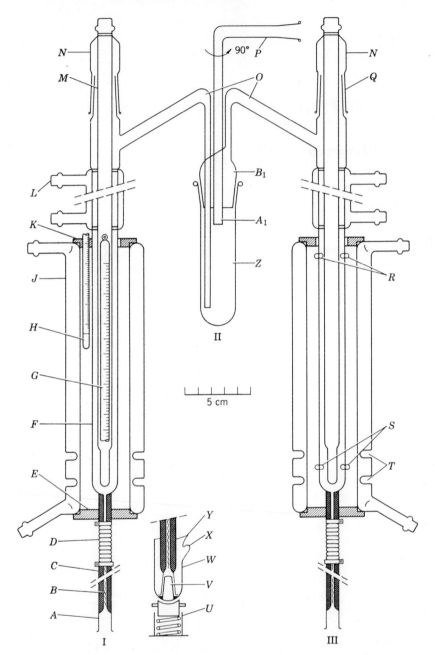

Fig. 27-1. Boiling point determination apparatus.

boiling liquid; *M* contains a sufficient amount of mercury to ensure that the thermometer reservoir is just covered by mercury;

A thermometer *G* containing a copper wire which extends beyond *M*; a condenser *L* closed at the top with a cover *N*. The tube *M* is welded through this cover; the cover *N* of parts I and III are marked *L* and *R*. When these letters point toward the front of the apparatus, the tube *M* is centered properly;

A spiral resistance wire (R_{ac}, "anticondensing coil") stretched between glass hooks; drops of liquid which might hinder a proper view of the thermometer can be dispelled with this wire;

A double glass wall *J*. In I this contains a thermometer *H* and a heating coil *R* wound on a mica core.

27-3b ELECTRICAL PART

The following switches and lights are mounted on a switchboard (see Fig. 27-2):

S_1: connects transformer to house current.

S_2: connects evaporation element R_v.

S_3, S_4: controls current in R_v by shorting of R_3 and R_4.

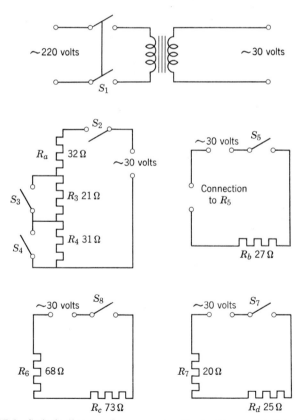

Fig. 27-2. Switch diagram for apparatus for boiling point determination.

S_5: connects heating coil in part I, using a variable resistance R_5.

S_6, S_8: switches controlling anticondensing coils I and III.

S_7: controls evaporation coil in part III.

27-3c CLEANING THE APPARATUS

Rinse the apparatus with alcohol and ether; clean tubes M (Fig. 27-1) in a similar manner. Dry, using a current of dry air.

If a grease spot remains in the apparatus, fill the apparatus with alcoholic alkali and allow to stand for 15 min. Remove the cover N, siphon empty, wash with water (three times), followed by alcohol and ether.

27-4 Procedure

Clean and dry the apparatus. By winding a cotton plug around a wooden stick, wetting it slightly, and dipping it in graphite, seal the ground glass joints A. Put the bumpers U into place. Fill the receivers with sufficient mercury to close off the joint of A.

Remove the covers N (do not interchange these). Fill each of the tubes M with sufficient mercury to properly surround the thermometer wells. Too little mercury may cause errors; too much does no harm provided that the *boiling* liquid surrounds the well completely.

Lubricate the joints N with vacuum grease (no silicones!). Place 3 ml. of the liquid to be investigated in tube I, and an equal amount of distilled water in tube III.

Check whether air bubbles remain inside the capillary (this happens when the spirals are not entirely clean; careful tapping may remove the bubbles).

Replace covers N and tubes M, turning the joints until they fit properly. Insert the appropriate Anschütz thermometer, using a copper wire long enough to facilitate removal.

Fill trap II with a layer of dry silica gel. Grease the joint. If necessary, cool II in a Dewar flask. Circulate water through condensers L. Adjust the pressure to within 1 mm. of the three pressures (20, 100, and 760 mm. Hg). If the pressure exceeds atmospheric pressure, take care joints, stopcocks, and stops do not loosen. Turn on current. Parts I and III are operated according to instructions in Tables 27-1 and 27-2.

For boiling points between 20 and 120°C. the jacket temperature (thermometer H) should be between 5 and 25° *below* the observed boiling point. For boiling points between 120 and 150°C. this range should be 10–30°. (Neglecting these temperature differentials might make the boiling point determination unreliable.) As soon as both liquids are boiling, take thermometer G readings every 30 sec. Check, using Table 27-3, that the pressure does not deviate too far from the standard pressure. Adjust if necessary. Estimate the thermometer readings to 0.02°. The determination is finished when five successive thermometer readings (H and G) do not change by more than 0.02. Now change the pressure a few millimeters (1–2 mm. at 20 mm. and about 10 mm. at 760 mm.). When this has

Table 27-1   Instructions for Operating Part I

Expected Boiling Point (°C.)	Instructions
20–40	Condenser water is circulated through J. S_2 and S_3 are closed. Close S_6 only to observe thermometer G.
40–50	Water is circulated through J. Close S_2 and S_3. Close S_6, but open it the moment thermometer H indicates a temperature higher than the boiling point.
50–100	Remove water from jacket J. Close S_2 and S_4. Do not close S_3. Close S_6; open S_6 only when the temperature (on H) is too high.
100–150	Close S_2, S_4, S_5, and S_6. Adjust the temperature as desired, using the variac R_5.
150–250	Close S_2, S_3, S_4, S_5, and S_6. Use R_5 as above.

Table 27-2   Instructions for Operating Part III

Pressure (mm.)	Boiling Point of Water (°C.)	Instructions
760	100	Close S_7 and S_8; J should be dry.
100	57	Close S_7 and S_8; circulate water through J.
20	22	Close S_7; circulate water through J. Close S_8 only to observe thermometer G.

Table 27-3   Boiling Point of Water

Pressure (mm. Hg)	Boiling Point (°C.)	dt/dp (°/mm. Hg)
760	100.00	Appr. 0.04
100	51.58	Appr. 0.2
20	22.14	Appr. 0.9

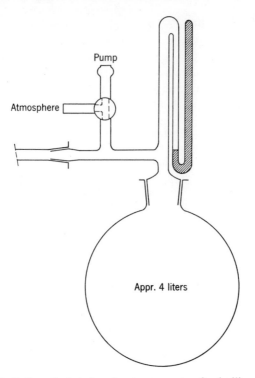

Fig. 27-3. Ballast flask belonging to apparatus for boiling point determination.

to be done at atmospheric pressure, it is easy to increase the pressure by using a rubber balloon.

At 20–100 mm. the pressure is increased by placing a finger on the ballast flask opening, and closing and opening the stopcock several times. Wait 1 min. for equilibrium to be re-established, and carry out a second determination. When finished, allow to cool for 10 min. Let the ballast vessel (Fig. 27-3) come to atmospheric pressure. Remove the bumpers and drain liquid into V. Remove the liquid, taking care that the mercury does not spill. Add the mercury to the used mercury bottle. Clean and dry the apparatus.

If the boiling point of water does not become steady in 10 min., either the apparatus leaks or the pressure changes in the vessel are too rapid. Check all joints and stopcocks.

27-5   Calculation

Round off the average of the last five readings to 0.01°. The boiling point at standard pressure is calculated using

$$t_X = T_{X,1} + \frac{t_W - t_{W,1}}{t_{W,2} + t_{W,1}} (t_{X,2} - t_{X,1})$$

where t_X = boiling point of substance X at standard pressure;
       t_W = boiling point of water at standard pressure (Table 27-3);
       $t_{W,1}$ = boiling point of water as determined from first set of observations;
       $t_{W,2}$ = boiling point of water from second readings;
$t_{X,1}$ and $t_{X,2}$ = boiling points for substance X.
   This equation is applicable only when

$$|t_{W,1} - t_{W,2}| < 4°$$
$$|t_{X,1} - t_{X,2}| < 4°$$

The standard deviations of the measurements performed by one person using a certain apparatus are about $< \pm 0.04°C$. Let the accuracy of the thermometer standardization be $\pm a°C$.; then the error in the boiling point determination is usually smaller than $\pm(3a + 0.04)°C$.

27-6 Exercise

27-6a

   Calculate the boiling points at 760, 100, and 20 mm. of the liquid under investigation. To this end determine the boiling points at five different pressures, e.g., two below and three above the standard pressure at the boiling point. Calculate the average of these six values standard (deviation)

$$s = \sum [\Delta^2/n(n-1)]^{1/2}.$$

   Report.   Report results as in Form 27-1.

Form 27-1

Name: Date:		Substance: Pressure: mm. Hg S.B.P.* °C.± °C.					
No.	Boiling Point of Substance	Boiling Point of Water	Combinations	t_X	Δ	Δ^2
				$t_Y =$	$\Sigma \Delta^2 =$	

* Standard boiling point

27-6b

   Determine the boiling point of the liquid at seven different pressures* in the neighborhood of a standard pressure (i.e., at 745, 750, 755, 760, 765, 770, and

* Use tables "Boiling Point of Water" and "Vapor Pressure of Water" in *Handbook of Chemistry and Physics*.

775 mm.) and make a graph plotting $\log p$ vs. $1/T$. The line (assuming a constant Q = molar heat of vaporization) obeys the equation

$$\log p = -\frac{Q}{2.303\ RT} + C = -\frac{A}{T} + C$$

$$0° = 273.18°K.$$

$$R = 1.987\ \text{cal.}/\text{mol}$$

Determine A, using the method of least squares, and calculate the molar heat of vaporization Q.

$$A = \frac{n \sum xy - \sum x \sum y}{n \sum x^2 - (\sum x)^2} \quad \text{when } y = Ax + c$$

Report.   Report results as in Form 27-2.

Form 27-2

Name:				Substance:						
Date:				A:						
				Q: cal./mole						
No.	Boiling point of Water	p (mm. Hg)	Log p	$y = \log p - \alpha^*$	t (°C.)	T (°K.)	$1/T$	$x = 1/T - \beta^*$	x^2	xy
						$\sum x =$		$\sum x^2 =$	$\sum xy =$	$(\sum x)^2 =$

*α and β are any constant numbers used to obtain smaller numbers, for instance, the smallest value of log p and $1/T$.

27-6c   EQUIPMENT

3 Anschütz thermometers for part III (water)   Magnifying glass
(0–50°, 40–100°, 100–150°)   Funnel
Pipette (3 ml.)   Bottle of mercury
2 Beakers (100 ml.)   Graphite

27-7 References

1. W. Swietoslawski and J. R. Anderson in *Technique of Organic Chemistry*, A. Weissberger, ed., Interscience Publishers, New York, 1959, Vol. I, Part I, p. 357.
2. W. M. Smit, ed., *Purity Control by Thermal Analysis, Proceedings of The International Symposium*, Elsevier Publishing Co., Amsterdam, 1957.

28

Molecular weight determination

A   EBULLIOMETER

28-1   Introduction

The ebulliometer is an apparatus used to determine the elevation of boiling point of a solution. It is usually desirable to determine the boiling point of the solvent simultaneously, since the boiling point varies with the atmospheric pressure.

28-2   Theory

The chemical potential of a solvent (1) is

$$\mu^g = \mu_0^g + RT \ln p$$
$$\mu' = \mu_0' + RT \ln (1 - x_2)$$

where x_2 = mole fraction of solute (2);
$\quad \mu^g$ = chemical potential in gas phase;
$\quad \mu_0^g$ = chemical potential of pure solvent;
$\quad \mu'$ = chemical potential in liquid phase;
$\quad \mu_0'$ = chemical potential of pure solvent in liquid;
$\quad p$ = vapor pressure of the solvent phase.
At the boiling point (T) $\mu^g = \mu'$. Therefore

$$RT \ln (1 - x_2) = (\mu_0^g - \mu_0')_T + RT \ln p$$

But under normal circumstances $p = 1$, and

$$R \ln (1 - x_2) = \frac{(\mu_0^g - \mu_0')_T}{T} = \frac{(\mu_0^g - \mu_0'{}_{T_0})}{T_0} = \int_{T_0}^{T} \frac{\Delta H}{T^2} \, dT$$

where $\Delta H = H_g - H_l$ = difference in enthalpy between liquid and gas phase;
$\quad T_0$ = boiling point of pure solvent.
But

$$(\mu_0^g - \mu_0')_{T_0} = 0$$

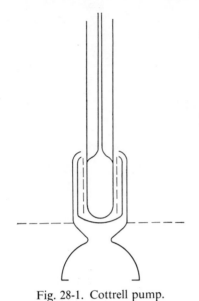

Fig. 28-1. Cottrell pump.

If ΔH is independent of the temperature and $x_2 \ll 1$, then

$$-Rx_2 = -H\frac{T-T_0}{TT_0}$$

$$\Delta t = x_2\frac{RT^2}{H} \qquad (28\text{-}1)$$

But

$$x_2 = \frac{\text{mole subst. 2}}{\text{mole subst. 1 + mole subst. 2}}$$

$$= \frac{\text{mole subst. 2}}{\text{mole subst. 1}}$$

When the amount of solvent is kept constant, the elevation of the boiling point is directly proportional to the number of gram moles of solute.

28-3   Principle

In order to measure the equilibrium temperature between liquid and vapor it is necessary to establish contact between these two phases and the thermometer. This is accomplished by using a Cottrell pump (Fig. 28-1). A mixture of vapor and liquid sprays from the tubes while the solution is boiling.

Table 28-1   Solvents for Ebulliometric Molecular Weight Determination

$$M = \frac{K}{\Delta t} \times \frac{\text{wt. of substance (g.)}}{\text{wt. of solvent (g.)}}$$

Solvent	K	Boiling Point (°C.)
Diethyl ether	2.02×10^3	35
Carbon disulfide	2.34×10^3	46
Acetone	1.72×10^3	56
Chloroform	3.63×10^3	61
Carbon tetrachloride	5.03×10^3	77
Ethyl acetate	2.77×10^3	77
Ethanol	1.22×10^3	78
Benzene	2.53×10^3	80
Cyclohexane	2.7×10^3	81
Water	0.52×10^3	100
Dioxane	3.20×10^3	101
Isobutyl alcohol	2.0×10^3	108
1,2-Dibromoethane	6.43×10^3	132
Phenol	3.56×10^3	181
Nitrobenzene	5.24×10^3	211

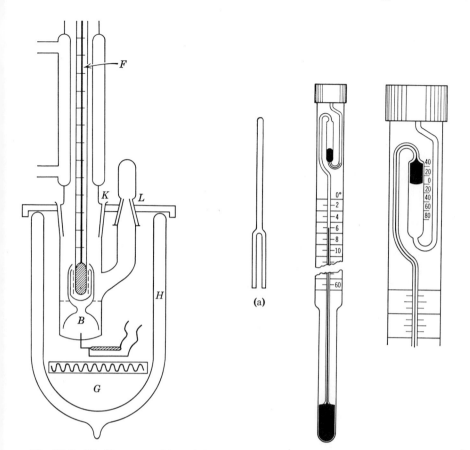

Fig. 28-2. Ebulliometer. (a) Weighing tube.   Fig. 28-3. Beckman thermometer.

28-4   Apparatus

About 100 mg. of substance (mol. wt. < 500) is needed in order to determine the molecular weight with the apparatus shown in Fig. 28-2. The apparatus consists of two equal parts; one part contains pure solvent, enabling corrections for barometer readings to be made readily.

The temperature is determined with a Beckman thermometer* (Fig. 28-3), which is placed between the arms of a Cottrell pump. The mercury well of the thermometer is surrounded by a jacket of glass wool. To prevent superheating a platinum wire which can be heated with a resistance coil is fused into the bottom of the container. The entire apparatus, including the heating coil (*G*, Fig. 28-2),

---

* For use of Beckman thermometer see (*a*) J. R. Partington, *An Advanced Treatise on Physical Chemistry*, Vol. I, Longmans Green & Co., New York, 1949, p. 249; and (*b*) D. P. Shoemaker and C. W. Garland, *Experiments in Physical Chemistry*, McGraw-Hill Book Co., New York 1962, p. 381.

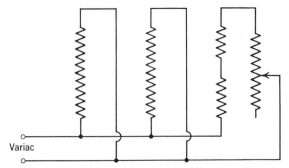

Fig. 28-4. Circuit for ebulliometer.

is placed inside a Dewar flask H. Heating is accomplished by using the circuit shown in Fig. 28-4.

28-5   Procedure

Clean and dry the apparatus. Lubricate all the joints (lightly, no silicones). Assemble the ebulliometers. Two ebulliometers are used to eliminate the influence of atmospheric pressure changes. One is filled with pure solvent.

(*a*) Carefully place the assembled apparatus in the Dewar flask and put the Beckman thermometer (with glass wool attached) in the ebulliometer.

(*b*) Pipette the appropriate amount of benzene with both ebulliometers.

(*c*) Adjust the variacs. Read the thermometers after 30 min. Repeat every 3 min. for 15 min. until the difference in thermometer readings is less than 0.003°.

(*d*) Turn off the variac, allowing the apparatus to cool.

(*e*) Weigh out about 100 mg. of naphthalene, using weighing-in rod (Fig. 28-2a).

(*f*) Blow warm air at stopper L until no drops are visible. Open L, add naphthalene, and reweigh rod.

(*g*) Turn on the variac and determine the temperature differences as in (*c*).

(*h*) Determine Δt for naphthalene, the unknown, and again naphthalene.

Form 28-1

T_1	T_2	$T_2 - T_1$	Average $T_2 - T_1$	Δt	Weighing rod filled: Weighing rod empty: Added:
				Δt_1 Δt_2	

28-6   Calculations and Report

Record thermometer readings as shown in Form 28-1.

a mg. naphthalene $= a/128$ mmoles $= q\,\Delta t_1$

c mg. naphthalene $= c/128$ mmoles $= q\,\Delta t_3$

b mg. unknown $= b/M_0$ mmoles $= q\,\Delta t_2$

$$q = \frac{1}{128}\left(\frac{a + c}{\Delta t_1 + \Delta t_3}\right)$$

$$M_0 = \frac{b}{q\,\Delta t_2}$$

B   SEMIMICROEBULLIOMETER

28-7   Introduction

With a semimicroebulliometer the molecular weight of a small amount of substance (15 mg., mol. wt. = 200–400) can be determined within 4%.

The elevation of the boiling point is determined by a differential method. The difference in temperature between solvent and solution is measured with two NTC* thermistors and a Wheatstone bridge. In order to maintain the thermistors at the right temperature they are kept in the mercury well, which in turn is surrounded by a mixture of vapor and liquid.

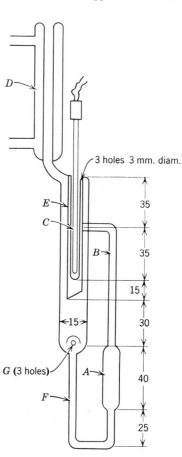

Fig. 28-5. Semimicroebulliometer (dimensions in millimeters).

28-8   Apparatus [6]

28-8a   GLASS PART

The semimicroebulliometer is shown in Fig. 28-5. A mixture of vapor and liquid passes through tube B when the liquid in flask A boils. This mixture collects on the wall of the mercury well C to protect it from the cold liquid in condenser D. Three openings at the top of the jacket allow vapor to escape.

Condensed liquid returns to flask A via a U-tube F. A small cap G at the top of this U-tube also contains three holes designed to prevent any boiling in the wrong leg.

The content of the ebulliometer measures 5–6 ml. when the apparatus is filled to 4 mm. above the glass stopper.

* A ceramic having a *N*egative *T*emperature *C*oefficient of about 4% a degree.

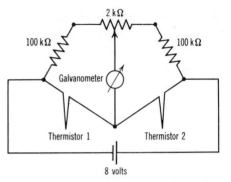

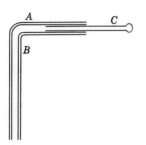

Fig. 28-6. Weighing-in rod.

Fig. 28-7. Bridge circuit for the semimicro-ebulliometer. The thermistors used have a resistance of 430 kΩ at 25°C (100 kΩ at 80°C). The galvanometer is a type Kipp A 70 HC.

28-8b ELECTRICAL PART

The electrical circuit is shown in Fig. 28-7. The potentiometer P balances the bridge. When balanced, the deflection of the galvanometer is proportional to Δt. The potential applied is p volts. The main flask A (Fig. 28-5) is heated by a heater using an 80-ohm variable resistance at 100 volts. Only the temperature just before and after the addition of the substance needs to be determined. This requires only a few minutes, enabling the replacement of the reference ebulliometer (containing only solvent) by a resistance. A potentiometer of 0.5 Mohms is used. Its position should remain unchanged after balancing the bridge.

28-9 Procedure

Fill both ebulliometers to about 5 mm. above the glass cover (G, Fig. 28-5). Bring the liquid to a boil by turning on the current. The variac setting varies with the solvent used.

Lower ebulliometers into the Dewar flask up to the condenser D. Place both NTC thermistors in the thermometer well. Insulate with some cotton. After 5 min. apply a potential across the Wheatstone bridge. Carefully switch the galvanometer to its most sensitive setting. When the liquid is boiling well in both ebulliometers, the deflection of the galvanometer should not exceed ± 5 mm. Adjust, using the potentiometer if necessary. Read the galvanometer with care.

When equilibrium has been reached ($1-1\frac{1}{2}$ hr.), place about 20 mg. of reference substance in the ebulliometer, using the weighing-in rod (Fig. 28-6). Place B in the condenser, leaving its lower part just 2 mm. above the condensing liquid. Using rod C, push the sample into A. Weigh B again afterwards. Any material clinging to the condenser is removed by interrupting the condenser water, thus raising the level of the condensing liquid. After addition of the sample, equilibrium is re-established rapidly (1–2 min.). When a constant galvanometer value is obtained, add a sufficient amount of the unknown to cause at least a one-quarter scale deflection of the galvanometer. When equilibrium has been reached, add a second portion of the reference compound. The molecular weight is calculated readily from the differences (§ 28-6).

Note. Weigh the three samples ahead of time. The actual determination need take only 15 min.

28-10   Calculations and Report

Record as shown in Form 28-2.

Form 28-2

Name:				Substance:				
Date:				Solvent:				

No.	Substance	Weighing tube		Weight of substance (mg.)	Galvanometer		Deflection (mm.)	Mg. substance Displacement
		Filled	Empty		Before	After		

Let M_y be molecular weight; then the molecular weight of the unknown is

$$M_0 = M_y \frac{(\sum a / \sum b)_0}{(\sum a / \sum b)_y}$$

C   MICROMOLECULAR WEIGHT DETERMINATION ACCORDING TO BARGER [3, 4]

28-11   Introduction

The vapor pressure of a solution depends on the molarity of the solution according to Raoult's law. Isothermal distillation occurs because there is a difference in vapor pressure between two solutions of different concentrations (in the same solvent). This type of distillation takes place when the solutions are put in a closed system, the liquid distilling from the solution of a lower concentration to the one with a higher concentration. The distillation velocity increases with increasing difference in concentration. This phenomenon is used to compare a solution of unknown molarity to several known solutions, thus determining the molecular weight of the unknown solute.

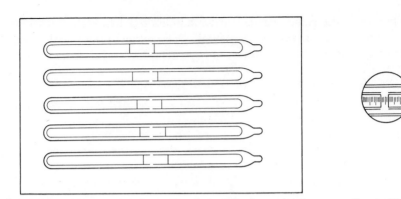

Fig. 28-8. Capillary tubes for molecular weight determination according to Barger.

28-12 Principle

A capillary tube is filled with a solution containing a known concentration (weight per volume) of the unknown. A similar tube is filled with a solution of known molarity containing the reference substance in the same solvent. The two tubes are placed inside a slightly wider tube, the open ends facing one another (see Fig. 28-8). This outside tube is sealed closed with a flame.

When both solutions have the same molarity, the menisci do not move. Usually one will have risen a bit and the other will have lowered. By comparison with several reference solutions the molarity and thus the molecular weight of the unknown can be determined within 10%.

28-13 Procedure

Weigh 15–150 mg. of the unknown (mol. wt. between 50 and 500) accurately into a 10-ml. volumetric flask, and make up the flask to the mark with distilled acetone.

Select two capillaries which just fit into one another. One should be about 30 cm. long with a constant inside diameter of 1–1.5 mm.; the other, 60 cm. in length with an inside diameter of 2.5–3 mm. A microscope can be used to check that the variation in diameter is less than 5%. Clean with acetone and dry.

Carefully divide each capillary into six pieces of equal length, using a glass cutter (or sharp ceramic edge). Using a microburner, close all tubes at one end. Divide into six pairs, making sure that the tubes fit well into one another. Again using a glass cutter, cut all inner capillaries into two approximately equal pieces.

Thus each outer tube now has two inner tubes. One of each of the inner tubes needs to be sealed at the end.

A micropipette (finely drawn capillary) fitting inside the inner tube is used to fill these tubes. Fill one inner tube of each pair with unknown solution to about 4 mm. from edge; place point of micropipette on bottom, thus avoiding air bubbles. Clean outside carefully with cotton (wet with acetone and dry), and carefully glide tubes inside outer tube with open side up. Fill remaining capillaries in the same way, using the five standard solutions, which contain 1, 2, 3, 4 and 5×10^{-2} mole azobenzene/liter of acetone. Clean the outside, and insert the tubes open end down into the outer tube, pushing them against the other tube with a thin glass rod.

Carefully close the end of the outer tube, using a microburner; soften the glass edge, draw out the glass with another glass tube, and then seal. Attach the five tubes to a glass plate, using Scotch tape; place this plate in a box lined with cotton and put the box in an oven at 40°.

Allow the system to equilibrate for 16–24 hr. Read the position of the meniscus, using a microscope. In each of the five tubes determine the distance of the meniscus from a reference point (e.g., the dividing line between the two capillaries).

Again equilibrate for 24 hr. and measure the position of the meniscus again. Repeat this step once more 24 hr. later. Do not carry out a determination on a tube whose liquid has run out.

28-14   Calculation and Report

Record as shown in Form 28-3.

Form 28-3

No.	Content	Position after			Displacement		Total displacement after	
		0 hr.	24 hr.	48 hr.	24 hr.	48 hr.	24 hr.	48 hr.
1	Unknown	A	B	C	$A - B$	$A - C$	$(A-B)-(P-Q)$	$(A-C)-(P-R)$
	y molar azobenzene	P	Q	R				

Plot the total displacement against the molarity of the standard solutions. Straight lines are obtained which intersect the horizontal at a point equal to the molarity of the standard (see Fig. 28-9). The molecular weight of the unknown is given by

$$M_x = \frac{c}{m}$$

where c = weight per volume of the unknown;
   m = molarity of standard.

28-15   Equipment

Glass plates

Glass cutter (file)

Glass tubing

Volumetric flask (10 ml.)

Scotch tape

Microscope with micrometer

Eyepiece

Capillaries

Standard solutions

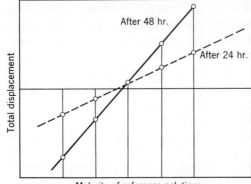

Fig. 28-9., Molecular weight determination according to Barger.

D   SPECTROMETRIC DETERMINATION OF MOLECULAR WEIGHT

28-16   Introduction

The absorption of non-conjugated chromophores is additive. Under certain conditions the absorption spectrum of a substance will not show any change when a structural modification is made in the molecule "far" removed from the chromophore. The molar absorptivity (ϵ) of a particular chromophore is therefore a constant (within limits) independent of the system. Thus all picrates show virtually the same molar absorptivity at 3800 Å (Table 28-2).

Table 28-2   Molar Absorptivity of Picrates in Alcohol at 3800 Å

Picrate	ϵ
Picric acid	13,450
Piperidine picrate	13,510
N-Ethylaniline picrate	13,430
Ethanolamine picrate	13,390
Morpholine picrate	13,400

28-17   Theory

Table 28-2 shows that the molar absorptivity of the picric acid part is nearly constant. The absorptivity of different picrates will vary with the molecular weight (see § 19-2), since

$$E_{1\ cm}^{1\%} = \frac{10\epsilon}{M} = \frac{\log (I_0/I)}{c'l}$$

where M = molecular weight;

c' = concentration (g./100 ml.);

l = path length (cm.).

The molecular weight of a variety of basic substances can be determined within 2%.

Although the absorption maximum of picric acid is at 3600 Å ($\epsilon = 16,000$), the measurements are carried out at 3800 Å to decrease the chance that the bases show any absorption at the wavelength used.

28-18 Procedure

Quinoline picrate is used as reference substance. Calculate the concentration needed, using Table 28-2. Since for the reference substance

$$10\epsilon l = \frac{M_1}{c_1'} \log \left(\frac{I_0}{I_1}\right) = \frac{M_1}{c_1'} D_1$$

and for the picrate of the unknown

$$10\epsilon l = \frac{M_2}{c_2'} D_2$$

Then

$$M_2 = M_1 \frac{c_2'}{c_1'} \frac{D_1}{D_2}$$

Measure the absorptivity (D_1 and D_2) at 20 wavelengths between 3400 and 3800 Å, and calculate the molecular weight from each pair of observations. When the series of results show no drift in any direction, calculate an average value.

Examples

Piperidine	2-Methyl pryidine
N-Methylaniline	4-Ethyl pyridine
Carbazole	Strychnine
Isoquinoline	Cocaine
8-Hydroxyquinoline	Acridine

28-19   References

1. R. U. Bonnar, M. Dimbat, and F. H. Stross, *Number-Average Molecular Weights,* Interscience Publishers, New York, 1958.
2. M. Dimbat and F. H. Stross, *Anal. Chem.,* **29,** 1517 (1957).
3. G. Barger, *Ber.,* **37,** 1754 (1904).
4. J. B. Niederl, D. R. Kasanof, G. K. Kisch, and D. Subba Rao, *Mikrochemie ver. Mikrochim. Acta,* **34,** 132 (1949).
5. K. G. Cunningham, W. Dawson, and F. S. Spring, *J. Chem. Soc.,* **1951,** 2305.
6. L. J. Sullivan, R. J. Fries, W. S. McClenahan, and C. B. Willingham, *Anal. Chem.,* **29,** 1333 (1957).
7. G. W. Perold and F. W. G. Schoning, *Mikrochim. Acta,* **1961,** 749–753.

VI

Tracer techniques

29

Vacuum line synthesis

29-1 Introduction and Principles

Small quantities of volatile compounds can be conveniently handled without loss by using high-vacuum techniques. The transfer of the volatile compounds from one container to another is carried out by evaporation and condensation in high vacuum. The better the vacuum, the faster these transfers can be made. By measuring the pressure, the quantity of the volatile substance is determined.

The vacuum is obtained by using a diffusion pump (oil or mercury, Fig. 29-1) in combination with an oil pump. Pressures of 10^{-5} mm. can be reached readily and are measured with a McLeod gauge (see Fig. 11-13).

29-2 Apparatus (Figs. 29-2 and 29-3) and Experimental Procedure

29-2a STOPCOCKS AND JOINTS

Check before every experiment that all stopcocks and joints are properly greased. If they are not, clean both parts, using cotton and ether. Warm slightly with a hair dryer and then use Apiezon M. Rotate the stopcock or joint until all air bubbles have been removed. *Always support both sides of stopcock housing.* Attach springs. Low room temperatures may cause freezing of joints. Never force a joint or stopcock; use a hair dryer to warm it.

29-2b START OF THE EXPERIMENT

N.B. SAFETY GLASSES MUST BE WORN AT ALL TIMES.

1. Check whether the boat b_2 is filled with dry P_2O_5 and whether the trap b_5 is clean and dry.

2. Check position of stopcocks:

a_1 and b_1 connected to oil pump.

a_6, b_4, and c_3 open.

p_1 and p_2 closed.

3. Start the oil pump and slowly open p_1. Turn on water in condenser b_3, and then turn on heater b_7. Surround b_5 with a Dewar flask containing liquid air. The system should be properly evacuated in 20–30 min. Read pressure gauge A.

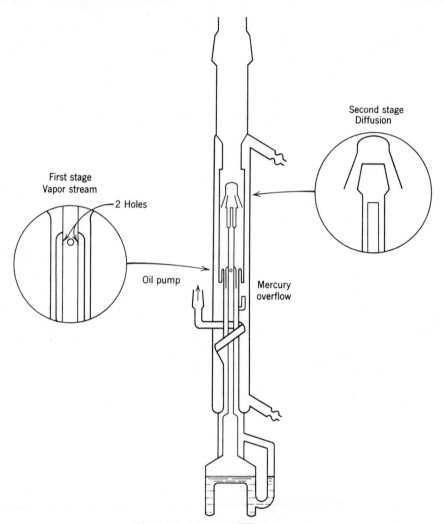

First stage
Vapor stream

2 Holes

Second stage
Diffusion

Oil pump

Mercury
overflow

Fig. 29-1. Mercury diffusion pump.

29-2c GAUGE

Bleed air into a_2 by opening a_1 slowly to the outside. Close a_1 when mercury in a_3 is level with mark on a_4 and read pressure in a_5. Close stopcock b_1, and then *carefully* turn a_1 again to oil pump. Open b_1 again when mercury has been lowered.

29-2d END OF EXPERIMENT

Turn off heater (b_7), close p_1, and *slowly* open p_2, turning off the oil pump immediately afterward. Bleed air into the apparatus *via* p_1, keeping p_2 open. Finally close p_1 and p_2.

N.B. BEFORE ADMITTING AIR, CHECK TO SEE THAT ALL STOPCOCKS ARE IN THE CORRECT POSITION.

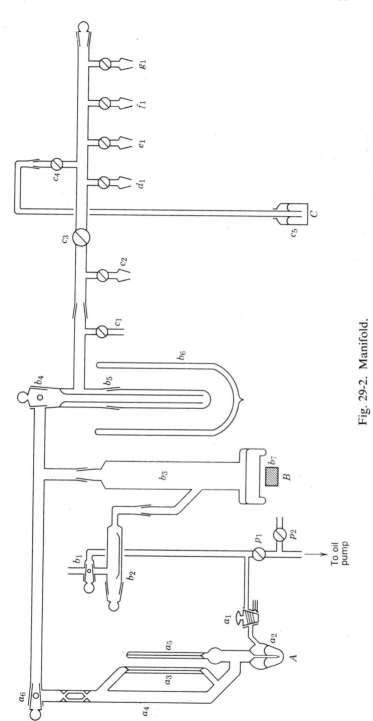

Fig. 29-2. Manifold.

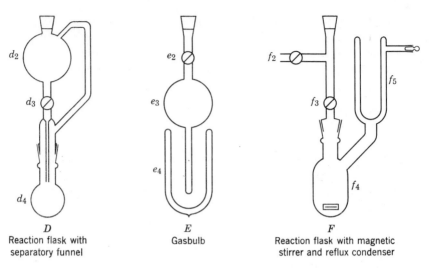

Fig. 29-3. Accessories belonging to manifold.

29-3   Experiments*

29-3a   BENZOIC ACID (C¹⁴) FROM BARIUM CARBONATE (C¹⁴)

$$BaCO_3^* \xrightarrow[\text{(1)}]{H_2SO_4} C^*O_2 \xrightarrow[\text{(2)}]{C_6H_5MgBr} C_6H_5C^*O_2MgBr \xrightarrow[\text{(3)}]{H_2SO_4} C_6H_5C^*OOH$$

Preparation. Attach pieces D, E, and F (Fig. 29-3) to connections d, e, and f_1 (Fig. 29-2).

Step 1a. Add 20 ml. of conc. sulfuric acid to d_2 (d_3 closed) and 2.0 g. of barium carbonate to d_4. Cover barium carbonate with glasswool to prevent spattering.

Open c_3, c_4, d_1, e_1, and e_2 and close c_1, c_2, f_1, f_2, f_3, and g_1.
   Evacuate the system and record pressure of gauge A.

Step 2a. Add 0.55 g. of magnesium to flask f_4 and then 50 ml. of dry ether, followed by 2 ml. of bromobenzene and a magnetic stirring bar. Add a crystal of iodine. Cool f_4 carefully in liquid air until the ether has frozen. Close d and c_4; open f_1 and f_3 in order to evacuate f_4. Close f_3; open d_1 and c_4. Melt the ether in f_4 in order to get rid of trapped air, cool again in liquid air, close d_1 and c_4, open f_3, and evacuate completely.
   Close f_1 and f_3; open d_1 and c_4. Warm f_4 to room temperature, cool f_5 in ice, and stir the boiling ether. At the end of the reaction, f_4 is cooled again in liquid air.
   Carry out step 1b during the period that the ether is stirring and boiling.

---

* Specific directions for working with radioactive compounds are found in B. M. Tolbert and W. E. Siri, *Technique of Organic Chemistry*, A. Weissberger, ed., Interscience Publishers, 1960, Vol. 1, Part IV, p. 3335 and Refs. 1, 4.

Step 1b. Read gauges A and C_5. Close c_3 and c_4. Cool the tip of e_3 in liquid air and open d_3 a little. The generation of the carbon dioxide should be very gradual. When all the H_2SO_4 has been added, warm d_4 carefully (beaker with warm water), close d_1, e_1, and e_2, and open c_3 and c_4; read gauges A and c_5.

Step 2b. Close c_3 again, remove the Dewar flask (e_4), open e and e_2, and read the manometer c_5 after all the CO_2 has evaporated. Read the outside temperature. Open f_1 and f_3, and condense all the CO_2 in f_4.

Close f_1 and f_3; bleed an air through f_2 and remove F from the manifold. Cool in Dry Ice-alcohol to $-20°C$., and shake occasionally for 15 min.

Step 3. Admit air through f_3. Maintain the temperature at $-20°$ and carefully add 15 ml. of $6N$ H_2SO_4 and 35 ml. of water. Extract the benzoic acid with ether, and remove again from the ether with the calculated amount of $0.3N$ sodium hydroxide. Check whether the aqueous layer is basic. Precipitate again by adding a slight excess of $6N$ H_2SO_4 (note the solubility of benzoic acid: 0.21 g./100 ml. at 17.5°C.; 2.2 g./100 ml. at 75°C. Cool the solution if the volume is too large.

Calculate the yield of CO_2 from the pressure measured (step 1b). The volume of C_3 needs to be determined, as well as that of the manifold tube, while e and e_2 are open and c_3, d_1, f_1, and g_1 are closed. Calculate the yield of benzoic acid based on CO_2. The yield based on $BaCO_3$ is 85%., m.p. 122–123°. Recrystallize from a little hot water if necessary.

29-3b ACETIC ACID $(C_1{}^{14})$ FROM BARIUM CARBONATE (C^{14})

Preparation. Attach D, E, and F to connections d_1, e_1, and f_1; attach a tube (g_2) containing 1.25 ml. of methyl iodide to g_1.

Procedure. Step 1a. As in experiment 1.

Step 2a. Add 50 ml. of ether, 0.625 g. of magnesium, and a magnetic stirring bar to f_4. Cool f_4 and the tube g_2 in liquid air until the ether and methyl iodide have solidified. Close d_1 and c_4, evacuate g_2 and f_4 via g_1, f_1, and f_3. Close g_1 and f_1; open d_1 and c_4. Remove the Dewar flasks around g_2 and f_4 and bring the methyl iodide and ether to room temperature. Again cool g_2 and f_4, close d_1 and c_4, open g_1 and f_1, and evacuate as completely as possible.

Close c_3, remove the Dewar flask from g_2, and distill the methyl iodide into f_4. Check the rate of distillation occasionally (manometer c_5); do not keep e_4 open too long.

Close g_1, f_1, and f_3 and proceed as in experiment 1, step 2a.

Step 1b. See experiment 1, step 1b.

Step 2b. See experiment 1, step 2b.

Step 3. Admit air *via* f_3, maintain the temperature at $-20°$, and carefully add 15 ml. of $6N$ sulfuric acid and 35 ml. of water. Add 4 g. of silver sulfate to combine with the iodine liberated. Make alkaline with $6N$ alkali and evaporate the ether. Acidify the aqueous layer, and steam-distill until the distillate is no longer acid. Titrate the distillate with $0.1N$ sodium hydroxide, using phenol-phthalein as an indicator. Concentrate to 25 ml., add some decolorizing charcoal, bring to a boil, and filter. The filtrate is concentrated to 10 ml. and dried completely in a vacuum desiccator.

The yield of CO_2 is calculated from the CO_2 pressure (step 1b). The volume of c_3 and the manifold tube needs to be determined beforehand. Also calculate the yield of sodium acetate (based on CO_2). The yield based on $BaCO_3$ is 85%.

29-3c   PROPIONIC ACID ($C_1{}^{14}$) FROM CARBONATE (C^{14})

Procedure. As in experiment 2. Use ethyl bromide instead of methyl iodide in step 2a. Do not add silver sulfate in step 3. The yield based on $BaCO_3$ is 95%.

29-3d   α-NAPHTHALENE CARBOXYLIC ACID ($C_1{}^{14}$) FROM BARIUM CARBONATE (C^{14})

Procedure. Step 1a.   See experiment 1, step 1a.

Step 2a. Since the Grignard reagent is formed with difficulty, it must be prepared at atmospheric pressure in order to apply heat. Instead of F use a two-neck flask with condenser and addition funnel.

Add 50 ml. of ether, 0.6 g. of magnesium, a crystal of iodine, and the stirring bar to the flask. Add 3 ml. of α-bromonaphthalene in 10 ml. of ether to the additional funnel.

Prepare the Grignard reagent as usual and carry out step 1b (see experiment 1, step 1b) in the meantime.

Step 2b. Attach the flask containing the Grignard reagent to f_1, using the connection with stopcocks f_2 and f_3; close the other neck of the two-neck flask with a stopper. Cool the flask in liquid air until everything has solidified, close c_4, open f_1 and f_3, and evacuate. Close f_1 and f_3, remove the Dewar flask around the two-neck flask, and warm the contents to room temperature. Cool in liquid air, open f_1 and f_3, and evacuate.

Close f_1, open c_4, and record the manometer reading (c_5). Close c_3, remove the Dewar (e_4), open e_1 and e_2, and record the manometer reading (c_5) and temperature reading when all the CO_2 has evaporated.

Open f_1 and condense all the CO_2 in the two-neck flask. Close f_1 and f_3, admit air *via* f_2, remove the two-neck flask from the manifold, cool in Dry Ice-alcohol to $-20°$, and shake occasionally for 15 min.

Step 3. See experiment 1, step 3. Recrystallize the acid from 1:1 alcohol-water. Calculate the yield of CO_2 from the CO_2 pressure (step 1b). Calculate the yield of α-naphthalene carboxylic acid (based on CO_2). The yield is 80% based on $BaCO_3$; m.p. 158–159° (uncorr.)

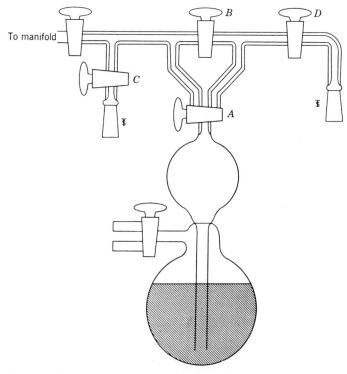

Fig. 29-4. Toepler pump. (Used with permission from K. W. Wiberg, *Laboratory Technique in Organic Chemistry*, McGraw-Hill Book Co., 1960)

29-3e   EQUIPMENT

2 Two-neck flasks (24/40)	2 Stoppers
Condenser	4 Dewar flasks
Round-bottom flask (100 ml.)	Siphon
2 Separatory funnels (400 ml.)	Magnetic stirrer
Separatory funnel (250 ml.)	Hair dryer
Calcium chloride tube	Low-temperature thermometer
Adaptor	Three-way plug
Graduated tube	Stirring rod
Steam-distillation apparatus	Hirsh funnel (5.5 cm.)
2 Weighing bottles	3 Erlenmeyers (500, 2 × 300 ml.)
Pipette (5 ml.)	1 Funnel
2 Graduate cylinders (25 and 100 ml.)	2 Vacuum desiccators
4 Beakers (800, 400, 2 × 50 ml.)	2 Crystallizing dishes
Suction flask (300 ml.)	Watchglasses

Note. When the gas to be transferred cannot be condensed properly, a Toepler pump (Fig. 29-4) can be used. See [3], p. 138, for use.

29-4   References

1. M. Calvin, C. Heidelberger, J. C. Reid, B. M. Tolbert, and P. E. Yankwich, *Isotopic Carbon*, John Wiley and Sons, New York, 1949.
2. R. P. Linstead, J. A. Elvidge, and M. Whalley, *A Course in Modern Techniques in Organic Chemistry*, Butterworths Scientific Publications, London, 1955, p. 77.
3. K. Wiberg, *Laboratory Technique in Organic Chemistry*, McGraw-Hill Book Co., New York, 1960.
4. J. G. Burr, Jr., *Tracer Applications for the Study of Organic Reactions*, Interscience Publishers, New York, 1957.
5. C. W. Sheppard, *Basic Principles of the Tracer Method*, John Wiley and Sons, New York, 1962.
6. H. Schmid, *Chimia*, **14**, 248–261 (1960).

30

Determination of deuterium

30-1 Introduction

This chapter deals with some of the procedures used in working with deuterium:

(a) Combustion of organic compounds.
(b) Purification of the water formed.
(c) Determination of the deuterium content of water by the falling-drop method.
(d) Determination of the deuterium content by use of a gradient tube.
Isotopic analysis by a mass spectrometer will not be discussed. See [10].

A COMBUSTION OF ORGANIC COMPOUNDS CONTAINING DEUTERIUM

The method is similar to that used for quantitative microanalysis of carbon and hydrogen. The substance is passed over cobalt oxide (superior to copper oxide) in a stream of oxygen. The water is frozen out, while the carbon dioxide is absorbed on asbestos containing sodium hydroxide.

Since hydrogen (and deuterium) in water rapidly exchanges with the hydrogen on the surface of glass, the system must be equilibrated carefully before reliable analysis can be made.

30-2 Apparatus

The apparatus consists of the following parts (see Fig. 30-1):

(a) Pressure bottle controlling oxygen flow. This may be replaced by a needle valve arrangement and flowmeter.

(b) Quartz tube filled with cobalt oxide (CoO) and surrounded by Nichrome (or Kanthal*) wire. Temperature is about $650°$.

(c) Condenser.

(d) Bubble counter filled with sulfuric acid.

* The Kanthal Co., Stamford, Conn.

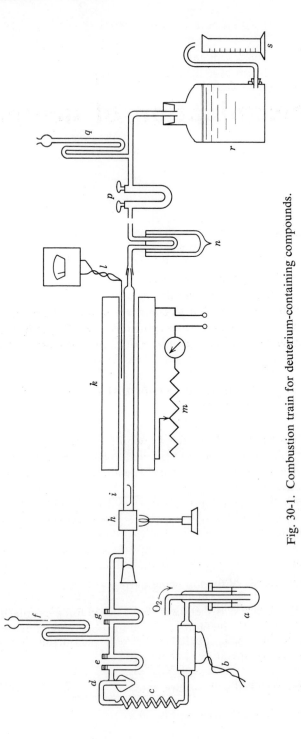

Fig. 30-1. Combustion train for deuterium-containing compounds.

(*e*) U-tube filled with asbestos impregnated with sodium hydroxide to remove the CO_2.

(*f*) Manometer filled with paraffin oil.

(*g*) U-tube filled with $Mg(ClO_4)_2$ to remove water.

(*h*) Movable copper cover.

(*i*) Boat with sample.

(*j*) Quartz tube, CoO, and silver gauze.

(*k*) Oven (700–750°C.).

(*l*) Pt/Pt-Rh thermocouple and millivolt meter.

(*m*) Variable resistance and ammeter.

(*n*) U-tube cooled with Dry Ice-alcohol.

(*o*) U-tube filled with sodium hydroxide asbestos and $Mg(ClO_4)_2$.

(*p*) Manometer filled with paraffin oil.

(*q*) Bottle to regulate final pressure (may be replaced by flowmeter).

(*r*) Graduate cylinder [see (*q*)].

30-3 Preparation of Cobaltocobaltic Oxide Catalyst

Oxalic acid dihydrate (88 g.) is dissolved in 300 ml. of water and added to a solution of 145 g. of cobalt nitrate hexahydrate in 200 ml. of water. The precipitate is filtered and washed with water and ethanol, mixed to a paste with water and with about the same weight of starch, and dried at 110–120°C. The preparation is ignited at 550–600°C. for 2–3 hr. and then sieved, the portion between 14 and 40 B.S. mesh being collected. A 5-cm. layer of catalyst followed by a 6–7 cm. silver gauze roll is used in the combustion tube at a flow rate of 10–12 ml./min.

30-4 Procedure

Detach tubes *n* and *p*. Clean *n* thoroughly, dry, and insert a small plug of glass wool into one leg of the U-tube (see Fig. 30-4). Fill *p* with sodium hydroxide-asbestos and $Mg(ClO_4)_2$ and weigh this tube.

Heat oven *k* to 700–750°C., turn on *b*, and pass oxygen through the system for at least 30 min. Replace *n* and *p* (using silicon or Apiezon grease) and regulate oxygen flow so that 20–25 ml. of water/min. is collected in *s*. The manometer *f* and *g* should indicate a pressure of 0.5 cm. of paraffin oil.

Weigh out a sufficient quantity of sample to collect at least 100 mg. of water. Solids are weighed out in a porcelain boat, and liquids in a glass capillary which is sealed after filling (Fig. 30-2).

The tube is held by tweezers at end *B* (solid), and bulb *A* is heated in a free flame. The end of the capillary *C* is then held in the liquid to be examined. (*Note.* Use only 1 ml. of liquid in this operation to avoid the possibility of fire from ignition of volatile liquids by the hot tube.)

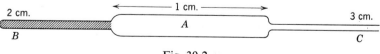

Fig. 30-2.

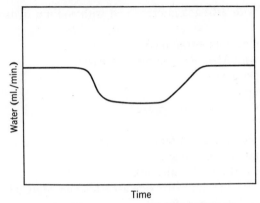

Fig. 30-3. Amount of water collected.

The burner is turned on, and *h* (Fig. 30-1) is slowly moved in the direction of the oven. The substance should gradually evaporate from its boat or capillary over a period of 1–2 hr. Record the amount of water per minute which runs into *s*. Use the flask *r* to regulate the oxygen flow so that the levels in *f* and *g* remain equal. The change in the rate of flow of the water will indicate when the combustion is complete (Fig. 30-3). Continue flushing with nitrogen for 30 min. more. If some water has condensed in the combustion tube, use a hot-air stream (hair dryer) to move this to *n* in the oxygen flow. Detach *n* and *p*. Close them well, and weigh *p* to check the completeness of combustion.

B   PURIFICATION OF WATER SAMPLES [1]

30-5   Principle

The water obtained from the combustion of the sample may be contaminated with halogen, nitrogen oxides, and fragments from incomplete combustion. Nitrogen oxides are removed by the addition of dry barium carbonate. Halogens are converted to copper halides with copper power. Organic compounds are decomposed by oxidation with chromium trioxide followed by potassium permanganate.

30-6   Apparatus (Fig. 30-4)

The purification takes place in train consisting of four U-tubes connected by standard taper joints. The first tube fits onto the end of the combustion tube. Clean all parts thoroughly, using dichromate-sulfuric acid overweight. Rinse with distilled water, followed by boiling nitric acid, and finally repeatedly with distilled water. Dry in oven.

Place wads of glass wool in tubes *A*, *B*, and *C*, at *x*, *y*, and *z*; this prevents the oxidizing agents, water and ice crystals, from being blown from tube to tube. Put 3–5 mg. of $KMnO_4$ and 3–5 mg. of CaO in tube *C*, 5 mg. of CrO_3 in tube *B*, and fill tube *A* with twice the calculated quantity of copper powder.

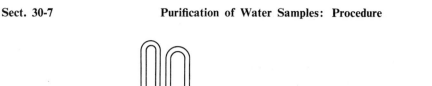

Fig. 30-4. Purification of water samples. *r*. KMnO$_4$ + KOH. *s*. H$_2$SO$_4$. *t*. Charcoal. *u*. Silica gel. *v*. P$_2$O$_5$.

Assemble the apparatus as shown in Fig. 30-4, using Apiezon on joints. By heating the train *in vacuo*, the last traces of water are removed from the system; to this end (*b*) is closed and the system is evacuated. Then heat *A* in a blue flame. Heat tube *B* carefully to prevent decomposition of CrO$_3$ to Cr$_2$O$_3$. Heat tube *C* strongly to convert the calcium hydroxide to calcium oxide. Continue heating until the calcium oxide particles no longer jump up and down. Keep the system evacuated for another 30 min. Finally permit dry air to enter slowly.

30-7 Procedure

The water formed during the combustion is collected in tube *A* (properly cleaned and filled with copper oxide before use). Close off *A* and allow to stand for at least 12 hr. Add a few milligrams of dry BaCO$_3$ to neutralize any hydrogen halides formed.

Connect *A* to *B* and cool *A* in Dry Ice-alcohol. Surround *B* by the Dewar flask and slowly evacuate the apparatus. The water distills into *B*. After the system is evacuated, the distillation may be accelerated by warming *A* with water (at 30°C.). Heat *A* with a free flame until the copper halide loses its green color, taking care to prevent decomposition. Finally bleed in air. Remove *A*, place Dewar flask around *C*, and heat *B* with a microburner, causing the water to reflux gently for 10 min. Freeze the water in *B*, place the Dewar around *C*, evacuate, and distill the water into *C*. When all the water has been removed from *B*, air is admitted, *B* is removed, and the open end of *C* closed with a stopper. The Dewar is moved over to *D*, and the water refluxed for some time in *C* and distilled into *D*. *C* is heated strongly, converting the calcium hydroxide to oxide.

When the weight of the water is immaterial, use receiver *E*; otherwise, receiver *F* (Fig. 30-5).

After the water has distilled into *F*, admit air and seal off at *p* and *g*. Remove all grease, dry, and weigh.

30-7a   PREPARATION OF KNOWN MIXTURES OF D_2O–H_2O

Five grams of doubly distilled water is weighed to 0.1 mg. Add the required amount of D_2O, weighing before and after on a microbalance to ±0.001 mg.

30-7b   CHECK ON PURITY

Determine the apparent D_2O content, using a gradient tube. A rapid determination with the falling-drop method may first be made. Repeat the purification of the sample and again determine the density.

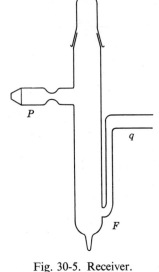

30-7c   OTHER METHODS

Kirshenbaum [10] describes in detail an alternative method of purification which uses oxygen and heated platinum wire.

C   DETERMINATION OF THE DEUTERIUM CONTENT OF WATER BY THE FALLING-DROP METHOD [2-5]

30-8   Introduction

The difference in density between H_2O and D_2O is 10% (100,000 p.p.m.). Since the density of liquids can be measured within 0.1 p.p.m., the deuterium content of water can be determined to an accuracy of

Fig. 30-5. Receiver.

0.0001%. Even when little water is available, the D_2O content can readily be determined to 0.01%.

30-9   Principle

The velocity with which a drop of water falls through a liquid immiscible with water is measured. According to Stokes' law,

$$6\pi\eta rv = \tfrac{4}{3}\pi r^3[d - d_m]g$$

where n = coefficient of viscosity of medium (dyne sec./cm.²);
  r = radius of falling drop (cm.);
  v = terminal velocity of falling drop (cm./sec.);
  d = density of drop (g./ml.);
  d_m = density of medium (g./ml.);
  g = acceleration due to gravity (cm./sec.²).
The velocity of a falling drop of known density (C_0) is compared to that of one with unknown deuterium content (C_1). If the time needed to cover a fixed

distance is measured, then:

$$(v_1 - v_0) \sim \left(\frac{1}{t_1} - \frac{1}{t_0}\right) \sim (d_1 - d_0) \sim (C_1 - C_0)$$

30-10 Apparatus (Fig. 30-6)

The "fall tube" (diameter 12 mm., length 57 cm.) is suspended in air surrounded by a water jacket and vacuum jacket. Water from a thermostat is pumped through the water jacket. The "fall tube" should hang vertically. The top of the air jacket must be closed off well.

Place a 2-cm. layer of dry sodium sulfate on the bottom of the fall tube to absorb the water droplets.

Fill the tube to within 2 cm. of the top with a kerosene-bromobenzene mixture of the desired density. Determine the time it takes a drop to fall. When this time is

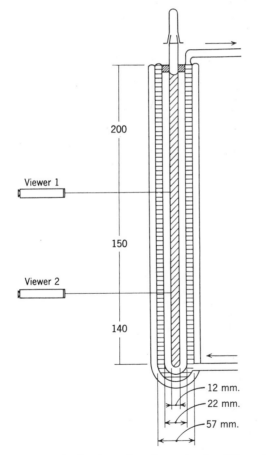

Fig. 30-6. Fall tube for deuterium determination (dimensions in millimeters).

less than 75 or more than 175 sec., pour the mixture into an Erlenmeyer and add either kerosene or bromobenzene in order to bring this time within the limits stated.

The falling time is measured over a distance of 15 cm. For the first 28 cm. through which the drop falls, the temperature of the drop adjusts itself to that of its surroundings. The last 10 cm. of the tube is unsuitable for measurement because of irregularities in the trajectory.

30-11   Procedure

Micropipette. A simple micropipette [10, p. 336] is shown in Fig. 30-7a. It is a 10-cm. length of $\frac{1}{2}$-mm. capillary tubing with a bulb and screw clamp arrangement as shown. After rinsing several times with water, the pipette is filled to a mark on the scale, and any water clinging to the five-capillary tip is carefully wiped off with hard filter paper.

The pipette is then placed in a holder (Fig. 30-7b). Water is expelled by turning the screw clamp until the water reaches a second mark on the scale. The drop which clings to the end of the capillary is released by raising the (submerged) tip in the liquid.

Drops of about 2.5 mm.^{3} give good results.

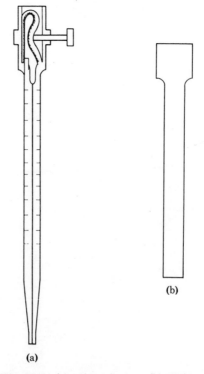

(a)

(b)

Fig. 30-7. (a) Micropipette. (b) Holder.

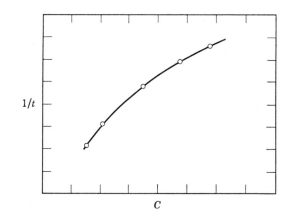

Fig. 30-8. Deuterium concentration as a function of fall time.

Temperature Control. Careful temperature control is necessary, since the viscosity and density are highly temperature dependent. A variation of less than $\pm 0.02°$ must be maintained during the experiments. The falling time may be changed by adjusting the thermostat to another temperature.

Measurement of Falling Time. Times between 75 and 175 sec. are chosen for the 15-cm. distance. Two small viewers are used (Fig. 30-6). Focus these viewers and start the stopwatch when the bottom of the drop crosses the horizontal cross hair. Make five separate measurements on each sample and average the results. The average deviation is usually $\pm 0.4\%$ or less.

If the deviation is larger than 0.5%, further observations must be made. Determine the falling time of two known H_2O–D_2O samples having a D_2O content lower and higher, respectively, than the unknown.

30-12 Calculation

If Stokes' law were entirely valid, a linear interpolation would be possible. Let the D_2O content of the known samples be C_1 and C_2 and of the unknown C_x; then

$$C_x = C_1 + \frac{C_2 - C_1}{1/t_2 - 1/t_1}\left(\frac{1}{t_x} - \frac{1}{t_1}\right)$$

Since Stokes law is not completely obeyed, a plot of $1/t$ against C is not linear (see Fig. 30-8). Thus K is not a constant in the equation

$$C - C_0 = K\left(\frac{1}{t} - \frac{1}{t_0}\right)$$

but increases as C increases. It appears that K increases virtually linearly with C. A close approximation is obtained by comparing the unknown (C_x) to five or six known samples. Let the falling time for normal water ($C_0 = 0$; in general only the difference in D_2O content is desired) be t_0 seconds; then

$$K_n = \frac{C_n - C_0}{1/t_n - 1/t_0} \qquad (30\text{-}1)$$

K_n, C_n, and t_n are the values for K, C, and t for the known samples. Plot K_n against $1/t_n$ and determine the constants p and q from the equation

$$K_n = p + \frac{q}{t_n}$$

using the method of least squares.

Now calculate K_y for the unknown with a falling time t_y, and determine C_y, using equation 30-1.

Table 30-1   Relationship between Deuterium Content and Density

D/(D + H)	Weight Percentage of Deuterium	$(d_4^{20} - d) \cdot 10^6$	Comments
0.00 000	0.000	0	
0.00 966	1.072	1.037	According to [3]
0.01 769	1.962	1.899	
0.02 972	3.291	3.192	$d = d_4^{20}$ for H_2O =
0.03 671	4.062	3.941	0.998230
0.04 418	4.884	4.743	
0.05 442	6.010	5.841	
0.06 389	7.048	6.855	
0.07 340	8.089	7.879	
0.08 135	8.957	8.733	
0.09 132	10.004	9.802	
		$(d_4^{25} - d) \cdot 10^6$	
0.20 192	21.888	21.770	According to [4]
0.40 243	42.800	43.370	
0.61 023	63.497	65.720	$d = d_4^{25}$ for H_2O =
0.82 358	83.837	88.630	0.99707
1.00 000	100.000	107.590	
		$(d_4^{25} - d) \cdot 10^6$	
0.00 017	0.0188	0	Natural water $d_4^{25} = 0.99707$
0.00 000	0.0000	−20	Completely pure H_2O $d_4^{25} = 0.99705$

D DETERMINATION OF THE DEUTERIUM CONTENT OF WATER BY THE GRADIENT TUBE METHOD [6–10]

In the border region of a mixture of liquids (usually kerosene-bromobenzene) a linear density gradient develops by diffusion. Objects having a density between that of the two liquids will float in this region. By comparing the equilibrium position of a drop of unknown density to the position of a drop of known density, the deuterium content may be determined. Only 1–2 mm.^{3} of water is needed. An accuracy of 0.01% D_2O may be obtained.

30-13 Apparatus

The gradient tube is properly thermostatted to within 0.02°. The drops are added with a micropipette. Their equilibrium position is determined with a cathetometer. A vibration-free setup is desirable. Consult the original literature for details [6–10]. Table 30-1 shows the relationship between deuterium content and density.

30-14 References

1. A. S. Keston, D. Rittenberg, and R. Schoenheimer, *J. Biol. Chem.*, **122**, 227 (1937).
2. M. Cohn in *Preparation and Measurement of Isotopic Tracers*, J. W. Edwards, ed., Ann Arbor, Mich., 1948, p. 51.
3. K. Fenger-Eriksen, A. Krogh, and H. Ussing, *Biochem. J.*, **30**, 1264 (1936).
4. S. Hochberg and V. K. La Mer, *Ind. Eng. Chem., Anal. Ed.*, **9**, 291 (1937).
5. F. Rosebury and W. E. van Heyningen, *Ind. Eng. Chem., Anal. Ed.*, **14**, 363 (1942).
6. C. Anfinsen in *Preparation and Measurement of Isotopic Tracers*, J. W. Edmunds, ed., Ann Arbor, Mich., 1948.
7. K. Linderstrøm-Lang, O. Jacobson, and G. Johansen, *Compt. rend. trav. lab. Carlsberg*, **23**, 17 (1938).
8. K. Linderstrøm-Lang and H. Lanl, Jr., *Compt. rend. trav. lab. Carlsberg*, **21**, 315 (1938).
9. L. G. Longsworth, *J. Am. Chem. Soc.*, **59**, 1483 (1937).
10. I. Kirshenbaum, *Physical Properties and Analysis of Heavy Water*, McGraw-Hill Book Co., New York, 1951, p. 358.
11. P. Jordan and C. Tgetgel-Schelling, *Helv. Chim. Acta*, **45**, 703–711 (1962).

VII

Kinetic techniques

31

Reaction kinetics

31-1 Introduction

The study of reaction kinetics provides a means by which we attempt to understand the processes taking place during a chemical reaction. The methods used to study the rate of a chemical reaction depend on the phase (gaseous, liquid, or solid) and the nature of the reactants, intermediates, and products. Direct and indirect methods are used. The hydrolysis of an ester produces an alcohol and an acid. The latter may be titrated and determined directly. Or the increase in conductivity may be measured to give an indirect indication of product formation. Other properties in which changes are used to follow the disappearance of reactants and/or the formation of products are the following:

(a) Light absorption.
(b) Optical rotation.
(c) Density.
(d) Refractive index.
(e) Pressure.
(f) Nuclear magnetic resonance absorption.
(g) Color.
(h) pH.
(i) Volume.

See [5] for examples.

31-2 Theory

The rate of a chemical reaction may be expressed as a differential equation

$$v = -\frac{d(A)}{dt} = K[A]^k[B]^l[C]^m \tag{31-1}$$

where [A], [B], and [C] are the concentrations of the substances reacting. The exponents k, l, and m indicate the order of the reaction with respect to the substances. The total order of the reaction is $k + l + m + \cdots$. The proportionality constant K is called the rate constant. The Arrhenius equation relates the rate constant to the temperature:

$$K = Ae^{-E/RT}$$

where E = (experimental) activation energy;
$\quad\;\; R$ = gas constant;
$\quad\;\; T$ = absolute temperature.
For a unimolecular reaction the theory of absolute reaction rates gives

$$K = \frac{RT}{Nh} \exp\left(\frac{-\Delta H^*}{RT}\right) \exp\left(\frac{-\Delta S^*}{RT}\right) \qquad (31\text{-}2)$$

where ΔH^* = activation enthalpy;
$\quad\;\; \Delta S^*$ = activation entropy;
$\quad\;\;\; h$ = Planck's constant;
$\quad\;\;\; N$ = Avogardro's number.
The total order of the reaction may be larger or smaller than the sum of the number of reacting molecules present stochiometrically. This is caused by the occurrence of consecutive reactions. The rate of such a reaction is determined by the slowest (rate-determining) step and by all preceding reactions. An investigation about the kinetics of a reaction thus furnishes information about the mechanism of the reaction, as well as the nature of the rate-determining step and previous steps.

31-2a nTH-ORDER REACTION OF A SINGLE COMPONENT [4]

First-Order Reaction. The rate expression (31-1) takes the following form for a single component:

$$-\frac{dc}{dt} = kc^n \qquad (31\text{-}3)$$

which upon integration for $n = 1$ yields

$$\ln c = \ln c_0 - kt \qquad (31\text{-}4)$$

To test data for a first-order reaction a plot of $\ln c$ or $\log_{10} c$ vs. t should be linear. The slope should be $-k$ or $-k/2.303$, respectively (see Fig. 31-1).

Second-Order Reaction. When $n = 2$ (in formula 31-3) the integration yields

$$\frac{1}{c} - \frac{1}{c_0} = kt \qquad (31\text{-}5)$$

This indicates that a plot of $1/c$ vs. t should be linear and with a positive slope equal to k (see Fig. 31-2).

Second-Order Reaction, First-Order with Respect to Each of Two Components. Consider the reaction A + B = AB. Then

$$-\frac{dA}{dt} = k\text{AB} \qquad (31\text{-}6)$$

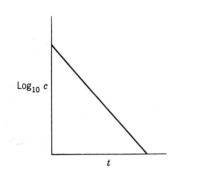

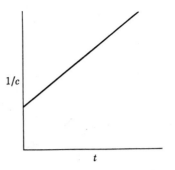

Fig. 31-1. First-order reaction plot.   Fig. 31-2. Second-order reaction plot.

Let x = decrease in concentration of a reactant in a given time;
  a = initial concentration of A;
  b = initial concentration of B. Then equation 31-5 becomes

$$\frac{dx}{dt} = k(a - x)(b - x) \qquad (31\text{-}7)$$

which on integration [4] yields

$$\frac{1}{a - b} \ln \frac{b(a - x)}{a(b - x)} = kt \qquad (31\text{-}8)$$

A plot of $\log \left(\frac{a - x}{b - x}\right)$ vs. t should be linear if the reaction is second order with k
equal to the slope multiplied by $\frac{1}{a - b}$.

31-2b KINETICS IN SOLUTION

For most ionic organic reactions in solution the specific properties of the solvent are important in determining both the rate of the reaction and the position of the equilibrium. If a neutral organic molecule dissociates into ions, the polarity of the solvent as well as the presence or absence of salts which influences the ionic strength of the solution will affect the rate and equilibrium of the reaction.

31-3 Examples

Discussion. The hydrolysis of alkyl halides serves as an example of a reaction in which the structure of the molecule, the solvent, and the ionic strength are involved in the order and the rate of the reaction.

31-3a PRINCIPLE: THE HYDROLYSIS OF *t*-BUTYL CHLORIDE TO *t*-BUTYL ALCOHOL

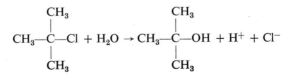

This is followed by measuring the decrease in the resistance (increase in conductance) of the solution.

Procedure. A mixture of 14.4 ml. of absolute ethanol and 21.6 ml. of distilled water is placed in a thermostatted cell maintained at 25.00 °C. The resistance (R_0) is measured (Chapter 23). At time t_0, 0.120 ml. (0.103 g. or 0.00110 mole) of t-butyl chloride is added. The resistance is measured at 1–3 min. intervals over a period of 20 min. Determine R_∞ after about 90 min. (10 half-lives).

Calculation. Plot log $(1/R_\infty - 1/Rt)$ vs. t. By multiplying the slope of the line thus obtained by 2.303, the rate constant k is obtained (see [5]).

Repeat the experiment, using a mixture of 14.4 ml. of absolute ethanol, 13.8 ml. of sodium hydroxide ($0.1N$), and 7.8 ml. of distilled water.

Repeat, using a mixture of 18.0 ml. of absolute ethanol and 18.0 ml. of distilled water.

Explain the change in half-life value.

31-3b SOLVOLYSIS OF *tert*-AMYL CHLORIDE

The cell is filled with a mixture of 14.4 ml. of absolute ethanol and 21.6 ml. of distilled water. Add 0.070 ml. (0.061 g. or 0.00057 mole) of *tert*-amyl chloride at time t_0. Measure the resistance for 20 min. at 0.5–1.5 min. intervals. Calculate the rate constant.

31-3c SOLVOLYSIS OF DIPHENYLMETHYL BROMIDE

Recrystallize diphenylmethyl bromide from petroleum ether (40–60°) until the melting point is 42–43° (lit. 42.5°). Keep in dark, closed container. Prepare a mixture of 200.0 ml. of absolute acetone and 50.0 ml. of distilled water. Using this mixture, carry out the following experiments with 110 mg. of diphenylmethyl bromide.

1. The solvent mixture plus 110 mg. of substance.
2. The solvent mixture, diphenylmethyl bromide, plus 84.4 mg. of sodium perchlorate.
3. Solvent, substance, plus 168.8 mg. of sodium perchlorate.
4. Solvent, substance, plus 71.2 mg. of sodium bromide.
5. Solvent, substance, plus 147.4 mg. of sodium bromide.

Calculate the rate constant as before and discuss salt effect (experiments 1, 2, 3) and common-ion effect (experiments 1, 4, 5) on the rate.

31-3d SOLVOLYSIS OF *n*-BUTYL CHLORIDE

1. Fill cell with 14.4 ml. of absolute ethanol and 21.6 ml. of distilled water. Measure the resistance. Add 0.100 ml. of *n*-butyl chloride and ascertain that the resistance has not changed. Wait 30 min. and then empty cell contents into a beaker containing 11 ml. of a $1N$ nitric acid. Add 10 ml. of silver nitrate solution.

2. Pour 14.4 ml. of absolute ethanol, 10 ml. of $1N$ sodium hydroxide, and 11.6 ml. of distilled water into an Erlenmeyer flask. Add 0.100 ml. of *n*-butyl chloride and keep at 25° for 30 min. Add 11 ml. of nitric acid and 10 ml. of silver nitrate.

Explain *all* observations in detail.

Suggested experiment: hydrolysis of an ester (see [6], p. 157).

31-3e EQUIPMENT

Thermostat complete with temperature control, pump
Thermometer
Conductivity apparatus (e.g., P.R.-9500, GM4249 Philips)
Double-wall conductance cell
Magnetic stirrer
Pipette graduated in 0.01 ml. (1 ml.)
2 Burettes (50-ml.)
Stopwatch
4 Stoppered Erlenmeyers (125 ml.)
2 Beakers

31-3f CHEMICALS

	Boiling Point (°C.)	n_{D}^{20}
tert-Butyl chloride	51	1.3860
n-Butyl chloride	78	1.4015
tert-Amyl chloride	86	1.406
Diphenylmethyl bromide (m.p. 43°)		
Sodium perchlorate (C.P.)		
Sodium chloride (C.P.)		
Sodium hydroxide ($1N$)		
Nitric acid ($1N$)		
Silver nitrate solution (10%)		

31-4 References

1. C. K. Ingold, *Structure and Mechanism in Organic Chemistry*, Cornell University Press, Ithaca, N.Y., 1953.
2. J. Hine, *Physical Organic Chemistry*, McGraw-Hill Book Co., New York, 1962.
3. A. Streitwieser, *Chem. Revs.*, **56**, 571 (1956) and *Solvolytic Displacement Reactions*, McGraw-Hill Book Co., New York, 1962.
4. A. A. Frost and R. G. Pearson, *Kinetics and Mechanism*, John Wiley and Sons, New York, 1961.
5. S. L. Friess, E. S. Lewis, and A. Weissberger, *Investigation of Rates and Mechanisms of Reactions*, Vol. VIII in *Technique of Organic Chemistry*, A. Weissberger, ed., Interscience Publishers, New York, 1961.

6. F. Daniels, J. H. Mathews, and J. W. Williams, *Experimental Physical Chemistry*, McGraw-Hill Book Co., New York, 1962.

7. J. L. Latham, *Elementary Reaction Kinetics*, Butterworths Scientific Publications, London, 1962.

8. H. Eyring and E. M. Eyring, *Modern Chemical Kinetics*, Reinhold Publishing Corp., New York, 1963.

9. B. Stevens, *Chemical Kinetics for General Students of Chemistry*, Chapman and Hall, London, 1961.

INDEX